Complete TV Servicing Handbook, Second Edition

COMPLETE TV SERVICING HANDBOOK, Second Edition

Walter H. Buchsbaum, Sc.D.
as revised by
John P. Steiner

Prentice-Hall, Inc.
Englewood Cliffs, New Jersey

Prentice-Hall International, Inc., *London*
Prentice-Hall of Australia, Pty. Ltd., *Sydney*
Prentice-Hall Canada, Inc., *Toronto*
Prentice-Hall of India Private Ltd., *New Delhi*
Prentice-Hall of Japan, Inc., *Tokyo*
Prentice-Hall of Southeast Asia Pte. Ltd., *Singapore*
Editora Prentice-Hall do Brasil Ltda., *Rio de Janeiro*
Prentice-Hall Hispanoamericana, S.A., *Mexico*

© 1987 by

PRENTICE-HALL, INC.
Englewood Cliffs, N.J.

Library of Congress Cataloging-in-Publication Data

Buschbaum, Walter H.
  Complete TV servicing handbook.

  Includes index.
  1. Television—Repairing.   I. Steiner, John P.
II. Title
TK6642.B795   1987   621.388'87   86-25337

ISBN 0-13-162843-7
ISBN 0-13-162496-2 PBK

Printed in the United States of America

ABOUT THIS BOOK

Electronics has become an integral part of our daily life, and television, in its many manifestations, is the most widely used (and one of the most complicated) devices in the electronic industry. TV receivers, monitors and display devices are found nearly everywhere. From its beginnings as a home entertainment device, television has grown to be many faceted. In addition to entertainment television, there are security television systems, video communications, business and professional systems and many others. Closed circuit TV systems are found in stores, airline terminals, industrial plants and wherever remote viewing is required. TV monitors are used to display stock market prices, medical data, flight schedules and a host of other information. One of the fastest-growing TV applications is the computer terminal, which is found in large quantities in businesses and in many homes.

The *Complete TV Servicing Handbook* has been completely revised, and this edition contains many circuit diagrams of the latest-model television sets, monitors and video display systems. Many chapters have been extensively modified to cover technology that is emerging in the video marketplace. For example, integrated circuit "comb" filters are found in the latest model televisions and monitors. Chapter 9 covers these sophisticated filter circuits.

The audio stages in television receivers have been given greater emphasis in new manufacture. Chapter 10 contains all the information you will need to understand and service television sound systems equipped with MTS stereo decoders. In addition, the MTS Separate Audio Program (SAP) channel is covered. You will learn how the SAP channel is used for second language sound transmission, and what other applications there are.

In addition to the above new items, expanded coverage of projection TV principles, Satellite reception, videocassette recorders (VCR) including the new 8mm, Beta and VHS formats, laser disc systems and many other accessories can be found in this expanded reference work. Many major changes in these technologies have occurred since the previous edition was released.

Many new television receivers also contain jacks and switches that allow them to double as a high-quality video monitor for use with a videocassette recorder or computer system. Standard video monitors are also commonplace these days. These devices are all essentially TV sets, and when they need repair or adjustment, anyone who really knows TV servicing can fix them. You will learn how to test, adjust, align, troubleshoot and install all of these "TV sets," whether they only show black and white pictures, whether they are part of a computer terminal or whether they involve a projection screen or full-color TV receivers. If you know the basics of electronics, can read circuit and block diagrams, use simple test equipment and know how to solder, this reference guide will increase your success in this huge and profitable business, part or full time, anywhere in the civilized world.

You will be shown, in a wide range of practical ways, without mathematics or theoretical physics, how to service any kind of device that has a TV screen. If you are active in an electronics speciality, such as audio, communications or computers, you will find this book a helpful guide to servicing the devices in your specialty that contain TV screens, no matter what their function. If you are in the TV service business, this book will be invaluable because it includes the latest integrated circuit TV designs and it reveals many shortcuts to faster servicing and greater profits.

The *Complete TV Servicing Handbook* begins with a quick, reliable way to diagnose most TV defects by using only the TV screen and the readily accessible controls. You will learn how TV receivers and monitors of all kinds work, what the essential monochrome and color TV functions are, and how different color TV picture tubes operate. Separate chapters cover tuners and IF sections, synchronizing, deflection and high-voltage sections, color circuits and audio circuits. The chapter on antennas and distribution systems will provide all the background you need to install systems with clear, ghost-free reception. Finally, you will learn how to troubleshoot those "impossible" defects in three easy, step-by-step chapters. A large number of illustrations, including color pictures of actual TV screen symptoms, help you along the way.

Walter H. Buchsbaum wrote three editions of the *Complete TV Servicing Handbook*, and his background and experience with television were instrumental in making the handbook a practical reference work for the practicing technician. Dr. Buchsbaum passed away in 1983. It has been a singular honor to be chosen to revise this edition, and it has been my goal to maintain the original organization and style of the handbook, while making sure that new technology is included, thus keeping it practical and useful for the technician.

State-of-the-art troubleshooting techniques are continually advancing. Today, the digital computer may be placed beside the digital voltmeter, the oscilloscope, and the TV generators on the troubleshooting bench. The practical value of the digital computer is its ability to completely analyze an electronic circuit in a fraction of a second, both for normal operation and for various malfunctions. Off-tolerance malfunction conditions are spelled out in terms of subnormal (or abnormal) measured values of voltage gain.

In the case of RC circuitry analysis, subnormal or abnormal Eout/Ein values are supplemented by computation of associated phase angles. Accordingly, a dual-trace oscilloscope can be used both to measure the Eout/ Ein value and the associated phase angle in order to close in on the fault. Note that all of the troubleshooting programs in the appendix provide for any choice of investigative tolerances.

In essence, this book is the result of all we have learned about the practical, essential data you really need in order to service TV sets. *Complete TV Servicing Handbook* covers the new generation of TV receivers and, because home TV sets are no longer the only application of television, we have included the latest information you need to service all types of monitors, including the alphanumeric displays used in computer terminals. With this book you can service any device, in whatever application, that has a TV screen.

John Steiner

TABLE OF CONTENTS

CHAPTER 1

TROUBLESHOOTING BY SYMPTOM AND FUNCTION

Most monochrome TV receivers have at least seven front panel controls and four or more secondary controls. Color TV sets usually have nine front panel controls and six or more secondary controls. Some of these controls are adjusted for the viewer's preference, some compensate for component aging, and some of these controls, front panel or secondary, interact with each other. This chapter shows you how you can diagnose over 75 percent of all TV defects by using only the TV screen, the speaker, and the front panel and secondary controls. You won't need any test equipment and you won't have to remove the chassis from the cabinet to accomplish this. Of course, depending on the defect itself, you may have to remove the chassis and replace components to cure the defect. But you can determine what is wrong with the set, how big a job it will be, and approximately how much it will cost. When you use the techniques described in this chapter, you will find that many troubles can be cleared up by proper adjustment of the controls, without elaborate tests and measurements.

Later chapters deal with the detailed operation of each of the functional blocks mentioned here. The information presented in Chapter 1 will give you a good understanding of all the TV receiver controls and get you an early start in TV servicing. You will be able to eliminate some of the obvious operator's errors before removing the chassis from the cabinet. Even if the set has to go to the shop, you will be able to give the customer a preliminary price estimate.

COMMON MONOCHROME DEFECTS

The typical monochrome TV receiver shown in Figure 1.1 contains all the functions shown in the block diagram of Figure 1.2. The same functions are also used for the monochrome picture in color TV sets, but more about color later.

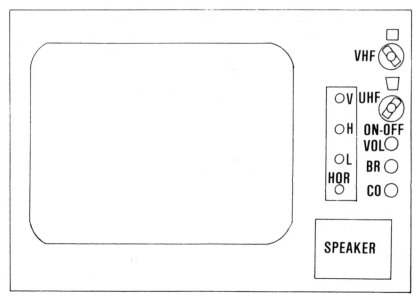

Figure 1.1: Typical Monochrome TV Set Controls

In the block diagram of Figure 1.2, we see the inputs at left; the outputs, sound from the speaker, and the picture on the screen of the picture tube are at the right. VHF and UHF signals are picked up by their respective antennas and brought to their respective tuners. While many TV receivers have electronic tuning systems, some still use a separate switch for the VHF and for the UHF channels. In addition, and not shown in Figure 1.2, there is a fine tuning adjustment for both tuners. All these controls are usually available on the front panel.

Power for the TV set comes in through the AC plug and is controlled by the ON-OFF switch, another front panel control that is often part of the volume control. The weak RF signal from the UHF tuner passes through the VHF tuner, and both rely on the IF amplifier for amplification of the video and sound TV signals. In the detector stage, the video signals are removed from the IF carrier and the sound signals are sent to the FM detector. From there the actual audio signal passes through the volume

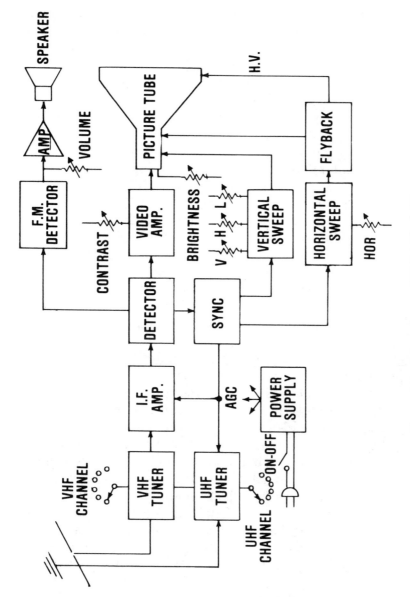

Figure 1.2: Monochrome TV Set Block Diagram

5

control and an amplifier that then drives the speaker. The video signals are further amplified before driving the picture tube. Video gain is adjusted by the contrast control.

The TV signal at the transmitter contains horizontal and vertical synchronizing pulses that are separated by the sync section and then supply the vertical and horizontal sweep section. The sync section also provides automatic gain control voltages (AGC) to the IF amplifier and the VHF and UHF tuner.

TV pictures are generated by a single dot tracing out horizontal lines, with 525 lines forming a complete frame or picture. Thirty complete frames are displayed each second, but, in standard TV practice, the 525 horizontal lines are broken up into two "fields" of 262½ lines each, requiring 60 vertical sweeps per second. The vertical sweep section accepts the 60-Hz vertical sync pulse and produces a 60-Hz sawtooth signal that sweeps the electron beam in the picture tube up and down. In almost all TV receivers there are three secondary controls. The vertical hold (V) controls the synchronization, height (H) controls the height of the picture, and vertical linearity (L) provides adjustment to keep the picture linear in a vertical direction. As you will soon learn, there is a great deal of interaction between these three controls.

The horizontal sweep section is locked to the horizontal sync pulse, which has a frequency of 15,750 Hz. Only the horizontal hold control (HOR) is available as a secondary control, but there are a number of adjustments, such as width, linearity, and a coarse frequency control, that are intended for adjustment only by the service technician. The sawtooth signal from the horizontal sweep section drives the flyback section that generates the horizontal deflection pulse and, from it, develops the high voltage necessary for the second anode of the picture tube. Most monochrome receivers have one or two adjustments that affect the flyback operation accessible only to the service technician.

The power supply section provides the DC power for

all the transistor and IC stages as well as the filament power for the picture tubes and any other vacuum tubes that might be used in the TV receiver. In most power supplies there are no internal adjustments.

In Table 1.1 we have summarized 12 sets of symptoms and indicated for each where the most likely trouble spot is. In the first instance, there is no sound and the picture tube is dark. Under the controls we have listed the ON/OFF switch, the circuit breaker, and the house fuse. This case is obviously one where no power is getting into the TV set or where the power is interrupted right at the power supply. Experienced service technicians know that many service calls have nothing to do with the TV set, but are simply due to either a defective wall socket or power cord or even an open fuse or circuit breaker, which shuts off the power to the wall socket to which the TV set is connected. Once you understand this particular problem, the troubleshooting steps are quite simple. First remove the TV set plug and, instead, plug in a lamp, radio, or other device that you know works correctly. If it fails to work, the AC power is simply not reaching that wall socket and the defect probably has nothing to do with the TV set at all.

If AC power does reach the wall socket, the most likely suspect is the power cord of the TV set. A simple visual inspection often shows the defect right there. Substituting a good power cord or repairing the break is an obvious remedy. Failure of the ON/OFF switch is quite rare, but it is possible that a fuse in the TV set's power supply has opened. In this case you have to get access to the chassis and replace the fuse. Many TV sets have circuit breakers that can be actuated externally, and that is, of course, one of the things you will try. If the fuse blows again or if the circuit breaker drops out, there is probably an overload in the TV set's power supply and more elaborate troubleshooting will be necessary.

The second symptom shows a case where the sound is normal but the picture tube is dark. At least part of the

SOUND	PICTURE	CONTROLS	MOST LIKELY TROUBLE SPOT
None	Dark	On-off switch Circuit breaker House fuse	1. Power supply 2. AC wall socket 3. Power cord
Normal	Dark	Brightness Contrast Channel sw.	1. Flyback 2. Horiz. 3. Video 4. CRT
None	Normal	Volume Channel sw.	1. Amp. 2. Audio 3. Det.
Normal	Gray raster no picture	Contrast AGC level Fine tuning	1. Video 2. Det. 3. IF 4. Tuner
Normal or scratchy	Weak, snowy picture	Channel sw. Fine tuning AGC level	1. Antenna 2. Lead-in 3. Tuner
Normal	Picture tears, weaving strips	Horiz. hold Contrast AGC level	1. Horiz. 2. Sync 3. Det.
Normal	Top or bottom squeezed or expanded	Vert. linearity Height Vert. hold	1. Vertical
Normal	Picture rolls up or down	Vert. hold Height Vert. linearity	1. Vertical 2. Sync
Normal	Picture too narrow	Horiz. drive	1. Flyback 2. Horiz. 3. Yoke
Normal	Picture fuzzy, out of focus	Focus Brightness Contrast	1. Flyback, 2. Power supply 3. CRT
Normal	Picture dim, too large	Brightness	1. Flyback 2. Power supply 3. CRT
Humming	Black bars across screen	------------------	1. Power supply

TABLE 1.1: TV TROUBLE-FINDER CHART (MONOCHROME)

TV receiver's power supply is working, and the problem is associated with the picture tube. Adjustment of the brightness and contrast controls should produce at least some kind of raster. Occasionally a defective channel switch can keep the picture tube dark, but if you can switch through several channels with correct sound and a dark picture tube, the most likely area of defect is the flyback section with its high voltage supply, the horizontal sweep section, or the video amplifier portion itself. A defective picture tube is quite rare, but you can perform a quick check by looking at the back of the tube to see if the filaments of the picture tube are bright. If the filaments are not lit, the defect may be in the picture tube itself or else in the filament circuit.

When the picture tube is normal but there is no sound, we will first try to adjust the volume control. If a channel is mistuned, the same symptom could occur, but you should hear some kind of hum or noise from the speaker. Try the channel switch for the VHF and UHF channels to see if the correct sound appears on some other channel. If none of this helps, it is clear from the block diagram of Figure 1.2 that the defect must be somewhere in the sound channel, in the audio amplifier, the FM detector, or possibly, even in the speaker itself.

In the fourth example, the sound is normal and there is a grey raster on the screen but no picture can be obtained. These symptoms will occur when the contrast control is set to absolute minimum, and therefore we will try adjustment of the contrast control first. If the AGC levels are high enough to cut off the gain of the tuners and the IF amplifier, video signals cannot reach the video amplifier. In most TV sets the AGC level adjustment is accessible only to the service technician, so we try first to see if the fine tuning can bring in the proper channel. Of course, if you can get a decent picture on one channel and not on another, it may be that your antenna has been damaged or is facing the wrong way, or that the tuner itself is misaligned. If none of these adjustments bring in the correct picture with sound, the defect is most likely in the video amplifier section, the detector, the IF amplifier, or possibly even in the tuner. Troubleshooting all these sections requires sophisticated test equipment and removal of the chassis onto the service bench.

The description of normal or scratchy sound coupled with weak, snowy pictures is typical for insufficient signal amplitude reaching the IF amplifier from the tuner, the antenna, or its transmission line. First we try the channel switch and the fine tuning to see if we are really tuned properly to the offending channel. If the AGC level control is readily available, we could try that too, though it is less likely to correct the problem. The most likely trouble spot is the antenna and the transmission line bringing the signal to the tuner. Very often visual inspection of the antenna and the transmission line shows a broken lead, loose connection, or broken antenna element that causes the weak signals. The tuner itself is only rarely at fault, particularly if the symptoms occur only on one or two particular channels.

The next four examples are probably among the most frequent reasons for service calls that don't require any real repair. In example No. 6 the picture tears and seems to appear in weaving strips. Adjustment of the horizontal hold control usually corrects this trouble. In some instances the contrast or AGC level is set too high, causing an overloading of the sync separator. In any case, this symptom is due to loss of horizontal synchronization. When certain of the components in the horizontal sweep section have aged or changed, the horizontal hold control may no longer have sufficient range to lock the sweep to the horizontal sync pulse. In such a case it is often possible to reach the coarse horizontal frequency adjustment by means of a long screwdriver inserted from the rear of the set. Turn this control until the horizontal hold control (HOR) is again within its adjustment range. When this is not possible, a defect in the horizontal sweep section, the sync separator, or the detector itself must be suspected, and more detailed troubleshooting on the bench may be required. Experienced service technicians find that in the majority of cases where these symptoms appear, a simple corrective adjustment of the horizontal hold control does the trick.

When the top or bottom appears squeezed or expanded, the vertical linearity (L) and the height (H) controls can be used to linearize the picture. Adjustment of these two controls will affect the synchronization and will often require readjustment of the vertical hold (V) control. It usually requires a brief period of trial and error with careful observation of the effects of the adjustments of these controls before the picture is linear and stable. If these controls cannot cure the problem, the defect can only be in the vertical sweep section.

Loss of vertical synchronization is indicated when the picture rolls either up or down or jitters in a vertical direction. The first control to adjust is the vertical hold (V), and after that the height (H) and vertical linearity (L) must be adjusted as well. Loss of synchronization may be due to a defect in the vertical sweep or, in a few rare cases, in the sync section itself.

When the picture does not fill the screen to the left and right edges, it appears narrow, and this defect usually originates in the flyback section or occasionally in the horizontal sweep section. As components age, their deterioration often causes the narrowing of the picture. In many of the older TV sets a service adjustment, the horizontal drive control, is available with the use of a long screwdriver. If the adjustment cannot be made, the TV receiver will have to go to the shop. In very rare cases, only one half of the picture appears linear with the other side, left or right, squeezed together. This symptom indicates open or shorted circuits in the deflection yoke that is mounted on the neck of the picture tube.

The symptoms described in examples 10 and 11 can be confused with each other, and both symptoms can be due to defects in the same areas. When the picture appears fuzzy and out of focus, it may be due to misadjustment of the brightness or contrast controls, but it may also be due to misadjustment of the focus control in those older sets that have these controls. Electrostatic focus is used in many sets, which means that one of the picture tube elements is connected to a resistive voltage divider. If one of these resistors becomes defective, this can cause loss of proper focus. In a few older TV receivers magnetic focusing is used, and it is possible to adjust focusing by means of the focusing rings. Defects in the high voltage coming from the flyback circuit, the DC power supply, or the picture tube itself can also cause the same symptom. When the picture is dim and generally too large, try adjusting the brightness control because excessive brightness may cause overload of the high voltage section and lowered high voltage. In most cases this type of defect is due to the flyback, the power supply, or the picture tube itself.

The final example in Table 1.1 illustrates the appearance of power supply interference. None of the controls can be adjusted to eliminate or alleviate this problem. The defect is always in the power supply itself and is usually due to an open filter capacitor. This causes excessive AC ripple on the DC voltages that are supplied to the video and sound channels, causing the humming noise and the black bars across the screen.

After you have been working in the TV service field for a while, you may wish to come back to the block diagram of Figure 1.2 and to the 12 examples of the TV troubles listed in Table 1.1. You will be amazed at how many of your service calls fit into these 12 categories, and you will agree that the first eight examples occur much more often than the last four.

COMMON COLOR DEFECTS

In subsequent chapters we will discuss the detailed operation of the color portion of your color TV receiver, but the block diagram of Figure 1.3 is sufficient to let you troubleshoot and diagnose a large number of common color TV troubles. A quick look at the controls shown in this illustration indicates that the contrast and brightness control, the vertical sweep controls, and the horizontal controls are the same as for a monochrome set. The tuner, IF and sound section are also the same as in the block diagram of Figure 1.2 and are not repeated here. The important sections of this block diagram are the color IF, the color demodulator and its red (R), green (G) and blue (B) driver amplifiers, together with the color sync and the color killer section. They all combine to provide the proper signals to the color picture tube.

In color TV transmission the black-and-white portion of the color signal is transmitted by amplitude modulation of the main RF carrier signal, just as for monochrome transmission. The color information is transmitted on a special 3.58-MHz color subcarrier that is both amplitude and phase modulated; two synchronizing signals, at 3.58 MHz, but at different phase angles, are required by the color demodulator. During each horizontal flyback period a brief burst of color sync information is transmitted along with the horizontal sync pulse. This brief burst is used to lock in a continuous 3.58-MHz oscillator in the color sync section. The tint control permits adjustment of the phase of this reference signal and thereby determines the proper balance of colors.

The color killer section contains a relatively simple circuit that "looks for" the presence of the color sync burst. When the burst is detected, the color killer permits the color IF section to amplify the signal. During monochrome TV transmission, when the burst is not present, the color killer circuit provides a high bias that effectively turns off the color IF amplifier. Without this feature, monochrome transmissions would appear with some unsynchronized dashes of color floating over the black and white picture. The killer potentiometer adjusts the level at which

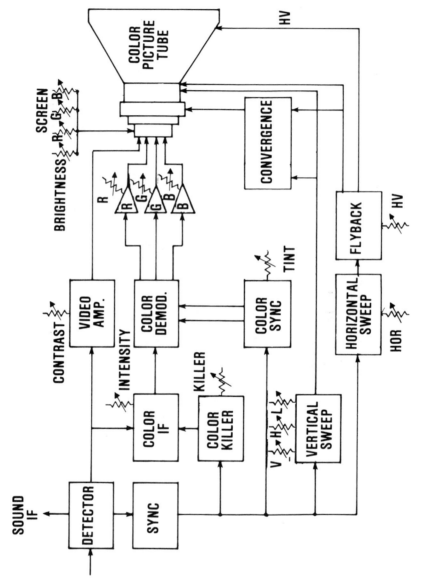

Figure 1.3: Color Section Block Diagram

14

the color killer circuits act to cut the color off on monochrome transmissions.

In the color demodulator section the 3.58-MHz subcarrier is demodulated by both phase and amplitude, and, by a method called color matrixing, the three basic colors are obtained. The fundamentals of color TV are described in Chapter 4 and the operation of the detailed color circuits is covered in Chapter 9. For the moment it is important to realize only that three video signals, corresponding to the R, G and B components of the final color picture, are obtained from the color demodulator. In most receivers separate amplifier stages are required, each with its own gain control, to provide the correct video signal to the color picture tube. Note that the color IF amplifier gain is controlled by a potentiometer marked "Intensity" or "Color." A front panel adjustment in most color TV sets, it determines the intensity or brightness of the colors themselves. Intensity and tint are usually front panel controls, but when the automatic color correction circuit is in operation, the front panel controls are generally inoperative, or have limited adjustment range.

The color picture tube of Figure 1.3 is of the type using three electron guns; this means that there are three separate screen grid controls, one each for the red, green and blue screens. The brightness control, which is on the front panel, generally acts as a master control for them. The three screen controls must be set so that, with no video signal applied to the color picture tube, the raster is a neutral grey or white color. The three gain controls on the R, G and B video amplifiers can only be adjusted properly with a special test signal, such as is available from a color bar generator.

Three-electron gun color picture tubes usually require some means of converging the three electron beams on the screen. For the sake of simplicity, we have shown a single block called "convergence" that receives vertical and horizontal sweep signals and that applies the proper signals to the convergence assembly on the neck of the color picture tube. Depending on the particular receiver model and the type of color picture tube, the screwdriver adjustments required for proper convergence may range from six to fifteen separate adjustments, almost all of them potentiometers mounted on the convergence assembly. Chapter 6 describes the different types of color TV picture tubes and includes a more detailed discussion of the convergence problem. Poor convergence is easily diagnosed just by looking at the picture, but proper adjustment always requires some special test equipment and is best performed on the bench.

Now that we have some idea of how the color portion of a TV set works, let's look at Table 1.2 and the ten examples of color defects that can be diagnosed by using only the screen and the front panel and secondary controls.

The first type of defect is the most obvious. We can receive proper sound and normal black and white pictures, but we cannot receive color on any channel. We first try the color intensity control because when it is turned to minimum, the gain of the color IF amplifier shown in the block diagram of Figure 1.3 is reduced and very little color signal can pass. If adjusting this control does not bring color in, we would next try to reach the color killer control usually accessible by screwdriver from the side or the rear of the chassis. Occasionally, the color killer level is set wrong so that the color killer circuit cuts off the color IF, even when color sync bursts are detected. While it is unlikely that the fine tuning would be misadjusted on all channels, it is possible, and it is easy to try to go through the fine tuning on each channel known to transmit in color. If none of these adjustments have any effect, the most likely trouble spot is, in that sequence, the color IF, the demodulator and the color sync section. Troubleshooting these sections will require some test equipment and removal of the chassis and is best performed on the bench.

Another frequent symptom is that the colors are weak

on all channels. If weak colors appear on only one or two channels and normal color pictures on others, the most likely problem is the alignment of the tuner. When all channels are weak it means that the defect is not very likely to be in the tuner. As indicated in Table 1.2, we would first try to adjust the contrast control and the color intensity. We usually don't worry about the color killer circuit because if any color appears at all, that circuit is working properly. The AGC level control should be adjusted, just as in the case of weak signals mentioned earlier in this chapter. As long as the colors appear correct but weak, the defect will not be in the color sync section and will not be in any of the stages following the color demodulator. As indicated in Table 1.2, the most likely loss of color amplitude is in the color IF. The video amplifier can also cause a loss of color because the final picture is the sum of the black and white portions coming from the video amplifier and the three primary color components. The third likely culprit could be the color demodulator if it contains an amplifier that is common to the three primary colors. Troubleshooting any of these three sections is usually best done on the bench.

The third symptom, weaving stripes of red, green and blue on the screen, indicates to the experienced service technician that the color sync circuit is not synchronized to the transmitted color reference burst. The first adjustment will therefore be the tint control, sometimes also labeled as "hue." In many color sets this control is on the front, with a master control having a much larger range, accessible with a long screwdriver from the rear of the chassis. If none of these adjustments lock in the color, the color sync circuit is not operating properly. This may mean that it does not receive the proper signals from the horizontal sweep section and from the sync separator. To determine this we normally need an oscilloscope, but a quick attempt at adjusting the horizontal hold and the AGC level may indicate where the problem lies. Table 1.2 shows that the most likely trouble spot for this type of

COLOR PICTURE	CONTROLS	MOST LIKELY TROUBLE SPOT
Black & white O.K. No color on any channel	Color intensity Color killer Fine tuning	1. Color IF 2. Color demodul. 3. Color sync.
Weak colors on all channels	Contrast Color intensity AGC level	1. Color IF 2. Video 3. Color demodul.
Weaving strips of red, green & blue	Hue or tint Horiz. hold AGC level	1. Color sync. 2. Sync. 3. Color demodul.
Exaggerated, strong colors on all channels	Color intensity Contrast AGC level	1. Sync. (AGC) 2. Color demodul. 3. CRT controls
Picture too purple or too green	Hue or tint	1. Color sync. 2. Color demodul.
Red, green or blue missing in picture	Red, green or blue CRT controls	1. R, G or B ampl. 2. Color demodul.
Strong colors, fine detail missing	Contrast Fine tuning AGC level	1. Video 2. Det. 3. IF
Gray raster contains colored areas	--------------------	1. Purity ring 2. Convergence ass'y.
Color fringing at either side	Horiz. convergence	1. Color convergence
Color fringing at top and/or bottom	Vert. convergence	1. Color convergence

TABLE 1.2: **COLOR TROUBLE-FINDER**

defect is the color sync circuit itself, with the sync separator and the color demodulator section less likely. The chassis will have to be removed for this type of troubleshooting.

The fourth symptom shows strongly exaggerated colors on all channels. This is exactly the opposite of the second symptom where the colors were very weak. The first attempt at correction will consist of adjusting the color intensity, the contrast, and the AGC level controls. While in the second example this control would be set for maximum gain, in the fourth example they would be set for reduced gain. If none of them seem to correct the problem, we have to look in the sync section, which also provides the AGC voltage, which may be insufficient to control the gain of the tuner and IF amplifier. Just as likely, however, is a misadjustment of the brightness, red, green and blue screen controls. The proper balance between the CRT controls and the video signal controls is important to get normal colors. If none of these controls seem to correct the problem, troubleshooting of the AGC circuits, the color IF and color demodulator has to be performed on the bench.

The fifth symptom is quite common and almost invariably due to misadjustment of the hue or tint control. In the normal range of adjustment, this front panel control should permit you to change the color balance of the scene so that it is either too greenish or too purplish with the center setting approximately correct. The best way to judge when this correct setting has been reached is to look at the flesh tones. They may be too reddish or too yellowish. Many modern color TV receivers provide automatic color balance controls, thus eliminating the need to set the tint control correctly. If the tint control setting cannot correct this problem, the most likely defect is in the color sync section. It is also possible, but less likely, that a defect in the color demodulator section causes the same symptom. If the tint control has no effect whatever and the automatic circuitry is not in operation, this type of symptom may indicate a serious defect requiring bench-type troubleshooting.

Peculiarly colored scenes appear when either the red, the green, or the blue component is missing or weak in the picture. You may find that the scenes tend to be somewhat brownish or somewhat pinkish or somewhat purplish, but the real clue is found in the color of objects that we know to be pure colors. Trees should usually be

green, the sky should be blue, and lips should be red.
Switch the station to a channel that is not used and observe the screen. If the screen has no color but is basically
greyish or white, then the three screen grid controls, R,
G and B, of Figure 1.3, are reasonably balanced. If, however, the entire screen appears yellowish or purplish or
pinkish, then one or two, or possibly all three, of these
controls are not properly adjusted. After you obtain a neutral grey or white screen, tune in a color picture from a
well-received station and see if adjustment of the R, G
and B video gain controls can correct for the missing color.
It is important that only a minimum amount of adjustment
be performed at this step. It is possible to completely mess
up the color adjustment when the video gain controls are
set without using a color bar test pattern. As indicated in
the Table 1.2, the defects are either in the three color video
amplifiers or in the color demodulator. Both require bench
testing.

The symptom described in example 7 of Table 1.2
indicates that the colors are correct but the fine detail that
is normally supplied by the monochrome signal is missing. This is equivalent to having a fuzzy picture in the
monochrome set. The first adjustment will be the contrast
control and fine tuning. The AGC level will be adjusted
next to optimize the monochrome video signal. If this does
not solve the problem, the defect is most likely in the
video amplifier or else in the detector and in the IF, all
of which require troubleshooting on the bench.

The eighth symptom, a grey raster that contains areas
of color, is seen only when there is no color picture on
the screen. It requires that you tune the TV set to an
unused channel or that you short-out the antenna terminals. This type of defect is due to improper adjustment
of the purity ring and convergence assembly in back of
the color picture tube. It can sometimes be observed on
a normal color picture when people move through the
screen and appear in different colors at different places

at the screen. Access to the rear of the color picture tube
almost always requires removal of the back of the set, and,
in some instances, disassembly of the entire cabinet.

The last two symptoms seen on color screens are both
due to convergence problems. Single electron gun color
picture tubes, described in more detail in Chapter 6, should
not display this kind of problem, but all other types of
picture tubes can. In the problem described under example 9, the colors at the sides of the screen appear somewhat like a misaligned color photograph in which the
areas between different colors show a third color. For
example, the area between a blue and green object appears
yellow. The horizontal convergence controls can be adjusted, if they are accessible, by removing the rear of the
set, but only very minimal adjustment is recommended
without a special test pattern generator that projects a
raster line or dot pattern.

The last defect has somewhat the same appearance
as color fringing at the side, but this time the color fringing
appears at the top or bottom, and, in a few very rare cases,
in the center of the screen. Convergence at the top and
bottom is controlled by the vertical convergence circuits,
and, again, only a small amount of adjustment should be
attempted without the availability of a color dot or line
generator. In general, the last three symptoms listed in
Table 1.2 cannot be cleared up by front panel controls or
by simple adjustment of secondary controls in the home.
For proper alignment of the purity and convergence circuitry, the entire color set should be taken to the shop
and the proper sequence of alignment steps should be
followed. These are all described in some detail in Chapter 6.

Experienced service technicians find that the ten
symptoms listed in Table 1.2 account for well over 75
percent of all color TV troubles. Often it is possible to
make adjustments that clear up the problem, but in many
cases actual circuit defects can cause these troubles and

that means removal of the set to the shop and a more elaborate troubleshooting procedure followed by the proper repair.

Experienced troubleshooters also know that in the majority of malfunction situations, a single component or device has gone out of acceptable tolerance. For example, a resistor may have changed in value, or a transistor may have developed reduced gain. If a capacitor becomes defective, it may open-circuit, short-circuit, or become leaky. Catastrophic failures are generally easier to localize than are marginal failures. As an illustration, a leaky capacitor develops a poor power factor, and also introduces a phase shift. For this reason, troubleshooting programs such as 3 and 4 in the appendix provide phase-angle computation to assist in localization of the defective component.

Since most malfunctions are caused by a single defective component or device, basic troubleshooting programs analyze output/input relations for individual off-tolerance conditions. One of the questions confronted at the outset by the troubleshooter is whether the trouble symptom is more likely to be caused by a faulty component such as a resistor, or by a faulty device such as a transistor. Accordingly, programs such as 3 in the appendix include computerized quick-checks to determine whether the device parameters are within acceptable tolerances.

CHAPTER 2

HOW TV RECEIVERS AND MONITORS WORK

This chapter deals with the basic ways in which TV receivers, TV monitors, and computer CRT terminals work. The principles described here cover all types of TV displays, including any kind of TV receiver, monitors for a closed circuit TV camera, a computer CRT terminal, fluoroscopy displays of an X-ray machine, or even the cardiac monitors displaying the heartbeat of critically ill patients in the hospital. All these displays use the same method of scanning, use the same cathode ray tube principles, and depend on synchronizing and video signals. Because TV receivers still form the bulk of the TV servicing business, this chapter also covers the principles and standards for TV transmission. Towards the end of this chapter we will discuss the common functions for TV displays, monitors, and CRT terminals.

Horizontal and vertical scanning of the electron beam in order to create a raster is essential for all the TV displays. The exact numbers of scans per second and the methods of scanning may vary, but the basic scanning arrangement of Figure 2.1 is almost universally used. The screen of the picture tube is filled by fine horizontal lines that are generated by moving the electron beam rapidly from left to right and back to the left. At the same time, the electron beam's scan is gradually moved downward, and, when it reaches the bottom of the screen, it is returned to the top. The left-to-right motion occurs when the actual picture or video signal is present, while the right-to-left motion, which is much faster, is generally called the horizontal retrace or flyback. The screen is blanked out during this retrace period. In Figure 2.1 the dotted lines display, in exaggerated vertical spacing, the odd-numbered lines that are scanned. They start at the upper left-hand corner and end at the lower right-hand corner. The solid lines in Figure 2.1 indicate the even lines that make up the raster. They start at the top center and end at the bottom center of the screen. This "interlaced" scanning method reduces the possibility of flickering of the

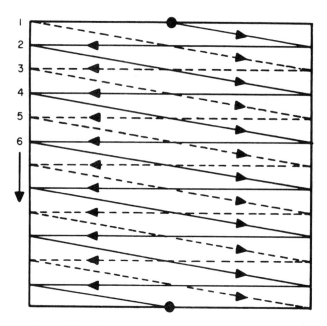

Figure 2.1: Interlaced Scanning.
Reprinted with the permission of Hayden Book Company from *Fundamentals of Television* by Walter H. Buchsbaum.

picture, similar to the rotating shutter used in movie projectors. Interlacing, or alternating the start of each vertical scan, is controlled by the vertical synchronizing pulses.

Commercial TV displays, such as monochrome and color TV receivers, use a raster, or frame, containing 525 horizontal lines. Thirty complete frames are displayed each second, but, because of the interlaced scanning method, 262½ lines, alternatingly odd and even, are shown 60 times a second. Each set of 262½ lines is called a "field." This means that the vertical scanning frequency is 60 Hz.

262½ lines, multiplied by 60 "fields" per second, result in a horizontal scanning frequency of 15,750 Hz. These are the standard scanning frequencies for the United States and Canadian system, based on the 60-Hz power line. In other countries, where the power line frequency is 50 Hz, this is also the vertical field frequency. In the most widely used foreign standards, the horizontal scanning rate is 15,625 Hz while the complete raster contains 625 lines.

The number of lines provided on a TV screen determines the amount of fine detail that can be displayed. This is based on the idea that the number of picture elements contained in each line is limited by the thickness of the line. Each picture element could only be a square with the thickness of the lines as the length of each side of the square. In actual practice, the maximum detail that is displayed on TV receivers and monitors is somewhat less than the optimum. European receivers clearly have an advantage concerning detail because they have a larger number of lines and are therefore capable of better resolution or fine detail. For certain high-resolution applications, usually in science and medicine, special monitors are available that have as many as 1,000 lines per raster. For many applications requiring relatively low resolution, such as in closed circuit TV systems used for security and in electronic games, the 262½-line field of interlaced scanning is simply repeated, without making the effort to interlace the lines.

THE PICTURE TUBE

The obvious key element of any type of TV display or monitor is the picture tube, which can be thought of as a bottle, the bottom of which is the screen. The cross-sectional view of a basic cathode ray tube in Figure 2.2 shows the phosphor screen that emits light at those points where the electron beam strikes it. If the electron beam contains more electrons, is more intense, the light emitted will be brighter. If the electron beam is weak, little or no light will be emitted from that spot. After striking the phosphor screen, the electrons knock secondary electrons off the phosphor and these are then attracted to the second anode, a metallic coating on the inside of the glass envelope that constitutes the cathode ray tube. The elements at the left of Figure 2.2 combine to make up the electron gun. Current through the filament heats up the cathode, which emits electrons. The electrons are attracted to the first anode, which is at a voltage much more positive than the cathode. From there they are accelerated by the high-voltage field of the second anode until they strike the phosphor screen. The number of electrons that reach the phosphor screen is controlled by the negative bias on the control grid located between cathode and anode, as in any vacuum tube. When the video signal is applied between the cathode and the control grid, this signal effectively determines how bright the phosphor screen will light up at every particular point of the raster. In most CRTs the first anode is split into two elements in order to provide an electron lens effect which will then focus the electron beam on a narrow spot over the phosphor screen.

The illustration of Figure 2.2 omits the means to move the electron beam from the center of the CRT. Without the deflection elements the CRT would be useless. In most oscilloscope CRTs the deflection elements are electrostatic plates, mounted inside the neck of the tube in such a way that large, varying voltages on these plates change the field

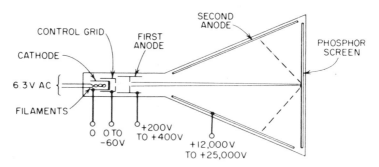

Figure 2.2: Basic Cathode Ray Tube (CRT).
Reprinted with the permission of Hayden Book Company from *Fundamentals of Television* by Walter H. Buchsbaum.

and cause the electron beam to move horizontally and vertically. A set of plates moves the beam from left to right, while another set of deflection plates moves the beam up and down.

In most TV type displays, the method of deflection is an external magnetic field, generated by four coils mounted in a single "deflection yoke." This deflection yoke, as will be described in more detail in later chapters, is mounted over the neck of the tube up against the point where the CRT flares out towards the screen. The coils above and below the neck of the CRT are connected together and combine to move the electron beam from left to right and back from right to left. Two deflection coils mounted on the left and right side of the deflection yoke move the electron beam up and down and back up again. Because a magnetic field moves the electron beam, its motion depends on the current through the deflection coils. Figure 2.3 shows the basic sawtooth current, both for 60 Hz and for 15,750 Hz. The slowly rising portion represents the motion of the electron beam from left to right, or from top to bottom, respectively. The short, rapid downward movement represents the retrace or flyback period when the beam moves from right to left and when the beam moves from the bottom of the screen to the top. During the motion from the bottom to the top, several horizontal sweeps occur; you can see this by turning up the brightness of your monochrome TV set.

A color TV picture is made up of a combination of the red, green and blue primary colors. They can be gen-

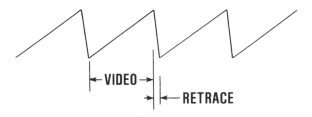

Figure 2.3: Basic Sawtooth Current

erated by three separate CRTs, having a red, green and blue light filter in front of the screen and with their pictures combined by optical means on a single screen. Many projection TV systems operate in just this way. The standard color receiver, however, has a single picture tube that produces the three primary colors; red, green and blue. Chapter 6 describes the various types of color TV picture tubes in detail. The principles involved in color picture tubes are the same as those for monochrome CRTs, with the additional complication of the need to produce, on a single screen, three different color pictures. If you look closely at a color picture tube, you will notice that the screen consists of either an array of red, green and blue dots or an array of red, green and blue vertical stripes. Color TV transmission standards are designed to utilize certain characteristics of the human eye to present a natural-appearing color picture. Chapter 4 explains these color TV standards and their application to color picture tubes.

SYNCHRONIZATION AND VIDEO SIGNALS

The picture on a TV type display usually originates at a TV camera or in a computer. In either case the display must be carefully synchronized, line by line, with the camera or computer. This means that, as the scene is scanned at the camera, the CRT must be scanned exactly in synchronism at the TV display. For this reason each horizontal line is initiated by a synchronizing pulse which rides on top of a blanking pulse, as illustrated in Figure 2.4. The short synchronizing pulse enables the circuitry at the receiver or monitor to lock in with the circuitry at the transmitter, camera, or computer. The wider blanking pulse is necessary to assure that all horizontal lines will start at exactly the same spot, and that the retrace or flyback portion, when the beam returns from right to left, is blanked out and invisible. If this blanking signal were absent, fine

lines representing the retrace lines would be seen superimposed on the picture.

Note that the illustration of Figure 2.4 shows the
video signal varying between the black level and the white
level. This amplitude range represents the gray scale that
can be accommodated in the particular TV system. Towards the center of the line we note that the voltage first
reaches the black level, then goes sharply toward the white
level, and then back to the white level again. If all the
lines of the particular raster were identical, this would
mean that the center of the screen contains a bright, almost
white, vertical stripe, surrounded on either side by a black
area which becomes progressively lighter on either side.
Note that the synchronizing pulse is beyond the black
level, in the so-called blacker-than-black region.

It is important that the horizontal synchronization
be maintained during the relatively long period of the
vertical synchronization and blanking portion. Figure 2.5
shows how this is accomplished. In all commercial TV
systems, the vertical blanking period contains a number
of pulses superimposed at the frequency of the horizontal
synchronizing signal. Beginning at the left of Figure 2.5
we see the last visible horizontal line which is followed
by a number of equalization pulses, very narrow pulses
which are used to keep the horizontal oscillator in synchronism while the electron beam moves from the bottom
to the top of the screen. The vertical synchronizing portion itself is a rather broad series of pulses that are interrupted by small serrations, again to permit the horizontal
oscillator to remain synchronized. The vertical sync portion is followed by more equalizing pulses, and then the
top of the picture starts. The first four lines, as illustrated
in Figure 2.5, are blanked out and are not visible. You
can verify their existence by reducing the contrast and
increasing the brightness of your monochrome picture.
You will see the lines that are normally blanked as well
as a "notch" at the top or the bottom of the screen, rep-

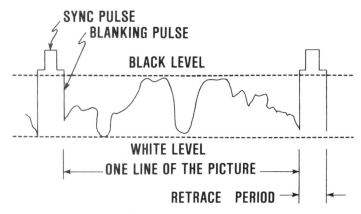

Figure 2.4:   Video Signal for One Picture Line

resenting vertical sync pulse and the beginning of alternate interlaced fields.

The vertical sync pulse illustrated in Figure 2.5 represents the signal transmitted from a commercial TV station. At the receiver, the horizontal and vertical sync pulses
are separated from each other. A high-pass filter or differentiating circuit separates the horizontal sync pulses
and directs them to the horizontal scanning oscillator section where these pulses serve to lock in the horizontal
scanning oscillator to the transmitted signal. A low-pass
filter or integrating circuit is used to remove the horizontal
components from the vertical sync pulse so that the vertical components from the vertical oscillator section can
use it to lock in. In some closed-circuit TV systems, particularly when camera and display are close together, the
vertical and horizontal sync signals are omitted and the
actual vertical and horizontal scanning signals (a sawtooth waveform) are connected on separate wires from the
camera to the monitor. In computer CRT terminals, the
horizontal and vertical sync pulses are usually generated
through a chain of counters and sent to the CRT over
separate wires, if the CRT is located close to the computer.
In those instances where the CRT terminal is remotely

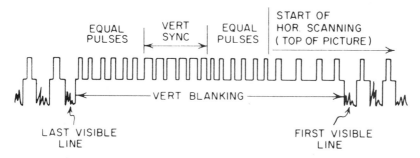

Figure 2.5: Vertical Sync Pulse.
Reprinted with permission of Hayden Book Company from *Fundamentals of Television* by Walter H. Buchsbaum.

located, a composite video signal is generated, complete with horizontal and vertical sync pulses.

TV TRANSMISSION

The following standards of the American Commercial TV System are used in most private or closed-circuit TV systems, usually because of equipment availability. The maximum bandwidth allotted for the basic monochrome video signal is 4 MHz, which represents the approximate theoretical maximum resolution for a 525-line raster. For transmission over radio frequencies this signal is combined with the horizontal and vertical sync pulses, as illustrated in Figures 2.4 and 2.5, and amplitude modulates the RF carrier. The audio signal (usually originating at a microphone and accompanying the picture signal) frequency modulates another RF carrier. The bandwidth of the audio carrier is ± 25 kHz. To save channel space, the lower sideband of the video RF carrier is suppressed by a "vestigial" sideband filter.

Figure 2.6 shows the spectrum distribution of a standard commercial TV channel. Chapter 4 covers in some detail the principles of color TV, but at this point it is sufficient to say that color information is transmitted

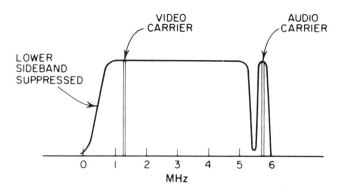

Figure 2.6: TV RF Channel.
Reprinted with permission of Hayden Book Company from *Funda-mentals of Television* by Walter H. Buchsbaum.

on a subcarrier, located at approximately 3.58 MHz above the video RF carrier, frequency-interlaced (explained in Chapter 4) with the monochrome signal so that there is no interference between the two. This color subcarrier is both phase and amplitude modulated and transmits two aspects of the color video signal.

As shown in Table 2.1, the TV stations in the United States are assigned channels 2 through 83, covering three different frequency bands. The lower VHF band, channels 2 through 6, ranges from 54 to 88 MHz. A special 4 MHz gap exists between channels 4 and 5. The higher VHF band covers channels 7 through 13 and ranges from 174 to 216 MHz. The remaining 79 channels, channels 14 through 83, are arranged in continuous 6-MHz-wide bands from 470 to 890 MHz. Some UHF channels in certain areas may be assigned to other services, but UHF TV channels generally operate at lower power and cover a smaller serv-ice area than the VHF channels. Because of the different frequency bands, different antenna lengths are required and these are discussed in Chapter 11. One of the prob-lems created by the channel assignment is the design of a suitable TV RF tuner. In most TV receivers one tuner covers the VHF channels 2 through 13, and a second tuner

Chan. No.	Frequency Band (MHz)	Video Carrier	Audio Carrier	Chan. No.	Frequency Band (MHz)	Video Carrier	Audio Carrier
2	54-60	55.25	59.75	43	644-650	645.25	649.75
3	60-66	61.25	65.75	44	650-656	651.25	655.75
4	66-72	67.25	71.75	45	656-662	657.25	661.75
5	76-82	77.25	81.75	46	662-668	663.25	667.75
6	82-88	83.25	87.75	47	668-674	669.25	673.75
7	174-180	175.25	179.75	48	674-680	675.25	679.75
8	180-186	181.25	185.75	49	680-686	681.25	685.75
9	186-192	187.25	191.75	50	686-692	687.25	691.75
10	192-198	193.25	197.75	51	692-698	693.25	697.75
11	198-204	199.25	203.75	52	698-704	699.25	703.75
12	204-210	205.25	209.75	53	704-710	705.25	709.75
13	210-216	211.25	215.75	54	710-716	711.25	715.75
14	470-476	471.25	475.75	55	716-722	717.25	721.75
15	476-482	477.25	481.75	56	722-728	723.25	727.75
16	482-488	483.25	487.75	57	728-734	729.25	733.75
17	488-494	489.25	493.75	58	734-740	735.25	739.75
18	494-500	495.25	499.75	59	740-746	741.25	745.75
19	500-506	501.25	505.75	60	746-752	747.25	751.75
20	506-512	507.25	511.75	61	752-758	753.25	757.75
21	512-518	513.25	517.75	62	758-764	759.25	763.75
22	518-524	519.25	523.75	63	764-770	765.25	769.75
23	524-530	525.25	529.75	64	770-776	771.25	775.75
24	530-536	531.25	535.75	65	776-782	777.25	781.75
25	536-542	537.25	541.75	66	782-788	783.25	787.75
26	542-548	543.25	547.75	67	788-794	789.25	793.75
27	548-554	549.25	553.75	68	794-800	795.25	799.75
28	554-560	555.25	559.75	69	800-806	801.25	805.75
29	560-566	561.25	565.75	70	806-812	807.25	811.75
30	566-572	567.25	571.75	71	812-818	813.25	817.75
31	572-578	573.25	577.75	72	818-824	819.25	823.75
32	578-584	579.25	583.75	73	824-830	825.25	829.75
33	584-590	585.25	589.75	74	830-836	831.25	835.75
34	590-596	591.25	595.75	75	836-842	837.25	841.75
35	596-602	597.25	601.75	76	842-848	843.25	847.75
36	602-608	603.25	607.75	77	848-854	849.25	853.75
37	608-614	609.25	613.75	78	854-860	855.25	859.75
38	614-620	615.25	619.75	79	860-866	861.25	865.75
39	620-626	621.25	625.75	80	866-872	867.25	871.75
40	626-632	627.25	631.75	81	872-878	873.25	877.75
41	632-638	633.25	637.75	82	878-884	879.25	883.75
42	638-644	639.25	643.75	83	884-890	885.25	889.75

TABLE 2.1: U.S. TV CHANNEL FREQUENCIES.
Reprinted with permission of Hayden Book Company from
Fundamentals of Television by Walter H. Buchsbaum.

covers the remaining UHF channels. TV tuners and their circuits are discussed in more detail in Chapter 7.

TV DISPLAY FUNCTIONS

In Chapter 1 we have presented the basic block diagram of a TV receiver, including some of the circuits required to produce a picture on the picture tube. In this chapter the block diagram of a TV monitor and a computer CRT terminal are shown and the important functions are discussed in some detail. All these are limited to black and white, monochrome pictures. Color TV is taken up in detail in later chapters.

The basic TV monitor block diagram of Figure 2.7

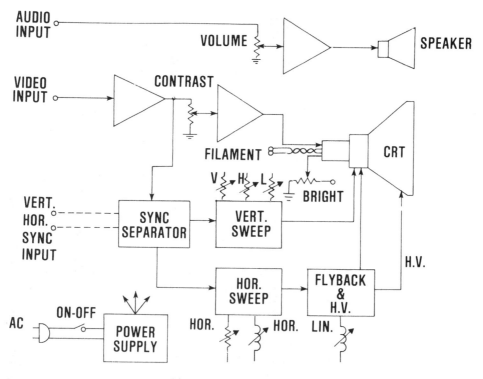

Figure 2.7: TV Monitor Block Diagram

shows an audio and video signal input as well as the AC power plug and ON/OFF switch. Separate inputs, connected by dotted lines, are provided for the vertical and horizontal sync signals. (More about this in a later paragraph.) The audio input signal is expected to be in the range of 0.5 to 1 volts, and goes either to a preamplifier or directly to the volume control and from there to the audio amplifier and speaker. Most monochrome TV monitors do not provide high fidelity or stereo sound reproduction.

The video input signal, with or without the horizontal and vertical sync pulses, is always applied to a preliminary amplifier which can drive the sync separator as well as the output amplifier. We have seen the appearance of a typical line of video signal in Figure 2.4, and for a standard TV monitor input the amplitude between the white level and the black level should be 1 volt. In some monitors inputs are provided for lower level signals as well as for higher level signals, with appropriate amplification or attenuation. A front panel control usually labelled "contrast" acts like the volume control to determine the final amplitude of the video signal reaching the CRT. In some monitors the video signal is applied to the grid, and in others to the cathode of the CRT. When the video signal is applied to the control grid, the black level must be in a negative direction so as to cut off the electron beam for the black and blacker-than-black portions. In that kind of circuit the cathode is usually connected to the brightness control that sets the DC level. In some designs this approach is reversed and the video signal is applied to the cathode, with the black level going positive, and the control grid is then connected to the brightness control, which allows adjustment from ground to a negative voltage for cutoff.

Most modern TV monitors use transistors and integrated circuits so that the filament voltage for the CRT is the only filament requirement, and it is usually connected directly to the filament winding of the power transformer.

We have explained earlier in this chapter how the raster is generated by 525 horizontal lines that form a frame. The vertical sweep section generates a sawtooth signal at a 60-Hz rate that provides the interlaced scanning. As described briefly in Chapter 1, the vertical sweep section contains three separate potentiometer controls. The one labeled "V" controls the vertical frequency and is adjusted so that the picture stands still and does not move either up or down on the screen. The potentiometer labeled "H" controls the height or the amplitude of the sawtooth current through the deflection yoke and is adjusted so that the picture fills the screen on top and bottom. The third control, labeled "L" for linearity, is adjusted to make sure that the top and bottom of the picture are neither squeezed nor expanded and that the horizontal lines throughout the screen appear equally spaced. Chapter 8 describes the actual circuit operation, adjustment, and troubleshooting of the vertical and horizontal sweep section as well as the sync separator portion. It is important that the vertical sweep oscillator, the circuit that generates the sawtooth, be locked in with the vertical sync signal. This signal is provided by the sync separator or is obtained directly as vertical and horizontal sync signals as indicated by the dotted lines. The sync separator performs three functions when it derives synchronizing pulses from the composite video signal. Referring to the illustration of Figure 2.4, we can see that the sync pulses extend into the black level, and this means that the sync separator must first clip or remove the sync pulses from the video signal. This clipping produces a pulse train that includes the vertical and horizontal sync pulses. After clipping, the two signals may need further amplification, and are then separated by high or low pass filters, or, as common TV terminology states, by an integrator and differentiator. The vertical sync pulse arrangement of Figure 2.5 clearly indicates that if this signal is fed into an integrator or low-pass filter, only the broad portion comprising the vertical sync pulse itself should pass through.

The high-frequency elements, which make up the equalizing pulses and the horizontal sync pulses, will be eliminated. In a similar manner, a differentiating network or high pass filter will not pass the vertical sync portion but only the high-frequency portions of the horizontal sync pulses.

Differentiating (lead) circuits and integrating (lag) circuits are extensively used in TV receiver networks for high-pass and low-pass filter action. We find these two basic types of RC filter arrangements in the sync section, as described above, in the chroma section, audio section, and AGC section. In all cases, the operating principles are the same, and troubleshooting of RC filter circuitry is often facilitated by the availability of appropriate computer programs such as provided by routines 3 and 4 in the appendix.

We will frequently find RC bandpass filter circuitry used in the vertical sync section of TV receivers. A typical filter of this type comprises a differentiating branch followed by two integrating branches. Since the integrating portion of the network interacts with the differentiating portion of the network, a comparatively elaborate computer routine is required to assist in troubleshooting of this arrangement. If you want to know more about this type of computerized circuit analysis, refer to *Designing Electronic Circuits* by Robert G. Middleton, published by Prentice-Hall.

The horizontal sweep section itself contains an automatic locking circuit that accepts the horizontal sync pulses and locks the horizontal sawtooth oscillator to them. The frequency of the horizontal oscillator is controlled by two controls, both labeled HOR in Figure 2.7. The coil is usually used as coarse adjustment, and the potentiometer, frequently available at the rear of the monitor, is used as fine adjustment. The output of the horizontal sweep generator is applied to the flyback and high voltage section that provides power amplification for the sawtooth signal to drive the deflection yoke mounted on the neck of the

cathode ray tube. During the retrace period the magnetic
field of the deflection yoke is reversed, and the energy required to do this is also used, through an auto-transformer
circuit, to generate the high voltage. Actual circuit description, adjustment, and troubleshooting are included
in Chapter 8. It is important to know that there is usually
a single control, a variable coil, that allows adjustment
for horizontal linearity. This control prevents squeezing
or expanding the picture at the left or the right side of the
screen.

> Caution: The high voltage required for the second
> anode of any CRT is in the range of 10,000 volts for
> small-screen monochrome CRTs up to 35,000 V or
> more for large-screen color TV picture tubes. This
> high voltage can cause severe burns and electric shock
> to anyone coming in contact with it.

To protect the service technician, the flyback and high-
voltage section of all CRT displays and TV monitors is
enclosed in a special, well-ventilated, high-voltage box.
A heavily insulated cable coming from it, with a plastic
or rubber cover for the anode cap, carries the high voltage
to the second anode of the CRT. Moisture, dust, and dirt
form leakage paths, causing occasional arcing or a corona
effect, a purplish glow around the affected area. Arcing
and corona are among the many troubles described in
Chapter 8 and present a very frequent problem for all
types of CRT devices.

A quick comparison between the TV monitor diagram and the block diagram of the TV receiver shown in
Chapter 1 shows that only the IF and RF portions of the
TV receiver are missing. All other functions are the same.
It is true that the power supply of a TV monitor can be a
little smaller since it does not have to supply power to
the TV tuner and IF section, but since the majority of the
power is required by the vertical and horizontal sweep

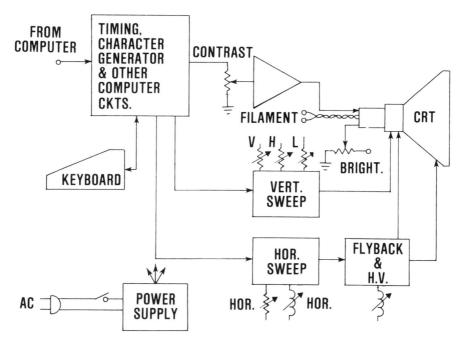

Figure 2.8: Computer CRT Terminal Block Diagram

section and the flyback and high voltage, the difference is very small.

When we compare these two block diagrams with the computer CRT terminal of Figure 2.8, we see that, again, the basic circuits required for the CRT are the same. A computer CRT terminal might have timing, character generator, and other special digital computer circuits as its source for the vertical and horizontal sync pulses as well as the video signal itself. The keyboard and the remote computer provide the information for this type of terminal. Many CRT terminals use small-screen picture tubes, some of them with green or amber rather than white phosphor so that we could speak of a green or amber screen rather than black and white. There are a number of detailed differences between a TV monitor or TV receiver display and a computer CRT terminal. The linearity

in a CRT terminal is usually more critical than that of a
TV monitor simply because a display of alphanumerical
character lines shows up nonlinearities much more than
a picture. The video amplifier portion of the CRT terminal
does not have to cover a gray scale since it only produces
information that is purely digital, on or off. Because computer CRT terminals must be ultrareliable, the circuitry,
components, and layout are usually carefully engineered
and of the highest quality. This applies, of course, to TV
monitors used for critical applications, such as medical
and scientific purposes, but does not always apply to commercial TV receivers.

CHAPTER 3

TV RECEIVER AND MONITOR FUNCTIONS

In Chapter 2 we have seen how TV receivers work, reviewed the current TV broadcast standards, and gained an understanding of the difference between TV receivers, monitors, and computer CRT displays. Now we will discuss specific TV receiver and monitor functions, together with the electronic signals involved in each function. Detailed circuitry is discussed in later chapters, but once we know how a particular stage functions and what the input and output signals look like, we can do a lot of troubleshooting without bothering about individual capacitors, resistors, and transistors.

Figure 3.1 shows a detailed block diagram of a typical monochrome TV set. Each rectangular box represents a particular function, but some may be performed by several ICs or transistors while others may consist of a single diode. In some advanced TV receiver models, several functional blocks may be combined in a single IC. To help us understand how a TV set works, each block in Figure 3.1 represents a specific change in the signal; this is indicated by the numbers enclosed in small circles. These numbers refer to paragraphs later in this chapter that deal with the specific electronic signals involved in each function.

OVERALL MONOCHROME TV SET FUNCTIONS

As illustrated in Figure 3.1, a separate UHF and VHF tuner is assumed for this particular monochrome TV receiver, although, in some of the most recent sets, the two functions are combined on a single chassis. Each tuner is connected through its respective transmission line to the appropriate antenna and converts the transmitted RF TV channel into the IF signal. This signal is then passed through the IF amplifier where it receives most of the amplification and bandpass limiting. Both the VHF tuner and IF amplifier gains are controlled by the automatic gain control (AGC) circuits.

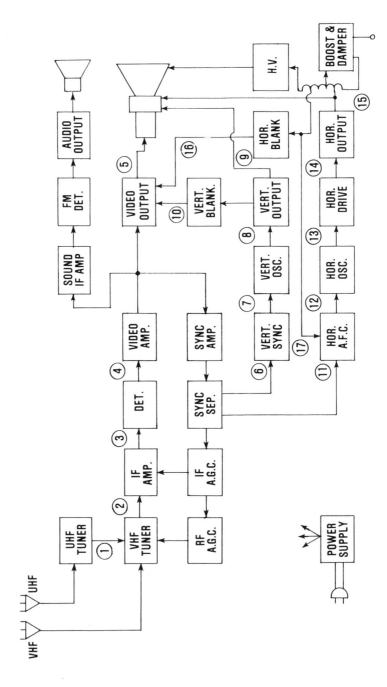

Figure 3.1: Detailed Monochrome TV Set Block Diagram

The output of the last amplifier stage passes through a peak detector that strips off the amplitude modulated envelope and eliminates the IF carrier. After some amplification, the output of the detector is divided into three portions. The composite video signal drives the video output stage, which in turn generates the black and white variations on the picture tube. The sound IF signal, the result of a 4.5-MHz beat between the video and sound IF carrier, is amplified, passed through an FM detector, and the resulting audio signal gets sufficient amplification to drive the loudspeaker. The third portion of the video signal goes through the synchronizing (sync) section where it provides the AGC signal and the vertical and horizontal sync pulses.

The vertical sweep section generates the vertical sawtooth current that drives one half of the deflection yoke while the elements of the horizontal sweep section perform the same function for the horizontal deflection. A high-voltage transformer uses part of the horizontal output to generate the high-voltage through the "flyback" system described in more detail later. The final portion of the block diagram contains the power supply that takes AC power and converts it to the required DC voltages and currents for each of the other receiver sections.

DETAILED MONOCHROME TV SET FUNCTIONS

1. The UHF tuner selects one of the UHF channels, a 6-MHz-wide frequency band ranging from 470 to 884 MHz. As illustrated in Figure 3.2, the output of the UHF tuner covers a frequency range of approximately 4.5 MHz in the IF band. Most UHF tuners contain a preselector, an oscillator, and a mixer. The frequency difference between the oscillator and the selected UHF station ranges from 41.25 to 45.75 MHz, the 4.5 MHz separation between the video and the audio RF carrier.

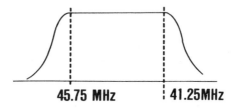

45.75 MHz ⋮ **41.25MHz**

Figure 3.2: UHF Tuner Output

The VHF tuner operates in a similar manner except that it usually contains an RF amplifier and covers the frequency bands from 54 to 88 MHz and from 174 to 216 MHz. When the VHF tuner is switched to the UHF position, its preselector and RF amplifier are usually tuned to the 41.25 to 45.75 MHz IF band and the local oscillator is disabled. This provides the same gain for the converted UHF signal that the VHF signal gets before it goes to the IF amplifier.

2. As we just learned, the VHF tuner contains a local oscillator, an RF amplifier and preselector, and a mixer or converter stage. Unlike the UHF band, the VHF band is not continuous and is broken up into the lower and upper VHF band. Channels 2 through 6, from 54 to 88 MHz, are in the lower band and channels 7 through 13, from 174 to 216 MHz, are considered the upper VHF band. The local oscillator is usually operated at a frequency above the selected VHF channel, and produces, in the mixer or converter stage, the IF as the difference signal. Typical amplitudes at the input of the VHF and UHF tuner would be 50 microvolts and up, while at the output of the VHF tuner, at point 2 in the block diagram of Figure 3.1, the minimum output signal will be approximately 20 millivolts.

3. When the IF signals pass through the IF amplifier section, they receive anywhere from 50 to 70 db of amplification and undergo considerable frequency selection. The output amplitude of video signals at point 3 in the block diagram of Figure 3.1 will range from 0.5 to 2 volts. The frequency response of the IF

section is illustrated in Figure 3.3. A separation or "dip" has been provided between the frequency band carrying the video signals and the audio carrier and its sidebands. In addition, the relative amplitude between the video and audio portion has been changed. If the audio IF signals were approximately the same amplitude as the video IF signals, the detected audio signal would appear as interference on the screen. RF and IF misalignment is often apparent when the audible signal appears on the screen in the form of interference. In general, at least 45 db amplitude difference is specified between the audio carrier and the video portion. In order to obtain the steep skirts of the video IF response curve, precisely tuned filter circuits are used at various stages of the IF amplifier. Chapter 7 describes these circuits in some detail and contains alignment and troubleshooting instructions for these receiver functions.

4. When the IF video signal is passed through a simple diode peak detector, the amplitude modulated envelope, the composite video signal shown in Figure 3.4, is stripped off. This signal contains the vertical and horizontal sync and blanking pulses and the actual video signal itself. Because a diode peak detector also acts as a heterodyne mixer, both the sum and the difference of the video and audio IF carrier are produced. The difference between them is 4.5 MHz.

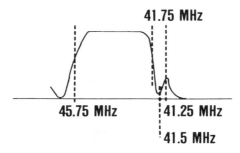

Figure 3.3: IF AMP Output

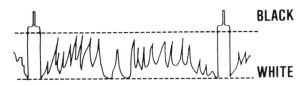

Figure 3.4: Detector Output

The sum is 87 MHz, a frequency that is easily filtered out and considerably higher than the response of any of the following stages.

The signal at point 4 consists of two main components, the composite video signal and the 4.5 MHz sound IF signal, frequency modulated by the audio signal. Both of these signals are passed through one stage of video amplification and then take different routes. The 4.5-MHz sound IF is selected by a resonant 4.5-MHz network, amplified by the sound IF amplifier, and passed on to the FM detector. This stage removes the frequency modulated audio signal and passes it to the audio output amplifier.

5. The video output stage simply provides the voltage amplification and driving power for the cathode ray tube and accepts the vertical and horizontal blanking signals. This means that the detected composite video signal shown in Figure 3.4 will appear without the synchronizing pulses and a slightly wider blanked portion than the transmitted signal, as illustrated in Figure 3.5. Depending on the particular TV receiver and picture tube, the amplitude of that signal may range from 30 to 150 volts at the blanking levels that are always in the blacker-than-black region.

The output of the first video amplifier also goes to the sync amplifier. In most TV receivers this stage provides amplification and clipping so that only the sync pulse, without the blanking pedestal, is supplied to the sync separator stage. This stage performs a number of functions. It develops a varying DC voltage, the amplitude of which depends on the ampli-

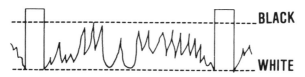

Figure 3.5: Video Output

tude of the sync pulse. While not shown in the block diagram of Figure 3.1, a portion of the horizontal flyback pulse is used to enable the AGC circuits only during the horizontal sync period. Detailed operation of this "keyed" AGC is explained in Chapters 7 and 8.

6. The main function of the sync separator is to separate the 15,750-Hz horizontal sync signal from the 60-Hz vertical signal. As we know from Chapter 2, the vertical sync pulse really consists of a number of serrations with pulses riding on them which occur during the vertical flyback period. As illustrated in Figure 3.6, the vertical sync pulse and its serrations are integrated into the proper waveform and applied to the vertical sync section. That stage amplifies and clips the signal so that a sharp 60-Hz pulse, with a typical amplitude of about 5 volts, appears at point 7 to synchronize the vertical oscillator.

7. This stage is usually a free running multivibrator or blocking oscillator type of circuit that generates a substantial pulse at approximately 60 Hz. In the absence of a vertical sync pulse, the vertical oscillator generates the signal required for the vertical deflection output. When sync pulses are available, the vertical hold control, discussed in some detail in Chapter 1,

Figure 3.6: Vertical Sync Input

is used to make sure that the picture does not jitter or roll up or down on the screen.

8. The output of the vertical oscillator, point 8 in Figure 3.1, looks essentially the same as the vertical sync pulse of Figure 3.7 except that the pulse is somewhat wider and at least 10 volts in amplitude.

9. The vertical output section is usually a power transistor stage and includes an R-C charging network to generate the vertical sawtooth. As illustrated in Figure 3.8, the vertical sawtooth signal is approximately 30 volts in amplitude and consists of two portions. A negative-going pulse portion is followed by the actual sawtooth signal. This combination voltage waveform, as illustrated, is necessary to generate a straight sawtooth current through the coils.

10. The vertical output section also provides a strong pulse during the vertical retrace or flyback period that is applied to the vertical blanking stage and from there (see point 10 in Figure 3.1) to the video output amplifier.

11. The sync separator selects the horizontal sync pulse from the vertical pulse by a differentiating network, discussed in more detail in Chapter 8. The appearance of this signal, with approximately 5 volts typical peak-to-peak amplitude, at a frequency of 15,750 Hz, is illustrated in Figure 3.9. This signal is applied to the horizontal automatic frequency control circuit (AFC) where its frequency is compared with a portion of the flyback signal from the horizontal output stage. When both the incoming sync and the feedback pulse are at the same frequency, the output of the

Figure 3.7:   Vertical Sync Output

Figure 3.8: Vertical Sawtooth

AFC circuit will be zero. If the incoming signal is higher in frequency the output may be positive, or, depending on the particular circuit, negative. The response curve of a typical AFC circuit is shown in Figure 3.10 and indicates the variation in positive and negative DC error voltage.

12. At point 12 in Figure 3.1, the error voltage controls the frequency of the horizontal oscillator. Most TV receivers have a filter with a selected time constant between the frequency detector and the oscillator so that a loss of synchronization for a few horizontal lines does not immediately affect the horizontal oscillator.

13. The horizontal oscillator is a free-running mulvibrator or similar circuit that usually includes an L-C network to stabilize the horizontal frequency during one or two frames. The waveform at point 13 in Figure 3.1 is shown in Figure 3.11 and illustrates the combination of a sine wave and the horizontal pulses. The horizontal hold control discussed in Chapter 1 sets the frequency of the horizontal oscillator. In addition to the accessible rear or subpanel control, there are also one or two coarse controls that determine the horizontal oscillator frequency.

Figure 3.9: Horizontal Sync

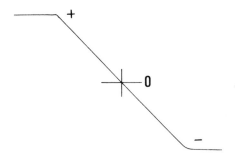

Figure 3.10: DC Error Voltage Response

14. The horizontal drive stage usually contains an R-C network to convert the pulse signal into a combination sawtooth and pulse signal, as described above for the vertical output stage. The major difference between the signals shown at point 14 and at point 15 of Figure 3.1 is the amplitude of the flyback pulse and the total power available in the sawtooth portion.

15. Figure 3.12 illustrates a typical horizontal deflection signal as it would appear at point 15 and across the horizontal deflection coils. The autotransformer shown in Figure 3.1 emphasizes the flyback pulse which is increased in amplitude up to 20,000 volts, rectified, and filtered to provide the high DC voltage for the second anode of the picture tube. The operation of the boost and damper, as well as more detailed information on the circuits, adjustment, and troubleshooting of the entire deflection and high-voltage portion, is contained in Chapter 8.

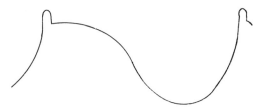

Figure 3.11: Horizontal Oscillator Output

Figure 3.12:   Horizontal Sawtooth

16. Horizontal blanking pulses are obtained from the fly-
    back transformer and passed through a blanking stage.
    Applied to the video output stage, the blanking pulses
    cut off the TV screen during the flyback period.

No TV set or monitor would be complete without the
power supply. In general, TV set power supplies use a
transformer to change the AC line voltage to the desired
voltage levels for rectification and filtering. Voltage and
current regulation is provided in many types of receivers
and monitors and in almost all CRT terminals. For a more
detailed discussion of power supplies, adjustment and
troubleshooting, see Chapter 10.

Portions of the detailed block diagram of Figure 3.1
are identical to the detailed block diagram of most TV
monitors. The UHF and VHF tuner, the IF and AGC sections are all omitted. In a closed-circuit TV system the
output of the camera would be connected directly at point
4 in Figure 3.1. If the camera is relatively close to the
monitor, separate lines for the vertical and horizontal sync
signals can be brought directly to points 6 and 11, respectively, in Figure 3.1, eliminating the need for the sync
amplifier and sync separator. Because a separate audio
channel would be used, if any sound is provided at all,
the sound IF amplifier and FM detector stage are omitted.
A typical TV monitor consists of the audio output stage
driving the loudspeaker, the video preamplifier and video
output stage, the picture tube, the vertical sync, oscillator
output and blanking section, and the equivalent portions

for the horizontal sync, complete with HV power supply, booster and damper circuits. Of course, an AC power supply is also part of the monitor. Once we understand the detailed functions of the monochrome TV set, we also appreciate how a TV monitor works. A computer CRT display, however, may contain some different functions as described below.

COMPUTER CRT DISPLAY

Monochrome computer CRT displays are grouped into two major types, monitors that are built into computer systems or other data display devices, and stand-alone monitors that are meant to be connected to computers. Color monitors are even further subdivided, and those units will be discussed in Chapter 5. Monochrome Data display monitors are almost universally found with green or amber long-persistence phosphors that reduce the effects of flicker, which can be annoying to persons who must spend many hours working in front of the terminal.

Stand-alone monitors have almost identical sections to television receivers. Referring to Figure 3.1, the monitor does not contain the tuner, IF amp, detector or AGC stages. The sound IF and FM detectors are also missing; however, some monitors contain an audio amplifier and speaker for connection to computer systems with audio capabilities. All other circuits are usually present, though typically, they are designed with wider bandwidth in the video stages, and usually high-reliability components.

The power supply section in stand-alone monitors is isolated from the AC line, a feature not usually found in current-model TV receivers. Isolation is required in a monitor that must be directly connected to other equipment that is also connected to the AC line, and is provided inside the monitor usually by a power transformer-based power supply circuit. This ensures that the chassis of all equipment that is interconnected together are safely tied to earth ground.

The monitor that is built into a computer, or other specialized data display device, is very similar to the stand-alone monitor; however, there are circuits ahead of the video portions that are responsible for delivering the appropriate data to the CRT display. Let's look at a typical computer CRT display in a commonly found microcomputer system.

The detailed block diagram of Figure 3.13 contains a power supply, a vertical sweep section, a horizontal sweep and high-voltage section, a video amplifier and picture tube, all basically identical to those used in the TV receiver of Figure 3.1. The main difference between the monochrome TV set of Figure 3.1 and the computer CRT display block diagram shown in Figure 3.13 lies in the eight logic blocks that generate the alphanumerical display and control the vertical and horizontal sweep section. A detailed circuit analysis of these logic functions is beyond the scope of this book, but a brief functional description will allow the reader to work on computer CRT displays and, in particular, align and troubleshoot the TV portion of it.

We can summarize the logic functions in a computer CRT display as follows:

- Data and address information are stored in the display RAM.
- At this point, a particular alphanumeric character is represented by its respective binary code.
- From the display RAM, the binary codes are passed on to the ROM character generator.
- This function converts binary codes into a series of pulse signals that result in a dot matrix, alphanumeric display on the TV screen.
- A shift register is interposed between the ROM char-

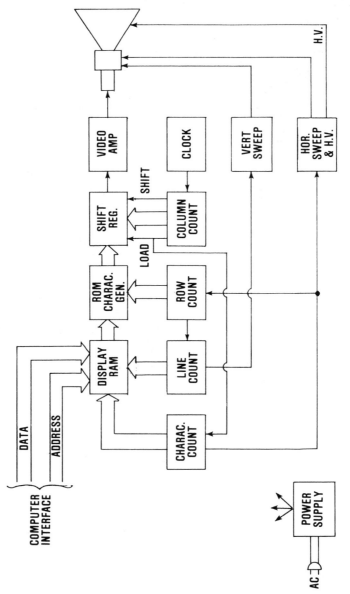

Figure 3.13: Computer CRT Display Block Diagram

acter generator and the video amplifier to convert the
pulse information into a serial pulse train that generates the desired alphanumerical display.

- A group of four separate counters, driven serially
  from a master clock, provides all the timing signals
  for the digital portion as well as for the horizontal
  and vertical sweep.

- Because of these internal relationships, there is no
  need for a sync section, and even the video signals
  are digital in nature. There may or may not be an
  audio channel.

While the actual TV portion of a computer CRT display is relatively simple, the digital circuitry on which
the final display depends can be just as complex as the
analog circuitry that is used in monochrome TV receivers.
Here is a more detailed outline of how the RAM, the ROM,
and the shift register operate:

DISPLAY RAM

This logic function is a random access memory (RAM)
that interfaces directly with the computer and receives
data and address information over the interface bus (a set
of standard, multiwire connections). The data consists of
a binary number that is translated into an alphanumerical
character in the next functional block. The address information from the computer indicates where a particular
binary number, representing data, should be stored in the
display RAM. When fully loaded, the display RAM represents, in binary codes, the contents of the display screen.
The display RAM is controlled by two counters. The line
counter locates the horizontal lines on which characters
will appear, and the character counter locates the spot
where each character should appear.

ROM CHARACTER GENERATOR

As indicated by the first three letters, this is a read-only memory (ROM) that stores the video information for each alphanumeric character. When a display RAM data word is entered into the ROM, the corresponding alphanumeric video information is read out of the ROM character generator, under the command of the row counter. Figure 3.14 shows how a typical character (the letter S) and a typical numeral (number 7) are represented on the TV screen. Note that each letter or numeral is nine horizontal lines high and seven horizontal lines wide. In other words, each character is composed by illuminating a number of selected dots in a 7 × 9 dot matrix. As the electron beam sweeps across the screen, it will be turned on to generate dots of light which then, on the entire screen, give the impression of letters and numerals.

Figure 3.14: ROM Character Generator Display

SHIFT REGISTER

This stage accepts the information from the ROM character generator in parallel form and then delivers it in serial form to the video amplifier. The control for the shift register comes from the column counter that receives its signal from the master clock. As illustrated in Figure 3.13, the clock to the shift register must have a frequency equivalent to the number of horizontal picture elements so that the output of the shift register is shifted by one for each picture element. The column counter also provides other timing signals to the shift register, and, more important, to the load control that enables each new character from the ROM character generator to be loaded into the shift register. The load signal also advances the character counter, which then informs the display RAM to move one character over and load another character from the display RAM into the ROM character generator. The output of the character counter drives the horizontal sweep section and the row counter. The row counter sends a signal to the line counter when a particular row is finished, causing the line counter to advance to the next TV line. When the total number of lines, usually 265, has been finished, the line counter sends a signal to the vertical sweep section to start another vertical sweep.

The video amplifier and vertical and horizontal sweep sections perform exactly the same funtions as in TV receiver or monitor, but their frequency response and linearity are usually much better. This is necessary because the human eye is more critical when reading text than when observing pictures. (More about this in Chapters 8 and 9 where the deflection and video circuits are covered in some detail.)

Electronic technicians who are unfamiliar with digital trouble shooting tend to suppose that this is one of the "black arts." However, digital troubleshooting is often easier than analog trouble shooting— although the digital troubleshooter must "learn the ropes." The "secret" of learning the ropes is to start at the beginning and to get the knack of digital test procedures and trouble analysis while becoming at home with digital circuitry and terminology. It is also a "must" to get your hands on some digital devices and digital test equipment. You can also put some of your familiar analog test equipment to good use in digital troubleshooting procedures.

CHAPTER 4

HOW COLOR TV WORKS

This chapter presents a brief overview of the fundamentals of colorimetry as they are used in color TV, and deals with the electronic signals that are required to produce the color picture on the TV screen. Because millions of monochrome TV receivers existed in the United States when color TV became available, it was necessary to set up color TV signal standards that would not interfere with monochrome reception. This "compatible" color TV system, originally known as the NTSC system, is unique in the United States and Canada and differs from the systems used in many European countries.

You may remember from physics that light is electromagnetic radiation, as are radio and TV signals, and that the visible spectrum merely represents a frequency range of electromagnetic radiation to which the human eye is sensitive. The colors visible to the human eye range from about 700 nanometers in wavelength, for the red and near-infrared, to about 400 nanometers, for the blue going towards the ultraviolet. All visible light is composed of the pure, or primary, colors shown in Figure 4.1 (see color insert). When we see white light, or some other color, we usually receive not a single, pure frequency but a mixture. The illumination provided by light-emitting diodes (LED) is usually pure, but the light coming from an incandescent bulb, a fluorescent bulb, a candle, or the fire in the fireplace is always a mixture of colors.

The human eye, like the ear, has some unique characteristics. Green, which lies at approximately the center of the visible spectrum, is the most visible color—the eye is most sensitive to it. This means that we can see a green light over a longer distance than we can an equivalent intensity of either red or blue. This is an important factor when colors are mixed.

HOW WE SEE COLOR

Light can reach the human eye in two ways. Transmitted light is light we see coming directly from its source, as when we look through a stained glass window or when we look directly at an LED display or a TV picture tube. When we look at colored objects we receive light via reflection. Reflected light acts somewhat differently from transmitted light. The color of the light shining on the object influences the reflected light we see as well as the color of the object itself. Stage lighting in the theater, in motion pictures, and in TV studios is a good example of this effect. When we look at transmitted light, however, somewhat different effects take place. When we shine a red light and a blue light on a ground glass plate and look at the plate from the other side, we will see a shade of purple. When we shine a red light and a green light on that same glass plate, we will see yellow. Color addition (the process just described, for transmitted light) follows some very important rules that will be described in detail a little later in this chapter and which form one of the fundamentals of color TV.

Like the human ear, the human eye has the ability to integrate different stimuli, different colors, into a single sensation. When you look at an array of small dots of different colors from a distance, the dots will disappear and color mixing takes place. For transmitted light, such as is used in color TV, only three primary colors—red, green and blue—are necessary.

The color diagram of Figure 4.2 (see color insert) is used as an explanation for the color characteristic of the human eye. All the pure colors appear along the outside, as indicated by their frequencies. The straight line between the 400 millimicron and the 700 millimicron colors represents mixed colors, combinations of red and blue, and these colors do not appear in the rainbow. This color diagram represents all possible colors at a fixed level of illumination. If we draw a straight line between the 580 and 450 millimicron colors, we see the white area. This means that, for transmitted light only, a 580 millimicron orange, when added to 450 millimicron blue, will appear white to the observer. White is often called a noncolor because it can be produced by mixtures of other colors.

While the color diagram of Figure 4.2 represents colors of equal intensity or illumination, the true range of visible colors, of course, also includes the colors that are mixed at different levels of intensity. When talking of the intensity of colored light, the term *luminance* is usually used as compared to *brightness*, which refers to the white only. Figure 4.3 (see color insert) is a representation, for purposes of explanation only, of the entire range of colors that we can see. At the apex of a pyramid would be black, the absence of any illumination; while at the base, in the large color diagram, the brightest white and the highest luminance the eye can tolerate would appear.

As the luminance or brightness is reduced, the range of visible colors shrinks, as indicated by the much smaller color diagram closer to the black. This is due to the anatomy of the human eye. Beyond a certain level of illumination, the human eye cannot distinguish colors but can still see black and white. The old saying that at night all cats are gray is based on this anatomical fact. We will refer to the color pyramid a little later when the actual color signal transmission characteristics are discussed.

For color TV, as well as color printing and color photography, it is not possible or necessary to reproduce all the colors in the color diagram. Most of the pure colors rarely appear in nature and practically never in the man-made environment. The color diagram of Figure 4.4 shows a triangle made up of red, green and blue, well within the actual color diagram. At the center of this triangle is white. These three colors, R, G and B, represent the primary colors used in color TV, and are the ones reproduced by the red, green and blue dots or stripes on your color pic-

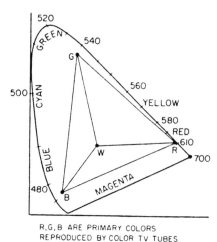

R,G,B ARE PRIMARY COLORS
REPRODUCED BY COLOR TV TUBES

Figure 4.4: Color Signal Relationships.
Reprinted with permission of Hayden Book Company from *Fundamentals of Television* by Walter H. Buchsbaum.

ture tube. White lies somewhere in the middle of this triangle as indicated. White can always be obtained on the color picture tube by illuminating at proper amounts the red, green and blue dots and stripes. It is clear from the color diagram that a proper mixture of red and green would produce yellow, a proper mixture of red and blue would produce magenta, and a proper mixture of blue and green would produce cyan. If we take the equation white = red + green + blue, and separate out the primary colors, we obtain the following equations:

$$B = W - (R + G)$$
$$G = W - (R + B)$$
$$R = W - (G + B)$$

These equations are often called the color difference equations, and they play an important part in the mixing and manipulation of electrical signals as explained later in this chapter.

When we translate the luminance of the three primary colors into voltages and label them accordingly, the relative magnitudes of red and green and blue voltages to produce one volt of white are indicated by the following equation:

$$E_Y = 0.3\ E_{red} + 0.59\ E_{green} + 0.11\ E_{blue}$$

Any of the colors in the triangle bounded by R, G, and B of Figure 4.4 can be reproduced by shining various amounts of these three primary colors on the screen. That is exactly how the color TV picture tube works. Different intensities of the red, green and blue dots are used to generate a whole gamut of colors.

The colors that lie within the color diagram represent only one level of brightness, but, as we have seen in Figure 4.3, the true range of colors is represented by a pyramid. To reproduce any of the colors in the pyramid, we could use the three primary colors of varying intensities and thereby select any point in the color space contained within the color pyramid. Another way of doing this, however, is to use the white portion, the brightness or "Y" signal, and let its magnitude indicate which of the many color diagrams that make up the pyramid is represented. Then we need only the distance from the white and the angle from a specified reference to indicate the selected color.

This concept, translating the red, green and blue magnitudes into a coordinate system consisting of the white magnitude, the location and magnitude of a vector, is the one used in the color TV transmission system that is standard in the United States and Canada. These three coordinates are called the brightness (Y), the hue and the saturation. Hue is indicated by an angular measurement and saturation is indicated by the distance from the white point.

STANDARD COLOR TV SIGNALS

In the early days of color TV, two standard signals were chosen, labeled the **I** and the **Q** signals. In vector representation, the **I** signal was displaced 57° from a reference signal, while the **Q** signal was at a 90° angle of the **I** signal.

In most modern color TV receivers, **I** and **Q** signals are not used, but the color difference signals, **R–Y**, **B–Y**,

and **G–Y**, are obtained by the color decoder circuit. Figure
4.5 illustrates these color difference vectors, their angular
reference to each other and to the reference signal itself.
Note that the blue difference signal is 180° away from the
reference signal while the **R–Y** signal is 90° away. Instead
of the **I** and **Q** vectors, the most commonly used notation
has been the **X** and **Z** vectors as illustrated in Figure 4.5.
The TV transmitter must send out a standard Y or brightness signal that is identical to the monochrome TV information. In addition, it must send out two other sine
waves representing either the **X** and **Y** vectors or the **I**
and **Q** vectors. These sine waves are modulated onto the
color subcarrier that is located approximately 3.58 MHz
higher than the monochrome video carrier.

This color subcarrier is both amplitude and phase
modulated by the color information and uses a method
called frequency interlacing to avoid interference with the
monochrome video signal. Frequency interlacing is based
on spectrum analysis of the actual monochrome video

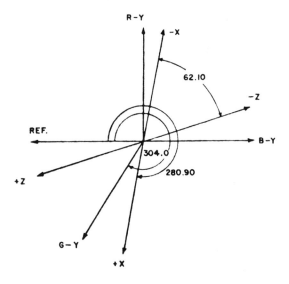

Figure 4.5: Color Difference Vectors.
Color TV Servicing, 3rd Ed., Walter H. Buchsbaum. Prentice-Hall, Inc.

signal. As illustrated in Figure 4.6, the actual mono-chrome video signal does not occupy a continuous frequency band from 0 to 4 MHz but rather consists of a series of narrow bands that are harmonics of the line frequency. Frequency interlacing is accomplished by placing the color subcarrier and its sidebands 15 Hz away from the monochrome video signal. As a result the color subcarrier information is interlaced, as seen on a spectrum analyzer, between the narrow bands of the monochrome video signal. To achieve this, the exact frequency of the color subcarrier is 3.579545 MHz, but for simplicity the 3.58-MHz figure is used in this book.

The signal shown in Figure 4.6 can be received by monochrome TV receivers that will not notice the effect of the color subcarrier at all. Only a color TV set, which has special circuits for detecting the color subcarrier and demodulating it, can use the color information.

In order to detect the color subcarrier, the receiver circuits must have an exact reference frequency of 3.579545

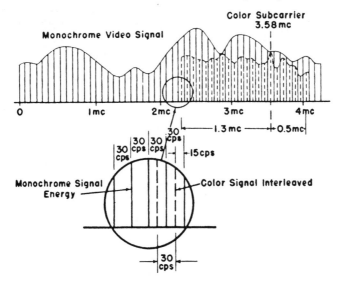

Figure 4.6: Frequency Interlacing.
Color TV Servicing, 3rd Ed., Walter H. Buchsbaum. Prentice-Hall, Inc.

MHz, exactly in phase with the reference signal at the transmitter. This color reference signal is transmitted from the TV station to your receiver by means of a short, 8-cycle burst that is modulated on the blanking pedestal, next to the horizontal sync pulse, as illustrated in Figure 4.7. A local oscillator in the receiver is synchronized with this "color burst" to generate the reference signal continuously and exactly in phase with that at the transmitter. With this reference signal it is possible to demodulate the color subcarrier and to determine the phase as well as the amplitude of the vectors that carry the **X** and **Z** information. The detailed discussion of these circuits appears in Chapter 9.

The basic color-demodulating functions are illustrated in the simplified block diagram of Figure 4.8. The composite video signal goes, as in monochrome sets, to a video amplifier that drives the picture tube. Although in this illustration the brightness or Y signal is shown going to the cathode of the color picture tube, this is merely a convenient convention. In three-gun color picture tubes, the three cathodes may be connected together to receive the Y signal. If the three control grids were all returned to a fixed suitable voltage, the Y signal alone would produce a monochrome picture on the color picture tube.

The composite video signal containing the 3.58-MHz subcarrier goes to the color IF amplifier where the 3.58-

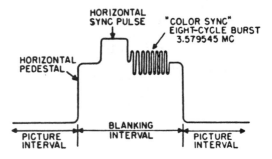

Figure 4.7: Color Sync Burst.
Color TV Servicing, 3rd Ed., Walter H. Buchsbaum. Prentice-Hall, Inc.

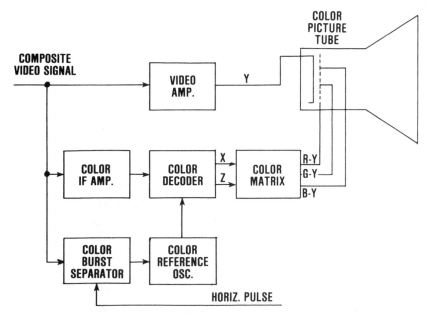

Figure 4.8: Basic Color Demodulating Functions

MHz color IF signal is amplified considerably. In standard color TV transmission, the amplitude of the color subcarrier is considerably less than that of the video signal, with which it is frequency interlaced. After amplification, the 3.58-MHz color subcarrier goes to the color decoder. This stage also receives the precise 3.579545-MHz reference signal which is necessary to remove the color information from the subcarrier. Detailed circuit operation will be described in Chapter 9.

The composite video signal also contains the horizontal blanking and sync pulse and the eight cycles of color reference signal that are transmitted on the blanking pedestal, as illustrated in Figure 4.7. In the color burst separator, the horizontal keying pulse obtained from the flyback transformer is used to remove the reference signal, which then sets the exact phase and frequency of the color reference oscillator. Since both phase and frequency are very critical, most color reference oscillators are controlled within a relatively narrow frequency and phase range due to the color burst itself.

Once the **X** and **Z** color vectors are removed from the color subcarrier, vector addition and subtraction is required to produce the red, green and blue color difference signals. This is performed in the color matrix section, usually a series of three amplifiers with appropriate adding and subtracting networks. When the three color difference signals, actual video signals, are applied to the control grids of the red, green and blue electron guns in the color picture tube, simple addition occurs between the cathode and the control grid. This is how the actual flow of electrons in each of the red, green and blue electron gun beams is made to represent, in magnitude, the original red, green and blue primary color components of each picture element. Another way of saying the same thing is to say that the Y or brightness signal is added electronically to the difference signals resulting in red, green and blue picture elements that finally appear to the viewer as a natural full-color presentation. These basic color-demodulating functions will become clearer after the reader goes over Chapter 5, which contains more detailed block diagrams and explanations, and Chapter 9, which discusses the actual circuit operation, adjustment and troubleshooting.

COLOR MONITORS AND COMPUTER CRT DISPLAYS

Many television sets manufactured recently contain connectors that allow a computer, VCR or video game to be operated directly from the video output ports. These ports connect directly to the video amplifier circuits before the sync takeoff point. More elaborate monitors also have the industry standard 9-pin RGB connector that is used for computer systems that develop their own color signals directly. This system is explained in more detail in the next paragraph. Composite color data monitors contain color detection and decoding circuitry, color, vertical and horizontal sync, and may also have an audio stage. Composite monitors are also used for VCR playback of direct video. Note Figure 2.7 for an example of a typical composite video monitor. Color circuitry is necessary, of course, to decode and display color.

RGB data display monitors expect the computer or other display driver to provide separate red, green and blue signals. Professional studio monitors for live video display also may use RGB monitors for a better color display.

Separate vertical and horizontal sync inputs are usually provided. To perform the same kind of functions with a color TV display, the simplified block diagram of Figure 4.9 shows that we need only three separate video amplifier channels, one each for the red, green and blue video signals. Particularly when the distance between the color TV camera or computer and the monitor display is not very great, a simple connection between the camera's red, green and blue video output signals and the red, green and blue input signals to the monitor, is all that is needed. Vertical and horizontal sync signals would be connected in the same way. When the distance between camera and display exceeds a few hundred feet, separate coaxial cables can be used, or a TV broadcast standard conversion to the 3.58 MHz color subcarrier is possible. In that case, the same color IF, decoder, matrix and color sync portion is required as illustrated in Figure 4.8.

Computer CRT terminals that feature a color display can be implemented in the same manner as illustrated in Figure 2.8 by adding two more contrast controls and video amplifiers. The timing, character generator and other computer circuits will provide proper video signals to the red, green and blue channels directly, without any need for a 3.58-MHz color subcarrier. To determine which colors should appear where, the computer program must simply allot particular pulse trains to the respective red, green and blue video channels. Computer CRT terminals almost

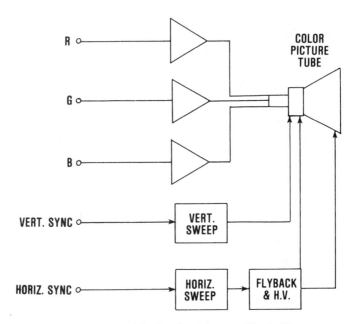

Figure 4.9: Simplified Color Monitor Block Diagram

never contain the elaborate color decoding and synchronizing circuits that are used in color TV receivers, but in
those cases where personal computers are used that connect to the color TV receiver through the antenna, the
personal computer must contain a 3.58 MHz color subcarrier generator and the appropriate encoders. This is
necessary so that the color TV receiver that acts as computer CRT display will receive the full range of TV standard broadcast signals for which it is designed. The same
requirement applies to TV games that interface with a TV
receiver over the antenna terminals.

It was previously noted that RC circuitry is generally
used in the chroma section to properly phase the outputs
from the 3.58-MHz color subcarrier generator. Comparatively simple lag and lead arrangements are used for this
purpose. Their normal and off-tolerance characteristics
can be computed by means of the basic troubleshooting
programs 3 and 4 in the appendix. Note in passing that

an oscilloscope with comparatively high-input impedance is required to accurately measure phase angles in chroma circuitry. This requirement is based on the relatively high operating frequency (3.58 MHz), and resulting spurious phase shifts introduced by loading of the circuit under test by the scope input capacitance.

CHAPTER 5

COLOR TV RECEIVER FUNCTIONS

We already know from Chapters 1 and 2 that many of the functions in the color TV receiver are the same as those in a monochrome set. We know that both of them use the same UHF and VHF tuners, the same IF amplifier, detector and sound section. We also know that the horizontal and vertical sweep, the power supply and the sync separator perform the same functions. In this chapter we will discuss the specific differences between the same functions in color and monochrome receivers and then concentrate on those functions that are unique to color receivers.

We will use the same format as for the monochrome receiver functions, and the same reference numbers will apply to the detailed color TV set block diagram of Figure 5.1 as were used in the monochrome TV set block diagram of Figure 3.1. In that illustration, specific functions and their signals were referred to by circled numerals, ranging from 1 through 17. The same corresponding numbers are used in Figure 5.1, but specific color functions are numbered starting at 20.

OVERALL COLOR TV SET FUNCTIONS

As in monochrome TV sets, the RF signals from the transmitter are received by UHF and VHF antennas and processed by their respective tuners. The output of the UHF tuner, in the IF band, is amplified by the VHF tuner when it is set to the UHF position. The IF amplifier section provides enough amplification to bring the signal from the relatively weak levels of the tuner up to the 0.5 to 2.0 V that are required at the output detector and first video amplifier. From there the 4.5-MHz intercarrier, audio FM modulated, signal goes to the audio section, the composite video signal goes to the sync amplifier and separator and also to the brightness or Y channel. A portion of this composite video signal also goes to the 3.58-MHz amplifier, which is tuned to the color subcarrier. When properly

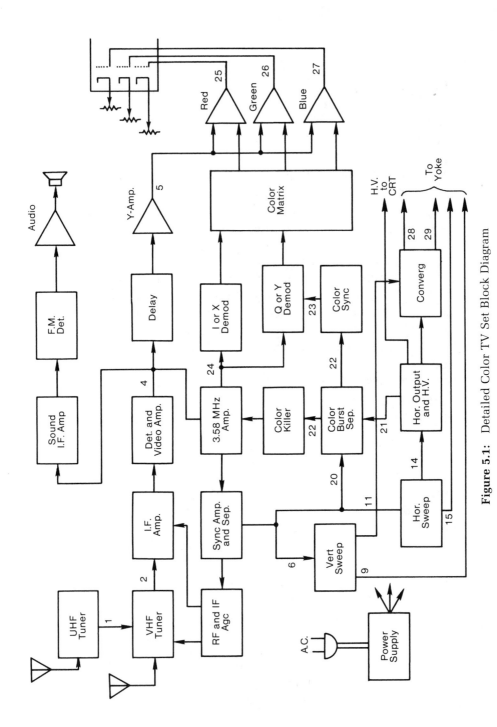

Figure 5.1: Detailed Color TV Set Block Diagram

82

amplified, this signal feeds the color decoder that, together with the input from the color sync section, then removes the color information from the subcarrier. The four amplifiers, labeled Y, R, G and B, all deal with video signals that are combined in the color picture tube to produce the colored picture.

The power supply, RF, and IF AGC circuit, as well as the horizontal and vertical sweep and horizontal output section, are all somewhat different physically than those used in a monochrome set, but they essentially perform the same functions. The block diagram of Figure 5.1 also contains several new and unique color functions. The color killer section monitors the presence of the color burst which is available only when a color transmission occurs. When the color burst is not received, the color killer section turns the 3.58-MHz amplifier off, preventing spurious color interference on an otherwise black and white picture. As we shall see in later chapters, this important function can cause a lot of trouble when the circuits are not properly adjusted.

The color burst separator removes the eight-cycle burst of color reference signal from the blanking pedestal and provides it to the color killer as well as the color sync section. With the aid of a crystal oscillator, as indicated in Figure 5.1, the color sync section maintains a very accurate frequency and phase-locked 3.58-MHz reference signal that is necessary for the color decoder. This section performs the synchronous detection necessary to remove the X and Z signals from the 3.58-MHz color subcarrier. In many color sets the matrixing circuits, which obtain the three-color-difference signals from the X and Z signals, are part of the decoder.

Another important color function is convergence. Different types of convergence circuits are required for different color picture tubes, but most color TV sets have the basic problem of converging the three electron beams—red, green and blue—in a uniform manner over the entire TV screen. Because convergence is related to the deflection circuits, signals from the horizontal and vertical sweep section are utilized to generate the required convergence waveforms. Single-gun color picture tubes don't need external convergence components.

A quick comparison between Figures 3.1 and 5.1 makes it obvious that the color picture tube receives many more signals than its monochrome counterpart. In effect, each color picture tube, regardless of type, must perform most of the functions of three separate monochrome tubes, which means there are that many more adjustments. The principles of an electron gun, an electron beam attracted by a high-voltage anode and a phosphor screen, are the same for both monochrome and color picture tubes, but the latter is so much more complex that an entire chapter is devoted to color picture tubes.

DETAILED COLOR TV SET FUNCTIONS

1. The UHF tuner selects one of the UHF television channels, and its output is the same as described in Chapter 3. The VHF tuner output also is identical to that described in Chapter 3 with reference to Figures 3.1 and 3.2.

2. Same as item 2 of the list in Chapter 3.

3. While the overall functions of the IF amplifier section are the same for monochrome and color TV receivers, the actual IF frequency response is different. As illustrated in Figure 5.2, the monochrome IF frequency response, 5.2 (a), requires only that the 41.25-MHz sound IF be about 40 dB below the top of the video passband. Because of the presence of the color subcarrier and its sidebands, however, the IF frequency response for a color TV receiver is much more critical, as illustrated in Figure 5.2 (b). Note that the frequency response must be flat up to about 41.75 MHz, and the sound IF carrier, at 41.25 MHz, should be down at least 60 db from the bandpass. As we shall

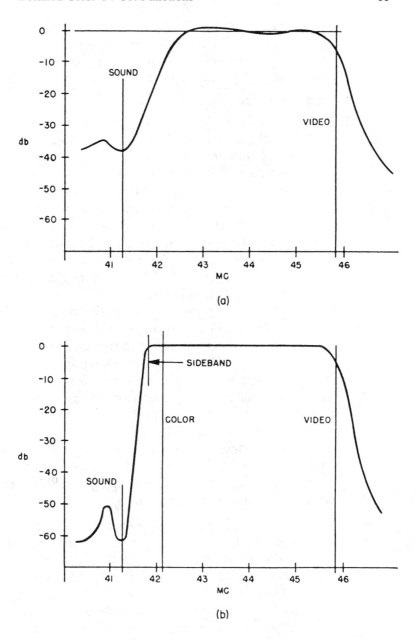

Figure 5.2: Monochrome and Color TV IF Responses.
Color TV Servicing, 3rd Ed., Walter H. Buchsbaum. Prentice-Hall, Inc.

see in more detail in Chapter 7, the IF amplifier section of a color TV receiver uses either a more elaborate network of resonant circuits or else depends on some special, sharp, cut-off filter for the required frequency response.

4. The output of the peak detector contains a number of different signals. As described in Chapter 3, the nonlinear characteristics of the detector cause a heterodyne action that produces a 4.5-MHz intercarrier sound IF signal. As in monochrome sets, this signal is selected and amplified by the audio IF amplifier and then passes through the FM detector, the audio amplifier, and the speaker. Because the audio IF carrier in the main IF amplifier is 60 dB down from the main signal, the 4.5-MHz IF amplifier will have to provide that additional gain.

   The composite video signal, with some amplification, is available at 4 and is supplied to the delay block and the video amplifier indicated by Y. (More about these functions in the next paragraph.) The same composite video signal is also applied to the sync amplifier and separator from where it goes to the AGC circuits and the sweep circuits, just as in a monochrome receiver. The 3.58-MHz color subcarrier is also detected and gets some amplification so that at point 4 it is part of the different signals available. It goes to a separate 3.58-MHz amplifier and contains all the color information.

5. The composite blanked video signal shown at point 5 of Figure 3.1 in Chapter 3 is essentially the same as that shown at point 5 in Figure 5.1. In fact, if the three other color signals were absent and appropriate DC voltages were supplied, a monochrome picture, just like the one in a black and white receiver, would appear on the color picture tube. The only difference between the video amplifier functions in a monochrome and a color TV set are the "delay" functions

illustrated in Figure 5.1. This block represents some sort of delay line or delaying device that delays the Y or brightness signal. If we look at the rest of the block diagram, we notice that the 3.58-MHz color subcarrier signal passes first through an amplifier, then through the color decoder, and then, once the three-color-difference signals have been obtained, they go through an amplifier similar to the Y signal amplifier. The delay of the Y or brightness signals simply compensates for the time it takes to obtain the three-color difference signals from the 3.58-MHz color subcarrier. A typical delay time for modern color TV receivers is approximately 1.5 microseconds.

6. The vertical synchronizing pulse is required to trigger the vertical oscillator that then drives the vertical sweep or deflection circuits. All these functions are the same as those described in item 6 of the list in Chapter 3.

7–10. All these functions, including the vertical blanking, are provided in the color TV set in the same manner as in a monochrome receiver. In order to keep the block diagram of Figure 5.1 reasonably simple, these functions have not been illustrated there.

11–19. All these functions have been explained in detail in Chapter 3 in connection with the block diagram of a monochrome TV receiver. The same functions are also used in the color TV set block diagram of Figure 5.1, but most of them have been omitted in the illustration to keep it simple. The major difference between the horizontal output and high-voltage section of color receivers and that of monochrome receivers is that of magnitude. Most monochrome TV receivers use second anode voltages from 12 to 17 KV. The color TV receiver second anode voltage is generally in the order of 25 KV. In addition, the color TV high-voltage section includes some circuits to regulate the anode voltage, because the beam current in a color picture tube varies greatly. This regulation is not required in monochrome receivers. Detailed circuit operation and troubleshooting of these circuits is covered in Chapter 8.

20. The sync amplifier and separator section essentially clips the blanking pulse in such a way that the video signals are removed and only the vertical and horizontal blanking pedestals and synchronizing pulses that ride above them are passed. These signals are then differentiated to bring the horizontal sync pulse to the horizontal sweep and integrated to deliver the vertical sync pulse to the vertical sweep section, as discussed in Chapter 3. We know from Chapter 4 that the color reference signal is transmitted from the TV station by means of a short, 8-cycle burst of 3.58-MHz sine wave. This burst rides on top of the blanking pedestal, next to the horizontal sync pulse, as illustrated in Figure 5.3.

21. The color burst separator receives the horizontal sync with the color sync burst riding along, and, in order to remove the color sync burst, it also requires a horizontal gating pulse from the horizontal output stage, as illustrated in Figure 5.4. The color burst separator is essentially an amplifier that can amplify only during the period when the positive gating pulse is present.

22. The output of the color burst separator is the color sync burst itself, which is applied to the color killer as well as to the color sync section. The color killer circuit is necessary in every color set so that no color

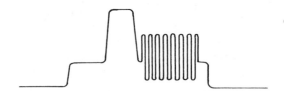

Figure 5.3:   Horizontal Sync and Color Sync Burst

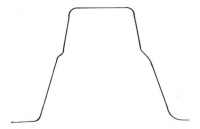

Figure 5.4: Horizontal Gating Pulse

information can appear on the screen when a monochrome transmission is received. On monochrome transmission, the color sync burst shown in Figure 5.5 will be missing, and this will cause the color killer circuit to set up a strong bias on the 3.58-MHz amplifier section, cutting off any color subcarrier signal to the color decoder. In most color TV receivers, the color killer has a potentiometer to adjust the level of the bias. If the level is misadjusted, it is possible to cut off the 3.58-MHz amplifier whenever the color sync burst signal itself is weak. In other words, the color killer changes color pictures into monochrome pictures whenever weak color transmissions are received—when not properly adjusted. If the color killer does not cut off the 3.58-MHz amplifier during monochrome transmission, we may see an effect best described as "colored noise" riding into the monochrome picture.

23. The color sync section also receives the color sync burst and uses it to control the frequency and phase of its own crystal-controlled 3.58-MHz oscillator. When operating correctly, the output of the color sync section will be a continuous 3.58-MHz sine wave that is exactly in frequency and phase with the reference signal transmitted from the TV station. This

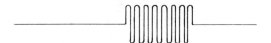

Figure 5.5: Color Sync Burst

reference signal is used in the color decoder for synchronous demodulation of phase and amplitude of the 3.58-MHz color subcarrier.

24. The 3.58-MHz amplifier is sometimes also called the color subcarrier IF amplifier or the chroma IF. The reason for this name is apparent from Figure 5.6, which shows the bandpass response of this amplifier. Note that it is similar to the overall IF response except that its bandwidth is only 1 MHz wide.

25. The signal at this point is a video signal that drives the red electron gun. Depending on whether cathode or grid drive is used in a particular receiver, different voltage and current values will be required. In general, however, this signal will have to be at least 20 V in amplitude and capable of driving a CRT electron gun.

26. The green color difference amplifier operates in the same basic fashion as the red difference amplifier described above.

27. The blue color difference amplifier also operates in the same manner as the red and green. The only differences between the three amplifiers are the relative output amplitudes that are in accordance with the equation of Chapter 4. Figure 5.7 illustrates the three-color video signals for a single horizontal line that would result in a vertical bar of red, next to a vertical bar of green, next to a vertical bar of blue,

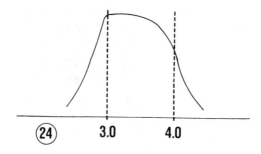

Figure 5.6:   3.58 MHz AMP Bandpass

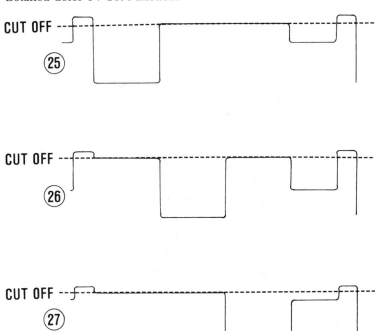

Figure 5.7: Color Video Signals

next to a narrow vertical bar of white. We have assumed that each of the three signals at 25, 26 and 27 have the same cutoff voltage and that each has the same relative brightness for that part of the screen when they are the only color appearing. On the narrower portion at the right of the picture in which all three colors make a contribution, the sum of the red, green and blue signals should be equal to the amplitude of either the red, the green or the blue bar. These values are used for purposes of illustration only and will probably differ with each manufacturer and with each model color TV receiver.

28. Another unique color TV function is the convergence section. It consists basically of a separate horizontal and vertical section that, in most receivers, produces a combined vertical and horizontal signal. Conver-

gence problems are discussed in more detail in Chapter 6 because they depend on the particular type of color TV picture tube used. Convergence refers to the proper focusing of the red, green and blue electron beams so that they illuminate the proper red, blue and green dots or stripes on the screen. Because the picture tube screen is essentially flat and the point of best convergence moves through an arc as the electron beam is deflected horizontally and vertically, some correction is necessary. Figure 5.8 shows a typical horizontal convergence signal. The notches at either end correspond to subsequent horizontal synchronizing and blanking pulses, and the curvature represents the amount of adjustment necessary in convergence as the electron beam moves from left to right. The vertical convergence signal would have approximately the same shape but occurs at the vertical deflection frequency. When the signals are combined, the 262 horizontal convergence signals modulate one 60-Hz vertical convergence signal so that each of the 262 ½ horizontal lines that make up each field is individually corrected for color convergence. Most color TV picture tubes require static and dynamic horizontal and vertical convergence adjustments. In addition, purity and focus must also be set. These topics are discussed in more detail in Chapter 6.

When we compare the color TV set block diagram of Figure 5.1 to the monochrome TV set block diagram of Figure 3.1, it becomes obvious that a color TV set has many more components because it has to perform many more functions. As a result, the power supply of a color TV set must provide more DC power. In addition to simply

Figure 5.8:   Typical Convergence Signal

providing more watts, the regulation of the different voltages and the filtering of the AC line voltage must be much better than for monochrome TV sets. While the power supply performs the same function and uses the same circuits in both monochrome and color receivers, the color TV power supply will invariably be larger and more complex.

When we look at the detailed performance requirements of color picture tubes in Chapter 6, it will become obvious that the horizontal and vertical deflection signals for color TV picture tubes are much more critical than those for monochrome picture tubes. The linearity of the sawtooth deflection wave itself must be practically perfect to assure good color pictures. As will be discussed in more detail in Chapter 8, color TV sets, particularly those using large-screen picture tubes, are subject to the so-called pincushion effect. This means that the horizontal and vertical deflection voltage, although perfectly linear, becomes more effective at the outer stages. This would result in a picture with edges that appear curved inward instead of straight. Special pincushion correction signals are provided by the horizontal and vertical sweep and fed directly into the respective deflection coils to reduce the effect. In most color TV receivers, pincushion adjustments are factory-preset and hardly ever require attention.

COLOR TV MONITORS AND CRT COMPUTER DISPLAYS

One of the latest trends in television is the addition of video monitor connections to the rear of the television set. Many units even have complex video switching networks that allow direct video input from several external video sources such as a VCR, computer, video game or other home video applications. These units also usually contain a tuner assembly for standard reception of VHF, UHF and even cable channels. Units with external video source jacks are often composite NTSC video format inputs, but many models also include the standard 9-pin digital RGB jack, with appropriate circuitry to display from an RGB output computer system.

All dedicated color TV monitors and CRT computer displays that operate in color use some of the basic functions of the color TV set block diagram of Figure 5.1. A dedicated monitor does not require the RF, IF or detector portions that would permit them to receive signals from an antenna. The NTSC input is essentially the same as the signal available at point 4 of the block diagram of Figure 5.1. The signal consists of a standard 4 MHz bandwidth brightness or Y signal with horizontal and vertical blanking and synchronizing pulses and with a 3.58-MHz color subcarrier interlaced as described in Chapter 4. The monitor processes the NTSC video from a computer or other video source exactly as if it had been delivered from a television tuner, IF and detector assembly.

CRT computer displays may accept the standard NTSC video, or the computer industry standard RGB input. Most of the less expensive home computer systems provide the NTSC standard signals, while the more expensive professional and small business microcomputers generate the RGB standard signal. The advantage of RGB is in resolution and clarity, since there are no intermediate conversion steps from computer output to NTSC standard and back to red, green and blue signals. Figure 4.9 contains the diagram of an RGB-type monitor. The computer circuits generate the appropriate red, green and blue signals with whatever bandwidth is required, and the character, row, line and column counters, driven by the clock, provide the vertical and horizontal sync signals. Depending on the type of color picture tube used, convergence circuits may be required. Because the color signals are generated by the computer, it is now necessary to have a 3.58-MHz amplifier, color killer, color burst separator, color sync or color decoder function. For computers with built-in monitors, the digital portion of the CRT display, of course, must be capable of providing separate and different signals to the R, G and B channels in accordance with the computer hardware.

Except for the difference in operating frequency, video and chroma amplifiers employ the same principles of circuit action. An R chroma amplifier (also termed a red output amplifier) typically uses a transistor with associated RC circuitry to step up the R signal, just as an audio output amplifier steps up the audio signal. The chief distinction between video and audio amplifiers is that the former use relatively low-value resistors in order to minimize the bypassing action of stray capacitances. Troubleshooting program 1 in the appendix can be used in either case to determine normal characteristics and off-tolerance characteristics.

CHAPTER 6

COLOR TV PICTURE TUBES

Using the principles of colorimetry discussed in Chapter 4, we can see that a color picture can be projected on a screen as illustrated in Figure 6.1. Each of the three light sources represents a slide projector, showing only the red, green and blue respective portions of the same color transparency. The total picture seen by the viewer will be a full color representation. Indeed, this technique is very similar to the way current model projection TV technology works, substituting red, green and blue CRTs for the slide projectors. Color picture tubes, and even solid state display devices all work in a similar manner. Each of these display devices are discussed in this chapter. First, let's take a look at the oldest technology, the color CRT in its many variations. Then current projection TV technology is discussed, and finally we will take a look at the newest technology, the solid state color display.

Getting back to our illustration of Figure 6.1, one of the problems with color CRTs, and color projection systems, is a built-in distortion. As illustrated, the red and blue projections will be distorted at the edges because, unlike the green projection, these projectors are at the top and bottom respectively. We will see later in this chapter how corrections are made for this problem.

In a color picture tube, the red, green and blue picture elements originate in three electron beams that are mod-

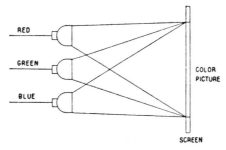

Figure 6.1: Principle of Color Picture Tubes.
Color TV Servicing, 3rd Ed., Walter H. Buchsbaum. Prentice-Hall, Inc.

ulated by the red, green and blue video signals respectively. When the red electron beam strikes the red phosphor dots on the screen, they are illuminated. The same applies to the green and blue electron beams. The composite of these three sets of color dots appears as a natural, full-range color picture to the viewer.

Figure 2.2 illustrates the cathode ray tube, and with slight variations, all these CRT elements are contained in color picture tubes. In current-technology CRTs, there is a common cathode and the filament is a single element, while in older systems, separate cathodes with their individual filaments are used. In the single-cathode system currently in use, there are three separate control grids to vary the current individually for each electron beam. A first anode and focusing element is also required for each electron beam. The first anode is often referred to as a screen grid, and separate adjustments for each of the color electron beams are provided. The three focusing elements are often connected together and controlled by a single focus adjustment. In color picture tubes, the second anode is often called the ultor, and is invariably common for all electron beams.

Although there are variations in the color picture tubes of different manufacturers, three major systems are currently in use. The oldest is the so-called Delta system in which the three electron beams are arranged in a triangle, forming the delta. Though the delta system is no longer found in current production television systems, we will use it as a standard of comparison for the other systems. Modern CRT systems use the so-called "in-line" system in which the three electron guns are arranged side by side. The third major system is generally called the single-gun system, indicating that a single electron gun provides three electron beams. This last system is in fact a version of the three-gun in-line system, as will be shown later in this chapter.

THE DELTA COLOR PICTURE TUBE

A greatly magnified illustration of the color dot arrangement of the system is shown in Figure 6.2. Each group of red, green and blue phosphor dots is arranged in triangular form, corresponding to the triangular arrangement of the three electron guns. To make absolutely sure that each electron beam strikes only its respective color dots, an aperture mask is located a short distance behind the color phosphor screen. As illustrated in Figure 6.3, the three electron gun beams converge at the hole and then pass through to strike the correct phosphor dots. We have seen from Figure 6.1 that convergence of the three beams over the entire screen area presents a problem. The point of convergence moves through a portion of a sphere, but the screen itself and the aperture mask behind it are not part of the sphere but are much flatter. This means that the point of convergence must move as the three electron beams move from the center of the screen to the left and right, top and bottom edges. As we shall see shortly, this requires both static convergence, in the area of the center of the screen, and dynamic convergence, at the edges.

Another problem in the Delta system is to make sure that the red beam will strike only the red dots, the green beam only the green dots, and the blue beam only the

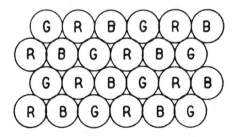

Figure 6.2:   Color Dot Arrangement.
Color TV Servicing, 3rd Ed., Walter H. Buchsbaum. Prentice-Hall, Inc.

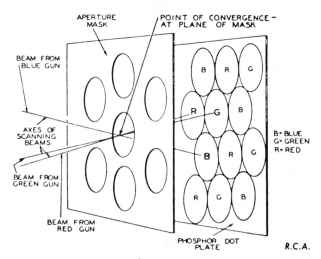

Figure 6.3: Aperture Mask in Delta System.
Color TV Servicing, 3rd Ed., Walter H. Buchsbaum. Prentice-Hall,
Inc.

blue dots. To achieve this, the manufacturer uses a so-
called purity magnet at the neck of the tube to generate
a magnetic field which will bend the electron beams just
enough to make sure that each beam goes through the
center of the correct aperture mask hole. The action of
the purity magnet is illustrated in the sketch of Figure
6.4.

Figure 6.5 illustrates the principle of the magnetic
convergence that assures that the three electron beams
reach the aperture mask at their proper angle so that they
strike only their respective color dots. Inside the glass
neck of the picture tube are metal channels in which the
electron beam moves, as indicated by the three dots. External magnets, consisting of both a permanent magnet
and an electromagnet, controlled by current through a
coil, are coupled through the glass neck to these internal
pole pieces. The lines of magnetic flux are at right angles
to the electron beam, which, in the illustration of Figure
6.5, would come out of the paper. This causes, depending
on the increase or decrease of the strength of magnetic

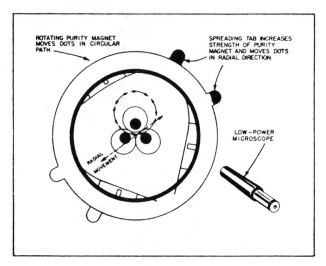

Figure 6.4: Purity Magnet Action.
Color TV Servicing, 3rd Ed., Walter H. Buchsbaum. Prentice-Hall, Inc.

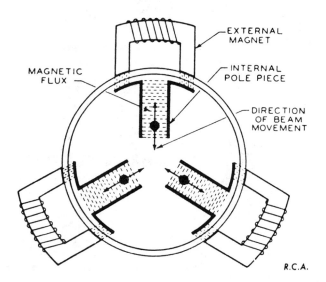

Figure 6.5: Magnet Convergence Principles.
Color TV Servicing, 3rd Ed., Walter H. Buchsbaum. Prentice-Hall, Inc.

field, an up or down motion. In actual equipment, the convergence assembly is mounted on the neck of the picture tube, between the end of the deflection yoke and the purity magnet assembly. (More about convergence adjustment towards the end of this chapter.)

From Figure 6.5 it is apparent that the radial motion of the electron beams generated by the convergence magnets is not really sufficient to assure that the three electron beams converge at one point at the aperture mask hole. This radial motion is satisfactory for two of the electron beams, but in order to make sure that the third one will also converge at the proper point, some lateral motion is required. For this reason, a third assembly, the blue position magnet, is used in most Delta color picture tubes. As illustrated in Figure 6.6, the blue position magnet uses magnetic coupling through the glass envelope between an external magnet and the internal assembly. This external assembly has to be located at just the right point on the

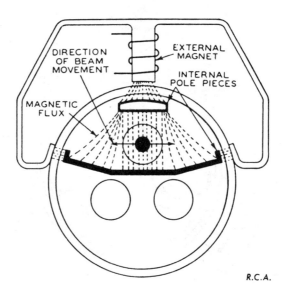

R.C.A.

Figure 6.6: Blue Position Magnet Principle.
Color TV Servicing, 3rd Ed., Walter H. Buchsbaum. Prentice-Hall, Inc.

neck of the picture tube to affect only the blue electron
beam. Some of the later Delta system color picture tubes
have done away with the blue position magnet by a more
precise assembly of the internal electron gun structure.

A typical Delta system color picture tube with its
external components is shown in Figure 6.7. The deflection
yoke with its mounting clamp is closest to the screen,
followed by the convergence coil and pole piece assembly, the purity magnet and the lateral (blue) magnet assembly. We know that even small magnetic fields can
affect the purity and convergence, and therefore a magnetic shield is usually used to enclose the area near the
screen of the picture tube. A variety of external magnetic
fields, either generated by electromagnetic appliances or
caused by moving the color set through different portions
of the earth's magnetic field, can affect the color purity
of the screen. To eliminate the influence of these magnetic

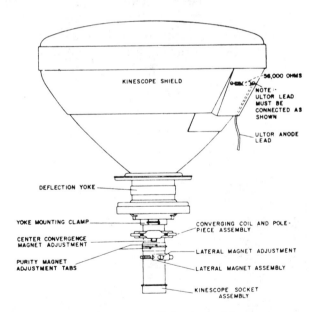

Figure 6.7: Delta Color Picture Tube Assembly.
Reprinted with permission of Hayden Book Company from *Fundamentals of Television* by Walter H. Buchsbaum.

fields on the color picture, an automatic "degaussing" system is used. This consists of a set of coils that are located around the edges of the screen and that receive a surge of 60-Hz current every time the TV set is turned on. (More about automatic degaussing at the end of this chapter.)

THE IN-LINE SYSTEM

Current television technology has replaced the Delta tube with either in-line or single-gun tube technology. In-line tube systems have three guns arranged in a straight line, as illustrated in Figure 6.8, which solves some of the problems of the Delta system. Instead of round holes, the aperture mask now uses vertical slits, and instead of phosphor dots, the screen has vertical lines. This method of arranging the three electron guns requires greater precision in the manufacture of the three electron gun assembly and the mechanical alignment of the electron guns, focusing elements, the aperture mask, and the screen. The advantages of the system are a great simplification in the amount

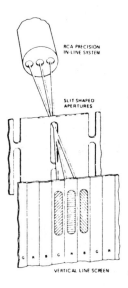

RCA PRECISION IN-LINE SYSTEM

SLIT SHAPED APERTURES

VERTICAL LINE SCREEN   R.C.A.

Figure 6.8: RCA Precision In-Line Color Tube.
Color TV Servicing, 3rd Ed., Walter H. Buchsbaum. Prentice-Hall, Inc.

of horizontal and vertical convergence, an elimination of the blue lateral magnet, and less critical purity adjustment.

SINGLE-GUN COLOR TV TUBE

Another modern replacement for the Delta tube is the single-gun color TV tube. There are several variations of this tube technology, the most well known of which is the "Trinitron," a trademarked single-gun color picture tube developed and manufactured by the Sony Corporation. The basic principle of this color tube is illustrated in Figure 6.9, which shows three separate cathodes, each responsible for the blue, green or red electron beam housed in a single control grid, G1. In this case, the three-color video signals are applied to the cathodes, with G1 held at a fixed-bias voltage. G2 in Figure 6.9 acts as accelerating grid, while G3, G4 and G5 form an electrostatic focusing system that interacts with all three electron beams. Following G5, there are four vertical plates, each connected to a separate high voltage, which form three channels through which the respective color electron beams must pass. These three channels form an electrostatic convergence system that, in effect, performs the same function

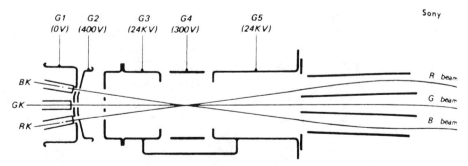

Figure 6.9: Cross Section of Trinitron Color Tube.
Color TV Servicing, 3rd Ed., Walter H. Buchsbaum. Prentice-Hall, Inc.

as the magnetic convergence system in the Delta color picture tube.

In the in-line color tube system, shown in Figure 6.8, the aperture mask consists of vertical slots, The Sony color tube uses an aperture grill, a structure of vertical strips, to assure that each electron beam will land only on its respective vertical phosphor strip on the screen. The precision of the assemblies in the single-gun tube must be very high. It is essential that not only the electron gun assembly but also the aperture grill and the vertical color strips must be precisely aligned. The great advantage of these picture tubes is their relatively simple convergence adjustment and the fact that misconvergence is quite rare.

COMMON CHARACTERISTICS

All color picture tubes have certain common requirements, inherent in the fact that three different electron beams are used. The second anode, or ultor, voltage is much higher than that required for monochrome picture tubes. Most color TV picture tubes require from 25 to 28 KV. Because three electron beams are involved, the total current drawn is also much greater, and some type of power supply regulation is required in each case. If one of the electron beams, the red, for example, requires a lot of current because a large portion of screen is bright red, this would normally reduce the second anode voltage slightly. This effect, however, would mean that the green and blue electron beams would also be reduced because the second anode voltage is dropping. When the entire screen is white, all three electron beams are on, and the second anode voltage would be reduced further because all three electron beams would be drawing current. When the second anode voltage drops, the magnetic deflection system will make the picture larger. In addition, the focus of the electron beams would change. Color fidelity will also be lost. These are the reasons why the high voltage power supply in color TV receivers is always regulated to provide a constant anode voltage over a relatively large range of current. Typical regulator circuits will be found in Chapter 8.

Another effect, common to all color TV picture tubes, is the pincushion effect which has already been mentioned in Chapter 5. Pincushion distortion can also be a problem on large-screen black and white TV receivers, but is most pronounced on color sets because of the particular construction of color deflection yokes and the large deflection angle. Clearly, the electron beam is farthest from the center and closest to the deflection coils at the four corners of the raster. And because it is closest at the four corners, the effect of the deflection coil magnetic flux causes it to move farther out. This results in a raster in which the four corners appear to be pulled outward, representing the familiar curve of a pincushion. Every color TV receiver contains some kind of circuitry or device to reduce this effect. In some receivers, permanent magnets are located near the corners of the raster to overcome the pincushion effect, while in others the horizontal and vertical deflection currents themselves are modified during the time periods when the electron beams reach the four corners of the raster. Chapter 8 contains some details of pincushion correction circuits.

The DC operating voltages are also common to all color picture tubes, although some variations exist according to the particular tube types. Figure 6.10 shows all the essential DC connections required for a typical current-production color picture tube. In this television receiver, high voltage ranges from 27.5 to 29 KV on the ultor. Focus voltage is a nominal 6 KV. Overall beam intensity is controlled by a single voltage applied to the screen grids, which is nominally around 400 volts. Red, green and blue video are applied to the cathodes, separately. There are red, green and blue drive bias controls to adjust each individual driver transistor output. Nominal voltage at the cathodes are around 150 volts. Gray

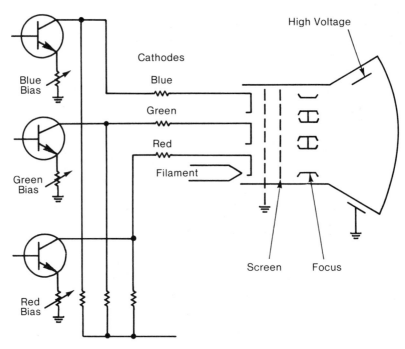

Figure 6.10:   Simplified One-Gun CRT Circuitry

scale and purity are adjusted magnetically in these systems. Those tubes with internal electrostatic convergence
plates will require corresponding potentiometers for adjustment.

In older delta systems, there are three screen controls,
one for each color. Video is applied to the three cathodes,
with a drive adjustment for each cathode. Brightness is
controlled by a voltage divider on the three control grids,
with color signals also being applied to the grids. The
Delta system requires external magnetic devices for proper
convergence.

PURITY AND CONVERGENCE ADJUSTMENT

All TV receivers now provide instructions, usually located somewhere on the chassis or inside the cabinet, to

help the service technician perform the important purity and convergence adjustments. The detailed directions will vary from set to set, but the principles for the three types of color picture tubes are described below.

A) DELTA SYSTEM PICTURE TUBES

The purity adjustment is performed by the proper setting of the purity magnet as illustrated in Figure 6.4. The separation of the tabs determines the magnetic flux intensity, and the rotation determines the effect of the magnetic field. In most instances it is not necessary to use either a low-power microscope or an enlarging lens to observe the action of the individual color dots as the purity magnet is manipulated. Purity is usually missing in only one part of the screen. The color illustration of Figure 6.11 (see color insert) shows a typical case of loss of purity in the lower right-hand corner. Careful manipulation of the purity magnet will soon show you which way it has to be turned to minimize the impurities and obtain a uniform red field.

   The convergence adjustment on any type of color picture tube is best performed by means of a crosshatch pattern such as the one illustrated in Figure 6.12, or a dot pattern such as the one illustrated in Figure 6.13. (See color insert.) In either case the static convergence, the convergence near the center of the screen, is adjusted first, and only after that has been optimized can we proceed to adjust the dynamic convergence near the edges of the screen. The static convergence is set by the permanent magnet pole pieces of the three convergence magnets, shown in Figure 6.5, and the blue lateral magnet, shown in Figure 6.6, to make sure that the crosshatch or dot pattern shows a pure white at the center of the screen. The dynamic adjustments, a series of potentiometers, should all be set so that the minimum amount of correction current flows through the coils on the magnets during the static adjustment. It takes a small amount of practice to manipulate the three static convergence magnets and blue lateral magnets until the center of the screen is properly converged, but the effects of each of the pole pieces are clearly evident in the movement of vertical and horizontal lines near the center of the screen.

At this point, the reader should remember that when the blue and red electron beams are converged, the result will be a magenta, or purple, line. When the blue and green electron guns are properly aligned, without the influence of the red, a yellow line will show. Figure 6.12 clearly shows these effects, and also illustrates that only when all three color electron beams are properly converged will a white line be apparent.

After the center of the screen is properly converged, the dynamic adjustments are next. Look at the convergence assembly and familiarize yourself with the location of the vertical and horizontal controls. In most Delta systems we will find three potentiometers for vertical convergence at the top of the picture and three for the bottom of the picture. Remember that the vertical lines on the raster are affected by the horizontal controls, while the horizontal lines on the raster can be converged by means of the vertical controls. The vertical convergence signals are obtained from the 60-Hz vertical deflection circuits, while the horizontal convergence signals come from the horizontal sweep and operate at 15,750 Hz. If a dot pattern is used, look at the vertical or horizontal dots in the same manner as you look at vertical or horizontal lines.

All controls are labeled with respect to the electron guns that they affect the most, and you will find that two each are labeled R/G for every one labeled BLUE. In effect, then, the red and green lines are converged onto the position of the blue, while in the other instance, the blue is converged onto the red and green lines.

First we set the bottom and top vertical controls, six potentiometers in all, and then the three left horizontal controls, also potentiometers. Finally, we have to adjust three right horizontal controls, which are usually inductors, and they require a rather careful adjustment. The usual sequence is to adjust first for convergence of the vertical center line and then adjust to converge the bottom and top horizontal lines. Touch-up adjustments are then usually relatively minor for the remaining controls. One of the difficulties in the Delta system convergence procedure is the need to go back and forth until optimum convergence is obtained. You will find that, even though the proper static convergence has been obtained with the pole piece and blue lateral magnet, adjustment of the dynamic convergence at top and bottom may have affected the center. Top and bottom adjustments also have some slight effect on the adjustment of convergence at the sides, and a fair amount of touch-up, going back and forth, is often necessary.

The enlarged view of the color dot pattern of Figure 6.14 (color insert) shows fairly good vertical convergence, but the horizontal convergence is definitely off. Note that the overlapping effect of red and green results in yellow, and of green and blue results in cyan. In the convergence dot pattern of Figure 6.15 (color insert), the vertical convergence of red and green is definitely off, as indicated by the fact that the center is yellow but the top of each dot is red and the bottom green. Figure 6.13 shows correct convergence when a pure white rectangular dot is obtained.

Although there should be no interaction between the convergence and purity adjustment, a touch-up of the purity or at least a check of its performance is suggested after the static and dynamic convergence adjustments have been optimized.

B) THE IN-LINE AND SINGLE-GUN COLOR TUBE SYSTEMS

These systems vary in convergence procedure from one manufacturer to the next. Figure 6.16 is representative of the RCA in-line system adjustments. Listed below are pu-

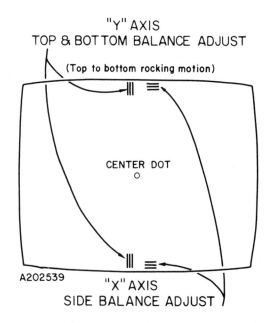

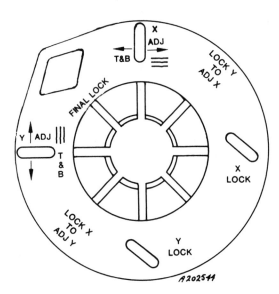

Figure 6.16: Dynamic Convergence, RCA In-Line Tube.
Courtesy RCA Consumer Electronics.
(a) TV Screen Convergence
(b) Rear Cover of Deflection Yoke

rity and convergence adjustment procedures similar to those found on many systems. Clearly, the dynamic convergence adjustment of an in-line tube is a lot simpler than for the delta system.

Purity Adjustments

1. Demagnetize the picture tube and receiver with an external degaussing coil. If you have replaced the CRT or yoke assemblies, be sure that the deflection yoke and purity magnet assemblies are mounted correctly according to manufacturer's literature.
2. Turn green and blue guns off and provide only green raster using the red and blue screen controls. Increase the green screen output to provide a green screen.
3. Slide the deflection coil backward as far as possible.
4. Rotate and spread the tabs of the purity magnets until the vertical green band is centered on the CRT screen.
5. Slide the deflection yoke forward until a uniform green screen is obtained.
6. Check out the red and blue screens in a similar manner to make sure they are also of uniform color. Slight readjustment of the yoke positioning may be required to obtain a uniform color display on all three screens.
7. Readjust the screen controls for proper gray scale.

Center Convergence Adjustment

1. Apply a crosshatch pattern generator to the antenna terminals.
2. Adjust the red and blue vertical lines in the center until they are superimposed over each other using the two inner magnet tabs.
3. Rotate both inner magnet tabs simultaneously to superimpose the red and blue horizontal lines at screen center.

4. In a similar manner to step 2, adjust the two outer pole magnet tabs to superimpose the green vertical lines over the red and blue lines.
5. Rotate the outer pair magnet tabs as in step 3, to superimpose the horizontal green lines over the red and blue lines.

Perimeter Convergence Adjustment

1. Loosen the deflection yoke and remove the rubber wedges from the front of the yoke.
2. Adjust the yoke to converge the detail in the outer area by making an orbital movement of the front of the yoke.
3. When convergence is correct, hold the yoke in position and reinsert the wedges at the correct points for holding the yoke in place.
4. Tighten the deflection yoke hold-down screw.

C) SINGLE GUN (TRINITRON)

The purity adjustment of trinitron picture tubes is the same as that for the Delta and the in-line color picture tubes, but the convergence itself is somewhat different. Static convergence is achieved by a single magnet assembly, somewhat similar to the way it is done for the in-line color picture tube. The dynamic convergence is adjusted by positioning the deflection yoke properly. After the optimum position of the deflection yoke is achieved, the deflection yoke holding screw is tightened and special spacers are installed to make sure that the deflection yoke remains positioned. As an additional adjustment, permanent magnet assemblies can be attached to some areas on the picture tube mounting assembly, closer to the screen, to compensate for minor misconvergence.

DEGAUSSING METHODS

As mentioned earlier in this chapter, stray magnetic fields can interfere with the purity and convergence action of all color picture tubes. These magnetic fields can cause metal portions of the color TV receiver assembly, and the picture tube mounting assembly, especially, to become slightly magnetized. To eliminate this effect, special degaussing coils are located around the screen of the color picture tube. In earlier sets, manual switches were used to activate these coils and direct a flow of 60- or 120-Hz current through them for a short burst, which would then neutralize the magnetic field. In the early days of color TV, service technicians carried in their tool kits special degaussing coils that were connected to the 60-Hz power-line, moved magically around the screen, and then withdrawn from it. The effect of all of this is to generate an alternating magnetic field that gradually diminishes, leaving the iron parts in the area magnetically neutral.

The automatic degaussing coils used in modern color TV sets are connected in fixed positions and are activated every time the color TV set is turned on. As illustrated in Figure 6.17, the degaussing coils are connected in series with the secondary of the power transformer, just before the AC current is rectified and filtered. When power is first turned on, the thermistor, a temperature-sensitive resistor, is at maximum resistance because it is cold. At the same time, the voltage dependent resistor in series with the degaussing coil is at minimum resistance. This allows AC current to flow through the degaussing coils. As even a small amount of current flows through the thermistor, it heats up, reducing its resistance. The voltage-dependent resistor increases in resistance, reducing the current flow through the degaussing coils. The combined action of the thermistor and the voltage-dependent resistor causes the current in the degaussing coils to decrease rapidly, and no current will flow through the degaussing coils after a

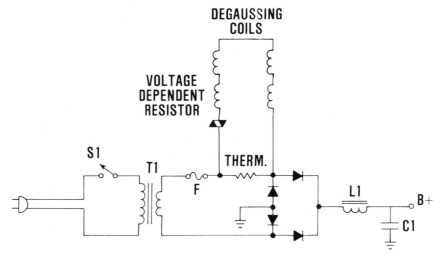

Figure 6.17:   Automatic Degaussing Circuit

few seconds. The result is a brief surge of AC current
through the degaussing coils.

The same effect is achieved in some color TV receivers by use of a thermal, bimetallic switch, which directs current into the coils until the heating element of
the thermal switch is warmed; then the switch directs all
the current away from the degaussing coils to the power
supply rectifier.

A third method used in some TV receivers for automatic degaussing employs a positive temperature coefficient resistor in series with the degaussing coils that are
connected directly across the power transformer. The
temperature coefficient of this resistor has to be extremely
positive to provide a cold resistance of approximately 25
ohms, allowing current into the coils, and a hot resistance
of 1 megohm or more, to keep current out of the degaussing coils.

Whichever method is used, automatic degaussing
circuits are ordinarily troublefree. It can happen that one
of the coils or a resistor opens, causing the loss of the
automatic degaussing action. Unless external magnetic
fields start to interfere, the viewer may never be aware of

this defect. The presence of color impurities or misconvergence, which is not easily adjusted, is usually an indication that the automatic degaussing circuit is not working
properly. A simple ohmmeter test can find this type of
defect.

PROJECTION TELEVISION SYSTEMS

Until just a few years ago, a 25-inch television display
was as large as was technically possible, and only recently
35- and 40-inch CRT displays have been introduced. With
the advent of projection technology, however, true home
theater-size television is a reality. Projection television
systems are inexpensive enough to be found in many
American homes, and range in size from 40 to 72 inches
diagonal measurement and larger.

Early systems consisted of a single 13-inch color CRT
with a rewired yoke that caused an inverted and reversed
display, which was projected correctly through a large
single lens. Systems such as this were very little more
complex than a standard TV system, but they had a very
dim picture, due to the inefficiencies of the large lens and
relatively low brightness CRT. This required viewing in
near total room darkness.

Another major problem with these early systems was
the fact that minor convergence irregularities not visible
on a 13-inch CRT were magnified with the projected picture. Many of these early systems had unacceptable convergence, even when adjusted to their best possible
convergence. There were very few of these televisions
sold, as the three-CRT projection system reduced or eliminated many of the disadvantages of the early systems.

Current technology systems use three CRTs and either two or three lenses. The CRTs are high-brightness
monochrome units, one each with red, green and blue
phosphor coatings. The CRTs are arranged in a manner
similar to the slide projectors in Figure 6.1, and the lenses

are mounted in front of each CRT, and the image is projected toward a highly reflective metal screen.

A variation on this scheme is the rear projection system, which uses a front mounted translucent screen, with the picture being projected from the rear. See Figure 6.18 for a comparison of these two types.

Figure 6.19 is an example of a two-lens system. One of the major costs in a projection system is the large glass or plastic lens that is required. These lenses can cost over $400.00 each, so some companies are using a dichroic mirror that passes red, but reflects blue light to eliminate one lens.

The special CRT units in these systems are either air or water cooled, as they are driven at very high voltage and beam current levels to gain adequate brightness levels to view in subdued room light. Ultor voltages run 40 KV and higher in current production units, with sharp focus electron guns and super bright phosphors.

CRT size ranges from about 5 inches to 10 inches diagonal measurement. Air blowing across the faceplates by a cooling fan prevents the CRT from overheating with the high beam current levels. This causes a cleaning prob-

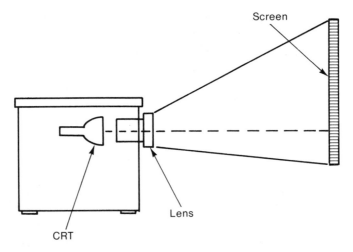

Figure 6.18A: Comparison of Front and Rear Projection Systems

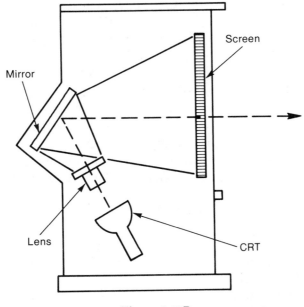

Figure 6.18B

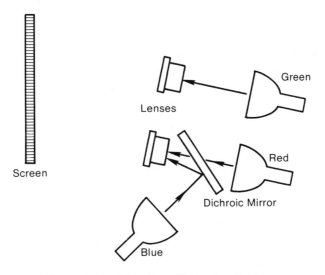

Figure 6.19: Two-Lens Projection System

lem, with airborne dust being attracted to the faceplate, as the air passes around the CRT. The relatively noisy cooling fan is also a problem in some units. Several manufacturers have gone to a liquid cooling system. Each CRT has a liquid-filled cavity over the faceplate. Elimination of the cooling fan reduces noise, and eliminates blowing dust toward static charged surfaces, keeping the lenses and CRTs cleaner, and requiring less maintenance. More importantly, liquid cooling keeps the phosphor coating from overheating, which would cause burning or cracking of the phosphor surface, thus destroying the tube.

PROJECTION TV REGISTRATION

Lining up the three CRTs to project an acceptable picture is more complex than the convergence process with a standard CRT. Convergence on a projection system is called registration, and is of greater importance to viewer enjoyment. The registration adjustments for a typical projection system are described below. Figure 6.20 contains a diagram of the effects of each of the registration adjustments. In addition to these adjustments, projection TV systems include controls for vertical and horizontal height, centering, linearity and pincushion as part of their registration procedure, just as in a standard color CRT system. There are separate adjustments for each CRT, as there are also three separate deflection output sections to accommodate the three picture tubes.

A. Vertical skew adjusts the vertical tilt of the entire image.
B. Vertical keystone adjusts the vertical tilt of the image at the top and bottom in opposite directions.
C. Vertical bow adjusts the bowing of the raster of the entire image.
D. Vertical pincushion adjusts the vertical bow of the image at the top and bottom in opposite directions.

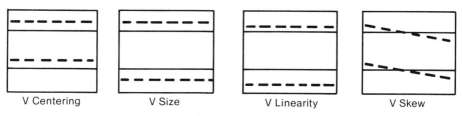

V Centering   V Size   V Linearity   V Skew

Note: Solid lines indicate properly converged lines. Dashed lines indicate one direction of movement of adjustment.

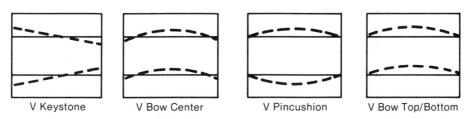

V Keystone   V Bow Center   V Pincushion   V Bow Top/Bottom

Figure 6.20A: Convergence Adjustments for Projection TV
A. Vertical
B. Horizontal

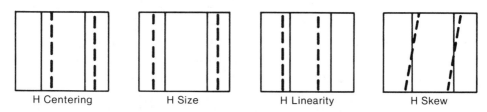

H Centering   H Size   H Linearity   H Skew

Note: Solid lines indicate properly converged lines. Dashed lines indicate one direction of movement of adjustment.

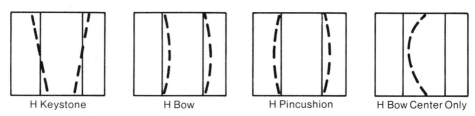

H Keystone   H Bow   H Pincushion   H Bow Center Only

Figure 6.20B: Convergence Adjustments for Projection TV

E. Horizontal skew adjusts horizontal tilt of the entire image.

F. Horizontal keystone adjusts the horizontal tilt of the image at the left and right in opposite directions.

G. Horizontal bow adjusts the horizontal bow of the entire image.

H. Horizontal pincushion adjusts the horizontal bow of the image at the left and right in opposite directions.

SERVICING PRECAUTIONS FOR PROJECTION SYSTEMS

Projection systems present a few specialized problems for the technician. Extra care must be exercised in high voltage circuitry, as the larger ultor voltage is more hazardous, and requires greater insulation than a standard CRT.

The lenses and faceplates of projection systems, especially in front projection air cooled systems require constant cleaning. Be sure to follow the manufacturer's cleaning instructions for these units. Be especially careful of plastic lenses, which are easily scratched. Wiping a dry cloth across a plastic lens can scratch it beyond usability (the scratches project very noticeably) and the lenses are very expensive to replace. Even glass lenses require special care when cleaning, and most lenses have multiple elements. Some are sealed, so internal cleaning is not necessary or possible, while others must be disassembled for cleaning. Be sure, also, to follow instructions carefully, when cleaning the CRT faceplates, as they are also expensive units, and not easily replaced.

Aside from the higher power supply requirements, and multiple deflection circuitry, there is much similarity between standard TV and projection TV systems. Rules for troubleshooting RF, video and audio circuitry can be used when troubleshooting projection TVs as well. Troubleshooting of video and audio circuitry is frequently facilitated by computerized analyses, as provided in programs 1 and 2 in the appendix.

It should be noted that partially bypassed emitter branches cannot be analyzed on the basis of the RC components alone, inasmuch as the RC emitter circuitry is loaded by the associated transistor. Precise analysis for normal cutoff frequency requires computer analysis as provided in program 2 of the appendix. This program also gives data for normal low-end and high end characteristics. The effects of off-tolerances on the measured cutoff frequency are computed.

LCD DISPLAYS

As this is being written, new technology is appearing that will eventually replace the CRT. Currently the forerunner of solid state picture display technology is the LCD display, though in some computer displays, gas planar technology is found. The LCD display has the advantage of low power consumption, and a thinner, flat display that enhances portability.

The majority of these displays are being found in computer displays, and several of these manufacturers are branching into television. The largest color display, which is currently in prototype as this is being written, is 13 inches diagonal, and is thin enough to hang on a wall. The average LCD display is less than ½ inch thick.

Poor resolution and lack of brightness presently plague LCD design. Manufacturers are working on both these fronts, however, and it won't be long before the 80-year refinement advantage of the vacuum tube CRT will be overshadowed by the low energy consumption, and simpler, smaller packaging of high-resolution LCD television.

Current technology LCD displays work by multiplexing a large number of pixels, with a thin film transistor at each pixel point. A pixel is a single point on the screen. In monochrome systems, a pixel can be either off, or on at some appropriate degree of intensity based upon the picture information. Color pixels are either red, blue or green, and are either on or off depending upon the current picture condition. Current generation units have about 50,000 pixels in a 2½ inch display, while the 13-inch prototype has over 250,000 pixels, which is about ¹⁄₁₀ the number available on a standard CRT. As large scale integration increases the number of pixels per square inch, the resolution of LCD displays will improve.

An LCD display works by blocking light, rather than emitting light. This means that an LCD display must have reflected light to work properly. LCD displays are actually better display units in very high light levels; for example, outside on a bright, sunny day. At low levels of room light, the CRT has the advantage, as it emits light. Low light levels cause LCD displays to become dimmer, and harder to see. Research is progressing on adding dyes to the host semiconductor material to improve the brightness and clarity by eliminating the need for a polarizing filter.

Newer, less expensive substrates are on the horizon that will allow a much less expensive display, giving the LCD display a cost advantage over the CRT, one of the major obstacles to LCD market penetration.

The major circuit differences found in LCD technology television are found in vastly different "deflection" circuitry, mostly contained in integrated circuits. In addition, since LCD TVs are so small, they are built using mostly large-scale integrated circuit technology.

Servicing Precautions for LCD Televisions

There are few discrete components that require service in LCD televisions, which contain many large-capacity surface mount technology integrated circuits. These new technology components require specialized servicing techniques. Surface mount ICs do not have sockets, nor are they mounted through holes in the circuit board. Instead, these ICs are mounted to foil pads etched on the board. Many of these ICs are square, and contain 40 to 64 pins or more. Special desoldering tools are required when removing surface mount ICs, and due to their difficulty of replacement, the technician must be quite sure that the IC is indeed defective. Once removed, a surface mount IC is not meant to be reinstalled. When troubleshooting, use only manufacturer recommended service literature and troubleshooting flow charts.

Once the defective component is found, remove it using the special surface-mount IC removal tool. A special tip on this iron heats all pins on one or two sides of the IC at a time, so they may be quickly and easily lifted from the printed circuit board. Once all leads have been de-soldered, the IC is twisted with pliers to break the seal of epoxy glue that holds it to the board. Do not pull directly up on a surface mount IC, as you will surely damage the circuit board, or break the IC before the epoxy fails. A quick twist of the IC with pliers will remove it properly. Once the IC is free, it may be replaced with a new one. Tools are available from many electronics suppliers, and most come with complete details on removal of surface-mount ICs.

CHAPTER 7

TV TUNERS AND IF CIRCUITS

This chapter covers signal processing circuitry in television receivers. The signal is presented to the television through the antenna terminals, and converted by the tuner to an intermediate frequency (IF) signal. Both of these signal blocks are missing in standard video monitors. We will first take a look at TV tuner principles, then look at some standard mechanical tuners, both turret and switch type, and continuously tuned UHF tuners. Late-model varactor switch electronic tuners are also explained, and a section covering the latest microprocessor controlled tuners is included. As many tuners manufactured today are remote control, we will look at how they operate.

IF amplifier circuitry has changed greatly in the last several years. Until only a few model years ago, tuners were composed of L–C stagger-tuned circuits that required careful alignment with expensive equipment to operate properly. Most of the newest televisions are currently using SAW (surface acoustic wave) filters that require no complicated alignment procedure, and are much more reliable. The chapter concludes with alignment instructions using a sweep generator and oscilloscope, and a section on effective troubleshooting methods applicable to all TV tuners and IF amplifiers.

TV TUNER PRINCIPLES

We know what the basic TV tuner is supposed to do from earlier chapters. Figure 7.1 shows how these functions are actually performed. The signal from the antenna is passed through an input filter and is then amplified by the RF amplifier, shown as an FET in this example. A bandpass filter is used between the RF amplifier and the mixer to obtain the 6-MHz bandwidth of the standard TV RF channel. Figure 2.6 showed the location of the picture and sound carriers and also illustrated the use of vestigial sideband suppression. This bandpass response is achieved by the combination of the input filter and the resonant

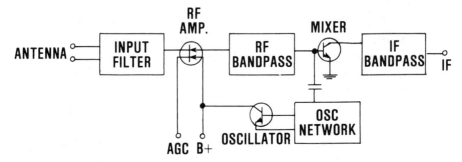

Figure 7.1: Basic TV Tuner

circuit between the RF amplifier and the mixer. In some tuners the input filter is broadly tuned over the TV band, while in others each channel is separately tuned. The RF bandpass filter is always tuned to each specific channel.

The local oscillator provides a frequency that is higher than the transmitted frequency so that the IF frequencies are available at the output of the mixer. This is based on the principle of superheterodyne receivers which is used in all AM and FM receivers as well as in TV sets. Obviously, the oscillator network will have to be tuned to a different frequency for each TV channel.

In Chapter 2, Table 2.1, we have listed all the 82 TV channels located in the United States. In the accompanying text, we have pointed out that, generally speaking, these channels are located in three different frequency bands. Channels 2 through 6 are located in the lower VHF band, channels 7 through 13 in the upper VHF band, and channels 14 through 83 in the UHF band. Because of the great difference in frequencies, most receivers have used separate UHF and VHF tuners. The most recent color TV models use combination VHF-UHF tuners, but even these use entirely separate resonant circuits for the bandpass and oscillator networks. In many TV receivers there is no RF amplifier for the UHF tuner, and this means that the output of the UHF tuner is then applied to the input filter of the VHF tuner. This was illustrated in Chapter 3 and shows the response curve in Figure 3.2.

In the listing of TV channels of Table 2.1, there is a gap between channels 6 and 7, from 88-174 MHz. This band of frequencies is currently allotted to the FM broadcast, two-way aircraft, business, and public service communications. In cable TV systems this frequency band is available for additional TV channels.

Many television systems manufactured today are "cable ready," and contain a tuner assembly capable of receiving the mid-band channels 14 through 60. These channels are only accessible through a cable system as they use frequencies that are assigned to other services for over-the-air transmissions. Most tuners have a switch to select between UHF and CATV. When the switch is in UHF position, channels 14 through 83 are available, while the CATV position allows channels 14 through 60 mid-band frequencies. (Early model tuners only covered through channel 36 mid-band, and as cable channels have expanded, manufacturers have supplied the additional channels.)

MECHANICAL TV TUNERS

The mechanical tuner is rapidly being replaced by the solid state electronic tuner. There are still many mechanical turret and switch type tuners in use, however, so we will look at two typical examples of these types.

The front panel VHF channel switch changes channels by connecting different resonant networks to the input filter, the RF bandpass, and the oscillator network. This operation can be mechanically implemented in two basically different ways. One method is illustrated as the VHF turret tuner in Figure 7.2. It derives its name from a mechanical rotary arrangement in which specific channel strips, as shown in this figure, are switched to stationary contacts that complete the active circuit. The Quasar TS 977 circuit shown in Figure 7.2 is typical of many turret VHF tuners. The antenna board provides both a 75-

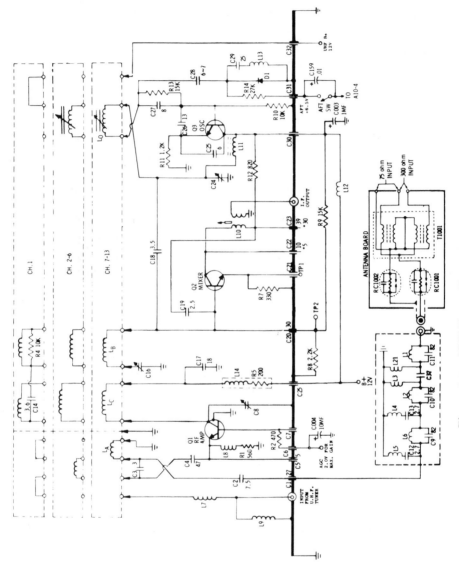

Figure 7.2: VHF Turret Tuner (Quasar TS-977). Courtesy of Quasar Company, Franklin Park, Illinois.

134

ohm and a 300-ohm input and changes from the balanced
to an unbalanced, grounded circuit. The input filter is
designed to reduce external interference.

In this particular circuit the input to the RF amplifier
is through the emitter with the base of the transistor, Q1,
grounded. The collector connects to a resonant circuit that
consists of a trimmer capacitor C8 and the turret strip-
mounted coil. Electromagnetic coupling between that coil
and the input coil to the mixer assures the broad band
frequency response of the RF bandpass circuit. Trimmer
capacitor C16 is for tuning the base resonant circuit of
the mixer. The collector output of the mixer goes to a
double-tuned transformer that covers the IF band and provides the proper impedance match for the IF output. Note
that the oscillator circuit of Figure 7.2 contains adjustable
coils on each turret strip as well as trimmer capacitor C24
for determining the exact oscillator frequency. In a typical
turret tuner, the tuning adjustment for the oscillator coil
on each turret-mounted strip is accessible through a small
hole in the front of the TV receiver and can be adjusted
for optimum reception at each channel with a small
screwdriver. A separate automatic fine tuning signal (AFT)
is applied through the bypass capacitor C3 to the variable
capacitance diode (varactor) D1. The resonant circuit
comprised of L13 and C29 is tuned by the DC voltage
across D1. This circuit is, in effect, shunted across each
of the oscillator resonant circuits through coupling capacitor C28. Variations in the DC voltage applied to D1,
when the AFT switch is closed, provide just enough frequency variation of the oscillator to perform the fine tuning function automatically.

Note that the turret-mounted strip marked "Channel
1" in Figure 7.2 is wired quite differently from the strips
for channels 2 through 13. When the VHF tuner turret is
set to channel 1, the tuner enables the input from the UHF
tuner and acts as an amplifier, with the oscillator circuit
disabled and the RF bandpass channel tuned to the IF
band.

An entirely different type of mechanical VHF tuner is illustrated in Figure 7.3. In this system, usually called rotary switch type tuner, the individual channel coils are connected in series, covering channels 2 through 13, and the rotary switch contact selects the inductance necessary for each particular channel. In an actual circuit there will be a 13th position for the UHF function, but this and a number of other circuit details have been eliminated for the sake of simplicity. Note that, as in the turret tuner, the oscillator circuits provide individual adjustment for each coil, again accessible through a hole in the front panel for optimization of reception for each channel. In the case of the bandpass circuit, S2 and S3, tuning is provided only for the coil for channel 13, which is not mounted on the switch itself, and for the channel 12 coil. The coil that covers the gap from channel 6 to channel 7 also has its own adjustment since it, in effect, tunes the entire lower VHF band, channels 2 through 6.

In a typical VHF tuner the rotary switch wafers containing S2 and S3 are mounted about ¼ inch parallel to each other. In the turret tuner of Figure 7.2 electromagnetic coupling was provided by the location of the RF amplifier output and mixer input coil on each turret strip. In the switch tuner, additional coupling is provided for the entire series of channels by capacitor C4, and, for the lower VHF channels, by capacitor C6, which is connected between the channel 6 contacts. The resonant circuits for the oscillator, connected to S1, are located at the front of the switch so that the individual coil adjustments are accessible. A metal plate isolates the oscillator from the RF portion, C3 provides the coupling from the oscillator to the mixer input, and, in most other respects, the circuitry of a switch VHF tuner is identical to that of a turret type. Automatic fine tuning (AFT), automatic gain control (AGC), and the input from the UHF tuner can be provided to the switch tuner in the same manner as shown in Figure 7.2 for turret tuner.

As we shall see at the end of this chapter under

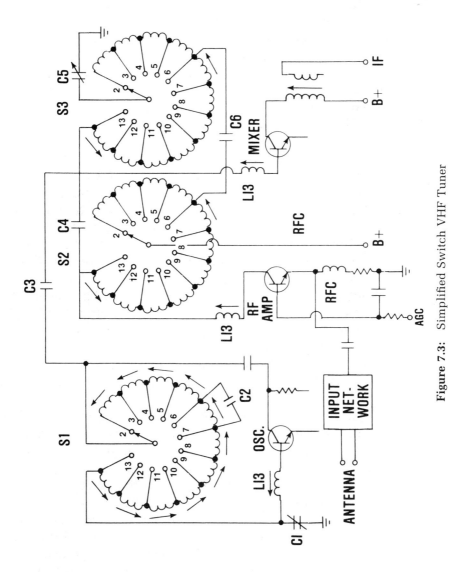

Figure 7.3: Simplified Switch VHF Tuner

137

"Troubleshooting," both mechanical types of VHF tuners fail most frequently where the switch contacts are. In general, turret tuner switching mechanisms are somewhat more easily cleaned and slightly more reliable than the rotary switch wafers. In both types of VHF tuners, contact troubles represent the majority of defects; this has given rise to special spray cans with such names as "tuner bath" to reduce the switch noise problems.

The UHF band covers 70 channels, and neither a turret nor a switch type mechanism would be suitable to cover that many positions. In essence, all mechanical UHF tuners depend on the use of capacitive tuning of resonant transmission lines. Because of the frequency range—the UHF channels go from 470 to 890 MHz in one continuous band—so-called "lumped" networks such as coils and capacitors are not suitable, and we generally use the transmission line or "distributed" constant circuits. In this system the electrical length of a transmission line can be varied by varying the capacity of it to ground at one end. That is the principle of the capacitor tuner circuit shown in Figure 7.4, one of the most widely used in TV receivers. Only the most recent UHF tuners have an active circuit as RF amplifier because transistors that can operate in the 470- to 890-MHz range are relatively expensive.

The UHF signal from the antenna is applied to a small coil that couples it to the resonant circuit consisting of the transmission line terminated in C ANT. The resonant circuit consists not only of the strip line but also of the walls and surroundings of the chamber in which it is mounted. A hole in one wall provides the same action as inductive coupling to the resonant circuit that is terminated in C MXR, the mixer tuned circuit. A similar resonant circuit is terminated in C OSC, which employs a UHF transistor as oscillator with its frequency controlled, to some extent, by the resonant circuits consisting of D2, a voltage variable diode (varactor), C3 and L3. In the mixer section, a portion of the oscillator signal is coupled through

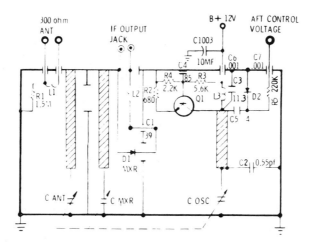

Figure 7.4: UHF Capacitor Tuner (Quasar TS-977).
Courtesy of Quasar Company, Franklin Park, Illinois.

a small loop, and since the tuned and preselected RF signal is also in the mixer chamber, D1, a UHF diode, provides the mixing of these two signals and the combination of C1 and L2 filters out the UHF portions and allows only the IF frequencies to go to the IF output jack.

As we shall see in the section on "Troubleshooting" at the end of this chapter, the three-gang capacitor providing the tuning for the oscillator, mixer, and antenna section of the UHF tuner shown in Figure 7.4 is a very likely source of trouble, even though no direct contact is usually involved. In most UHF capacitor-type tuners, the rotation of this capacitor covers either 180° or more than 240°, which, on the dial at the front of the TV set, is usually translated to at least 360°. This implies some kind of gear or dial-cord pulley mechanism, and, as with most mechanical devices, a variety of troubles can occur in this area. Some manufacturers use special mechanical arrangements to provide the appearance of UHF switching, while still using the ganged variable capacitor. This may be another area of frequent defects.

ELECTRONIC TV TUNERS

The key element in many of the electronic tuners is the varactor diode. All diodes contain a certain amount of capacitance, but varactor diodes are specially designed so that the amount of capacity depends on the voltage across the diode. We have already encountered a varactor diode in the VHF turret tuner of Figure 7.2. Here, the diode D1 was used for the automatic fine tuning circuit. In the UHF capacitor tuner of Figure 7.4, diode D2 performs the same function. In the most recent electronic tuning VHF and UHF tuners, varactor diodes are used extensively, as illustrated in the circuit diagram of Figure 7.5. Two different sets of varactor diodes are used in this VHF tuner. One set receives the switch voltage (BS) to change from the lower to the upper VHF band, and the second set receives the tuning voltage (BT) to tune the individual channels. We can see that the switch voltage goes to the input tuned circuit of the RF amplifier through a 4.7-K resistor. The tuning voltage (BT) also goes to the input stage through a complicated DC decoupling network. The double-tuned output transformer of the RF amplifier also receives BS through two 4.7-K resistors and BT through the same isolating network. In each case the resonant circuits consist of two series coils. One coil is tuned by the switch voltage (BS), and the other coil is tuned by the tuning voltage BT. The same principle is used for the two coils that make up the resonant circuit of the oscillator.

In the tuner of Figure 7.5 (Quasar TS-975), the switch voltage (BS) ranges from minus 21.1 volts for the low VHF channels to + 19.0 volts for the high VHF channels. The tuning voltage (BT) varies from 2.11 volts for channel 2 to 16.8 volts for channel 6, and from 8.2 volts for channel 7 to 19.7 volts for channel 13. It is clear that the source of this voltage must be very precisely controlled and accurately maintained. We shall see in a later paragraph how this voltage is provided.

The VHF varactor tuner circuit of Figure 7.5 uses a

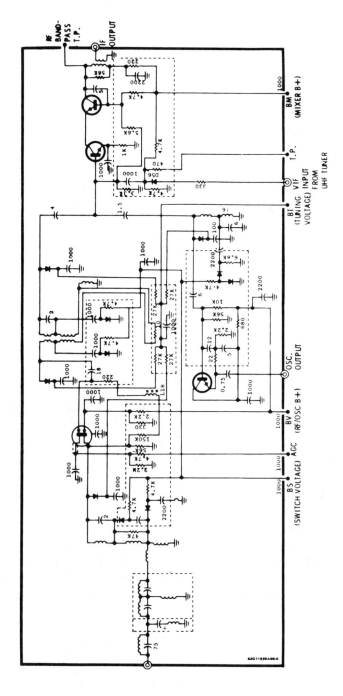

Figure 7.5: VHF Varactor Tuner (Quasar TS-975). Courtesy of Quasar Company, Franklin Park, Illinois.

two stage circuit for the mixer and IF output amplifier. Because the UHF tuner used in the Quasar TS-975 has its own UHF RF amplifier, the output of that tuner is applied, as illustrated in Figure 7.5, directly to the input of the mixer. When UHF channels are selected, the voltage to the RF amplifier and oscillator (BV) is cut to zero.

The UHF varactor tuner used in the Quasar TS-975 circuit, illustrated in Figure 7.6, also uses varactor diodes for tuning. In this case, however, there is no need for a switching voltage since channels 14 through 83 can be continuously tuned. A single tuning voltage (BT) is applied and controls varactor diodes for each of the four resonant circuits used in this tuner. Note that a UHF transistor is used as RF amplifier in a grounded base configuration. Each of the four resonant circuits has a trimming capacitor, adjustable from the outside, for the alignment of the UHF tune. The output of the oscillator is coupled to the emitter circuit of the mixer where it is mixed with the output of the RF amplifier section. A standard IF signal is obtained from the collector double-tuned transformer of the mixer, as in any VHF tuner.

According to the manufacturer, UHF channels 14 through 83 can be tuned by varying BT from 2.2 to 26.7 volts. This means that 24.5 volts covers the range of 69 channels, which means that 0.356 V increments tune from one UHF channel to the next. Clearly, as in the case of the VHF tuner, ultra-precise voltage control is necessary for electronic tuning.

Figure 7.7 shows the VHF and UHF tuning control circuit used with a rotary switch channel selector covering UHF and VHF in 18 positions. This provides the standard 12 VHF channels and six selected UHF channels. The 18-position selector switch is on the same shaft as the band switch SW2 which selects the low and high VHF control voltages. There are separate potentiometers for each of the channels so that the service technician can optimize the tuning for each channel. In the power supply for the control voltages used in this system, the $+33$ V

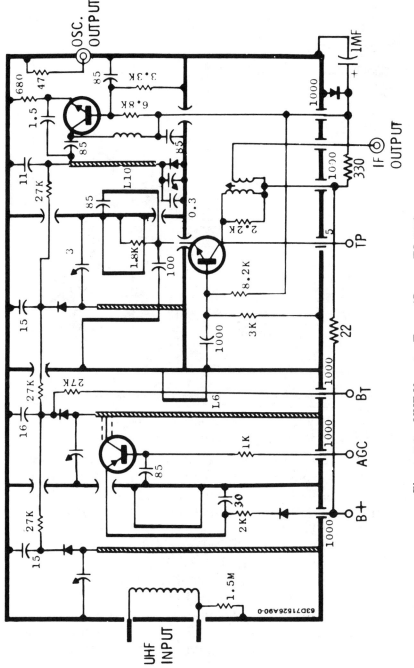

Figure 7.6: UHF Varactor Tuner (Quasar TS-975).
Courtesy of Quasar Company, Franklin Park, Illinois.

143

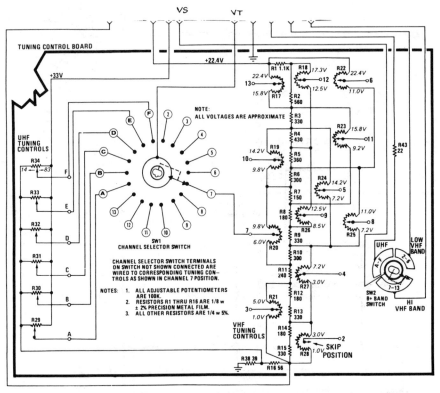

Figure 7.7: VHF and UHF Tuning Control (Quasar TS-981).
Courtesy of Quasar Company, Franklin Park, Illinois.

and +22.4 V sources are controlled by electronic power supply regulator circuits. Automatic fine tuning voltage signals are mixed into the tuning voltage VT so that, at the varactor itself, the actual voltage will vary, according to the AFT signal.

Any six of the 69 UHF channels can be selected for accessibility at points A, B, C, D, E, and F, because each of the six potentiometers covers the entire voltage range, corresponding to channels 14 through 83. During the installation, the service technician simply adjusts these potentiometers to tune in six UHF channels that are locally available. In most areas, there are no more than that.

MICROPROCESSOR-CONTROLLED TUNERS

Tuning of a particular channel is achieved by adjusting the local oscillator frequency. As this is a very critical adjustment for a stable, properly tuned picture, newer-model televisions often use frequency synthesis to generate a stable picture. Frequency synthesizers are widely used in industrial, military and test equipment to provide a very large number of precise, constantly controlled frequencies.

Many of these phase-lock-loop synthesizers with microprocessor control include onscreen channel display, remote control and many other features. A typical microprocessor control system is found in the Mitsubishi FS–VI tuning system. We will first look at its features, and then go through its design and functions.

The FS–VI system contains a programmable EAPROM (electrically alterable programmable read only memory) to allow the owner to program only active channels into the system. Volume level and last channel tuned are also stored in the EAPROM. An onscreen display generator can provide status of the following parameters: channel number, time of day, shut-off time if timer is being used, volume, tint, color and brightness levels, external monitor status, audio mode (stereo, SAP and so on) and cable or broadcast TV modes. The Mitsubishi FS–VI system is also remote controlled. Some models also control certain VCRs in the Mitsubishi line. As with most companies, Mitsubishi makes some or all of these features available in a given model television set. In other words, though the tuner may support display of stereo mode, if the television is not stereo equipped, the mode display will be disabled in the system.

Servicing microprocessor-controlled circuitry requires a base of knowledge on how microprocessors work. There is not enough space to cover this topic here. It is recommended that those who are not familiar with mi-

croprocessors locate appropriate reading materials that
will introduce the topic at a basic level. The discussion
of the FS–VI system will assume a basic knowledge of
microprocessor operations. A simplified functional block
diagram of the FS–VI tuning system is illustrated in Figure 7.8. Commands from the remote control or television
control console are received by a keyboard matrix. The
microprocessor internally generates a signal that is applied to pins 18–20 and 23–26 of the microprocessor IC
701. After being sent through the keyboard, the signal is
received at pins 1–4 and 40 and 41 of the microprocessor.
The scanner inputs then determine which, if any, command buttons are being pressed, and if so, direct the microprocessor to act accordingly. For example, when the
consumer selects a channel change operation, the microprocessor determines bandswitching at pins 38 and 39,
which directs IC 703, the bandswitching IC, to select the
appropriate band of channels at pins 15 and 17, and apply
the correct voltage to the varactor tuner assembly at pin
11.

Phase lock loop (PLL) technology works because a
sample of the tuning voltage is fed back into the frequency
generator and compared and readjusted automatically, allowing the generator to lock onto the desired frequency.
See Figure 7–9 for a simplified block diagram of typical
PLL and frequency synthesizer circuits. Digital frequency
dividers provide many different feedback frequencies, allowing the phase lock loop circuitry to generate any desired channel frequency.

A basic PLL circuit contains a voltage-controlled oscillator that feeds a frequency comparator. The comparator also receives a crystal-controlled frequency as a
reference. The output of the comparator is a DC voltage
that is used to adjust the frequency of the VCO.

If we place a divide-by-N frequency divider between
the VCO and frequency comparator, we can generate mul-
tiples of the reference frequency. This makes it possible
to obtain a very wide range of frequencies all based upon

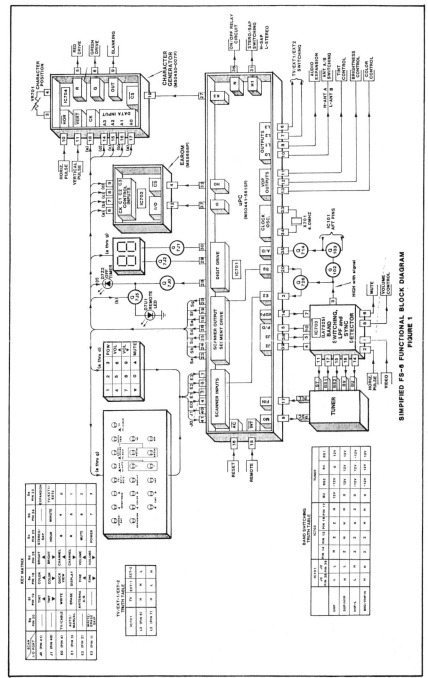

Figure 7.8: Mitsubishi FS-6 Electronic Tuning System.
Reproduced from the "Expander," a technical reference newsletter,
courtesy of Mitsubishi Electric Sales America, Inc., Cypress, California.

147

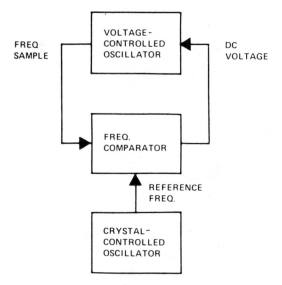

(a) BASIC PHASE LOCKED-LOOP (PLL)

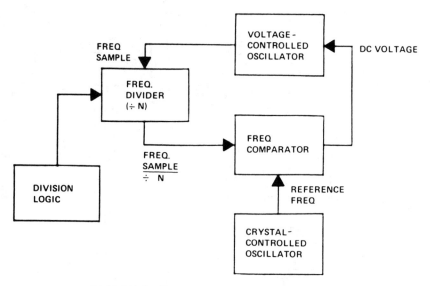

(b) FREQUENCY SYNTHESIZER

Figure 7.9: Block Diagram of Frequency Synthesizer.
Courtesy General Electric.

the division ratio by adjusting the division logic. The Mitsubishi tuner uses this technique to tune any desired station. The feedback sample is generated inside the tuner, and sent to the microprocessor at pin 17. Fine tuning is accomplished by changing the frequency division ratio. The microprocessor applies pulses to pin 9, the Pulse Swallow Control (PSC). The changing number of pulses at this point are what the tuner requires to determine the desired channel frequency.

An EAPROM is used to remember certain consumer-control settings during the times the TV set is unplugged. The EAPROM is enabled by the microprocessor at pin 32, and the memory is altered whenever choices affecting Sa through Sd are made. The logic at pins 7,8 and 9 controls the operational mode of IC702. Data is transferred in and out of the EAPROM via the I/O terminal at pin 12.

The scanner outputs of the microprocessor are also responsible for supplying data to the video display IC (IC 704) and also to the seven-segment fluorescent channel indicator, the OFF timer and remote LEDs.

This receiver uses onscreen displays of time, channel and other operating parameters. Data from IC 701 pins Sa through Se scanner outputs are also provided to the character generator IC, which contains the logic to display a graphic implementation of the settings of these controls. When the microprocessor places a LOW at pin 27, the character generator is enabled. Horizontal and vertical signals are applied to pins 10 and 11 of IC 704, and are used to determine position of the characters on the CRT display. Red and green drive are applied to the CRT at the appropriate time, and a blanking signal is generated to eliminate video underneath the character display to make sure the display is readable. The display may be adjusted horizontally on screen via VR 701 at pins 3 and 4, however vertical positioning is not adjustable.

Volume, brightness, color and tint adjustments are also processed through the microprocessor via a variable duty cycle pulse. The volume pulse is found at pin 14.

The signal is filtered by the low-pass filter (LPF), and the DC level is then applied to the audio circuitry.

Tint, brightness and color are variable duty cycle pulses at pins 11 through 13. A more positive duty cycle increases the level of the specific function (volume, color, brightness), or drives the tint control circuitry toward cyan. When the television is turned off, these levels are maintained; however, if the set should become unplugged, only the volume level will be remembered by the EAPROM. All other controls will return to midposition. Reset buttons are also provided for brightness and color, which will return these controls to midposition as well.

Automatic fine tuning and automatic detection of signal presence is also provided in the tuner. Stereo and SAP, and power ON–OFF are also controlled through the microprocessor.

Figure 7.8 also contains several truth tables that are helpful to the technician in determining whether a fault appears in the microprocessor or other control circuitry.

REMOTE CONTROL SYSTEMS

As we have seen, the FS–VI system can be remote controlled if desired. Many current production televisions use digital circuitry for tuning, and incorporate a remote control in their basic design. Earlier remote control systems used ultrasonic transmitters to send information to the remote receiver built into the television. An electric motor was used to turn the shaft of the mechanical tuner. As the mechanical tuner was replaced with varactor type tuners, the remote mechanism became much simpler in design, and thus less expensive to include.

Ultrasonic systems are prone to being triggered by external noises which cause random triggering of the remote circuitry. Later model units transmitted a digital code that must be received and verified by the ultrasonic receiver before the appropriate action occurred.

Nearly all current-model remote receivers are based upon infrared technology, as is the case of the Mitsubishi system. The RCA Color Track system also depends upon infrared radiation transmission for its remote control system as demonstrated in Figure 7.10.

The block diagram of Figure 7.10 shows the infrared transmitter and receiver, and the remote control and central control modules. In the remote control module, the pulse code modulated signals from the receiver are decoded, and, along with the inputs from the manual controls on the receiver itself, are passed on either to the chassis power supply or to the central control module. The central control module receives the binary channel code, the signals whether to step one channel up or one channel down in the sequence, and the volume control voltage. From these signals, the central control module then generates the correct control voltages for the VHF/UHF varactor type tuners and for the audio circuits.

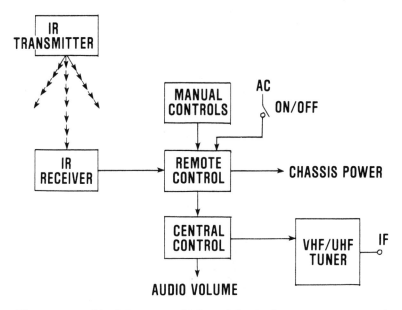

Figure 7.10: Block Diagram of RCA "Color Trak" IR Remote Control System

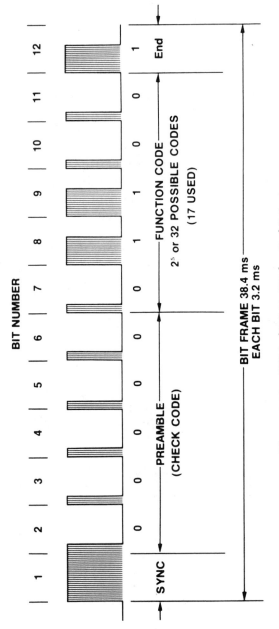

Figure 7.11: PCM of RCA's "Color Trak" System.
Courtesy RCA Consumer Electronics.

The remote control unit has a 17-key keyboard and a single IC that provides the encoding. Three infrared LEDs transmit a 40-KHz, crystal-controlled pulse code modulated signal, the format of which is shown in Figure 7.11. The sync pulse is 3.2 milliseconds long, a logic "1" pulse is 1.6 milliseconds wide, and the pulse that occurs when a logic "O" is indicated is 0.4 ms wide. As indicated in Figure 7.11, there is a 5-bit preamble or check code, followed by a 5-bit function code, of which only 17 possible codes are used. Manufacturer's instructions have to be consulted for the specific meaning of each code, but the operation of the color track system can be checked out by observing the decoded binary signals in response to different key depressions.

Like the Zenith Space Command and most other advanced remote control systems, RCA's Color Track system also uses digital ICs to a great extent. The principles of troubleshooting remote control systems are covered at the end of this chapter.

IF AMPLIFIER SYSTEMS

The key function of the IF amplifier in any TV receiver is to provide substantial amplification, usually 40 to 60 db, and to limit the bandwidth of the amplified signal to conform with the desired response curve. IF response curves have been shown in Figure 3.3 and again in Figure 5.2, where the difference between the IF response of a monochrome receiver and a color TV receiver have been demonstrated. In earlier TV receivers, the amplification was provided by several stages of vacuum tubes or transistors and the bandpass response was assured by the use of a variety of resonant circuits. Figure 7.12 illustrates some of the resonant circuits that have been used in vacuum-tube as well as transistor-type receivers. The bifilar transformer and absorption trap shown in Figure 7.12 (a) has been used quite widely in many kinds of receivers as

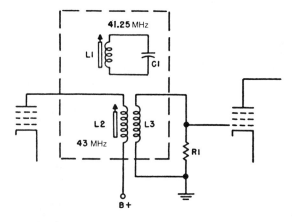

(a) BIFILAR TRANSFORMER AND ABSORPTION TRAP

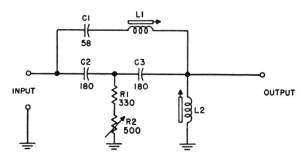

(b) BRIDGE-T TYPE IF FILTER

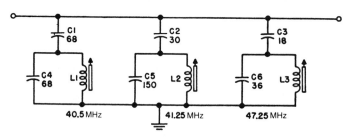

(c) COMBINATION SOUND AND ADJACENT CHANNEL TRAPS

Figure 7.12: Typical IF Tuned Circuits.
Color TV Servicing, 3rd Ed., Walter H. Buchsbaum. Prentice-Hall, Inc.

interstage coupling. The bifilar transformer itself acts as a single tuned circuit with unity coupling, while the absorption trap, with its coil wound on the same tube as the transformer, absorbs the 41.25-MHz audio IF signal. The bridge-T type IF filter shown in Figure 7.12 (b) is tuned for maximum rejection of the undesired audio IF or adjacent channel video or sound. A combination sound and adjacent channel trap, set up in a series of parallel resonant circuits, is illustrated in Figure 7.12 (c).

Since IC amplifiers that could cover the 45-MHz band have been available, a single IC performs all amplification. Such a circuit is illustrated in Figure 7.13 and includes a double-tuned, broadband, input transformer, T1, preceded by an adjacent sound IF filter consisting of the coil L1 and the two series capacitors. Three more resonant circuits are used in this IF section. Interstage coupling transformer T2 provides a broadband response, and part of its signal is absorbed by the trap consisting of L3 and the 120-pF capacitor; L2 and the 3.9 pF capacitor make up the third resonant circuit.

Many of the monochrome and color TV sets currently in use contain IF sections like the one shown in Figure 7.13, while some older sets use a series of discrete IF transistor stages. In each case, every resonant circuit was designed to be tuned to a particular frequency so that the total combination of resonant circuits adds up to the correct bandpass response. It is absolutely essential that the manufacturer's instructions concerning which circuit is tuned to which part of the frequency band be followed carefully.

In many recent TV receivers, all the resonant circuits have been eliminated and replaced by a single, small, solid-state filter that does not require any adjustment. These so-called SAW filters are based on a surface acoustic wave, traveling a fixed distance on a piezoelectric substrate. The principle of the SAW filter is illustrated in Figure 7.14. The frequency response curve is a function of the delay or spacing between the input transducer and the output

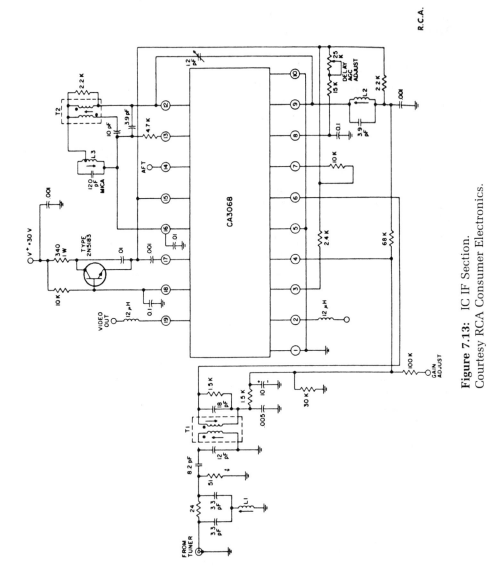

Figure 7.13: IC IF Section.
Courtesy RCA Consumer Electronics.

156

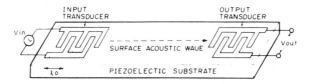

Figure 7.14: Principle of "Saw" Filter.
Courtesy Hitachi Ltd.

transducer while the interdigit spacing, λ, between the
transducer elements is related to the wavelength of the
surface acoustic wave. By proper design of input and output transducer, their separation, and the piezoelectric
substrate, it is possible to obtain a relatively broad band
frequency response, with a series of sharp nulls at the
desired distance from the center frequency. This feature
eliminates the requirement for traps because these nulls
are designed so as to fall at the point of the adjacent
channel sound and picture. Once a SAW filter is con-
structed, no further adjustment is necessary or possible.
This means that for IF systems using the SAW filter, there
is no tuning of the IF resonant circuits. The principles of
surface acoustic waves are beyond the scope of this book.
If a SAW filter becomes defective, it must be replaced by
the proper replacement part.

One of the drawbacks of SAW filters is a relatively
large insertion loss that must be compensated for by the
IF amplifier. The block diagram of Figure 7.15 shows the
IF IC used in RCA's CTC-108 chassis. Three stages of IF
amplification are followed by a synchronous video detector. This type of detector differs from the common peak
detector used in older TV receivers, but it provides the
lowest possible distortion in the video output signal. From
the video detector the video signal is amplified, passes
through a noise inverter, and then goes through the final
video amplifier as the composite video output signal. A
4.5-MHz trap eliminates the sound carrier information
that then goes to further signal processing circuits. The

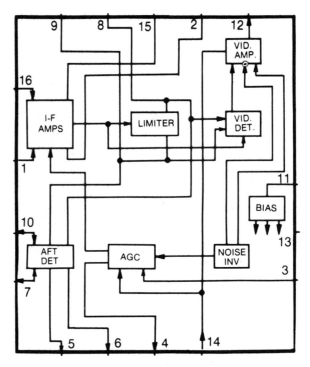

Figure 7.15: IF-IC Block Diagram (RCA U301).
Courtesy RCA Consumer Electronics.

same IC also includes a noise inversion circuit, a bias supply, AGC detector and amplifier, and a comparison voltage against the setting of the RF AGC control to develop the tuner AGC voltage. Unlike many earlier IF AGC systems, keyed AGC, controlled by a horizontal keying pulse, is no longer used. The automatic fine tuning (AFT) detector receives signals of both polarities from the limiter.

A variety of different IF IC devices are on the market, some of them incorporating the 4.5-MHz audio or other functions as well. In each case, when a defect occurs in this IC, only an exact replacement part can be used.

ALIGNMENT

The most widely used alignment method for TV tuners and IF amplifiers employs a sweep generator and oscilloscope. The block diagram of Figure 7.16 shows the basic operation of the system. A constantly varying frequency is generated by the sweep generator. In most systems the frequency band for the unit under test, VHF, UHF or the IF band, is approximately 5 to 6 MHz wide, and the sweep generator provides a constant amplitude output that sweeps through this band 60 times a second. The 60 Hz sweep signal is supplied to the horizontal input of the oscilloscope where it controls the horizontal deflection.

Figure 7.16 shows a matching pad that also allows a marker generator to be connected. A typical matching pad is illustrated in Figure 7.17 (a) and (b). In the 75- to 300-ohm pad, a separate input is provided for the marker generator. Some sweep generators provide internal, very accurate crystal-controlled marker frequencies. The out-

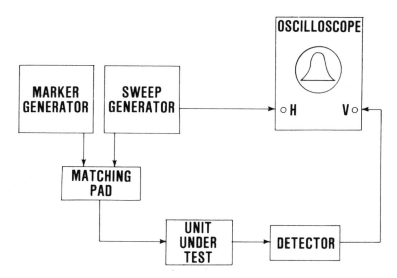

Figure 7.16:   Basic RF and IF Alignment Test Set-Up

put of the matching pad is applied to the UHF or VHF tuner. When only the IF section is aligned, the matching pad is usually not necessary since the output of the sweep generator can be applied to a specific test point on the tuner or the IF section itself.

The detector shown in Figure 7.16 is a small circuit, illustrated in detail in Figure 7.17(c) and (d), and different ones will be used for the tuner or IF section. If the final signal is taken off after the video IF detector, the detector probe may not be necessary. Both matching pads and detector probes are often supplied with the instruments they are used with. Many sweep generators are provided with a 300-ohm matching pad, and most oscilloscopes are available with suitable detector probes.

Manufacturer's instructions must be carefully followed to obtain proper bandpass response curves for VHF and UHF tuners and the IF section. The VHF tuner band-

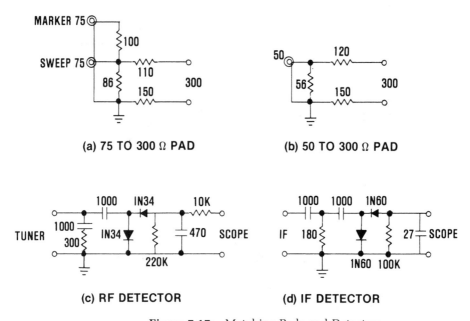

Figure 7.17: Matching Pads and Detectors

pass limits for a particular RCA series of receivers are
shown in Figure 7.18. As indicated, for maximum bandwidth, the picture and sound carriers should be no less
than 1.0 MHz from the peak of the double-dip curve. For
minimum bandwidth, the picture and sound carrier should
be at the 70% point of the curve. The types of slopes that
are possible between picture and sound are indicated in
Figure 7.18 (d) and (e).

The desired and the worst case curves for the RCA
UHF tuner bandpass are illustrated in Figure 7.19. Note
that in this case the desired RF center frequency is 887
MHz, but the picture and sound carriers are shown in
terms of their IF frequencies.

When a SAW filter is used, IF alignment is not necessary, but in all other TV receivers several adjustments
must be made to assure the proper IF bandwidth response.
It is essential that manufacturer's instructions be followed
carefully so that each resonant circuit is aligned to the
frequency prescribed by the manufacturer. The sequence
of performing the adjustments should also be that prescribed by the manufacturer, although some touch-up adjustments are usually necessary.

Figure 7.20 illustrates the ideal frequency response
for a color TV receiver. Note that the 41.25-MHz sound
portion appears to be attenuated very strongly, a necessary
feature to avoid interference from the color subcarrier at
42.17 MHz. Adjacent video and adjacent sound traps are

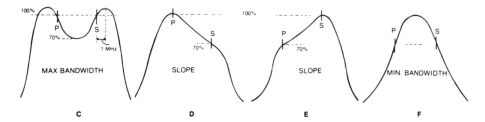

Figure 7.18: VHF Tuner Bandpass Limits.
Courtesy RCA Consumer Electronics.

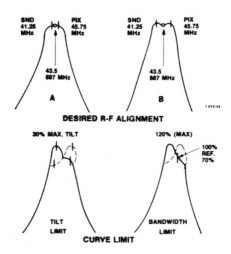

Figure 7.19: UHF Tuner Bandpass.
Courtesy RCA Consumer Electronics.

important to assure that, particularly when cable TV is being received, there is no interference from adjacent channels. The 45.75-MHz video IF carrier should be approximately halfway down on the response curve.

Most manufacturers specify the bias conditions under which tuner and IF alignment must be made. In some instances this requires substituting a battery box for bias

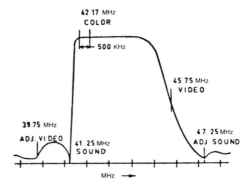

Figure 7.20: Correct IF Response Curve.
Color TV Servicing, 3rd Ed., Walter H. Buchsbaum. Prentice-Hall, Inc.

on the AGC bus, but in most modern sets this is not necessary.

When aligning an iron-core or ferrite slug in an IF or RF coil, never use a metal screwdriver. Suitable alignment tools are available from all electronic distributors. Only those adjustments in which a grounded metal screw is used should be made with a metal screwdriver.

TROUBLESHOOTING

TV tuner defects are usually easily localized if there are UHF and VHF stations in your area. It is a rare occurence when both tuners fail simultaneously. If it does occur, the most likely problem is missing tuner supply voltage in the power supply. When only one channel is received poorly, or when the low or high band VHF channels are received poorly, chances are the problem is in the tuner. A color generator that generates frequencies in VHF low and high bands and the UHF band is useful in tracking down tuner problems.

In televisions that contain mechanical tuners, the most common problem is switch contact corrosion. The usual symptom when this problem occurs is intermittent poor reception on one or more channels. The problem may temporarily clear up when pressure is applied to the channel selector knob, or another channel is chosen. Cleaning the contacts with a suitable spray or by applying a cotton swab soaked with cleaning fluid to the contacts is the most frequent solution. When the contacts become too noisy or corroded to be corrected by chemical cleaning, the tuner may have to be rebuilt or replaced. Before taking this step, be sure to also check for poor solder connections, poor grounding strap connections and loose cable connectors. Tighten all ground shields that connect between the main chassis and the tuner and control assemblies.

In electronic tuners, problems can occur either in the

pushbutton selecting keyboard, or in the switch that selects the various tuning voltages. In most cases, however, electronic tuners fail due to problems with circuit components, or problems with the tuner PC board or interconnecting wiring. Electronic tuners experience far fewer problems than the mechanical types. Complex tuning assemblies, especially microprocessor-controlled tuners, will require availability of detailed circuit diagrams, troubleshooting flow charts, and complete manufacturers documentation. These complex circuits make it necessary for the technician to have a much higher degree of expertise in troubleshooting to complete a successful repair.

As tuner problems are many times difficult to find, and take a lot of time, it may be best to utilize the facilities of one of the many tuner rebuilding services around the country. These companies will either replace your defective tuner assembly with a rebuilt unit, or completely rebuild your unit to original specifications. As these companies specialize in tuner repairs, they carry a large assortment of electrical and mechanical parts, and can do a quality job with a minimum of expense and a relatively short turnaround time. Most rebuilding stations also will completely realign your tuner assembly upon repair. If you use a rebuilding service, be sure to make a diagram of the tuner disassembly, including wire coloring and any plug connections that are not immediately obvious. Tube tuners should have new tubes in them before shipment, to eliminate these easily replaced components from suspicion. Pack the unit carefully for shipment. Turnaround time is less than two weeks in most cases, including shipment. Order an exchange tuner if you wish faster turnaround.

Regardless of the type of tuner used, its performance can be evaluated by means of the RF alignment procedure described above. If the alignment results in the proper response curve, we can assume that all portions of the tuner, except the oscillator, are functioning correctly. Using the same alignment set up to test the IF section, we can determine if that functions correctly. The final step is to check the local oscillator itself. If the VHF or UHF sweep generator is connected to the antenna terminals, and the detector and the oscilloscope at the output of the IF section, tuning to the frequency set in the sweep generator should produce an output on the oscilloscope. Failure to do so indicates a defect in the oscillator section. This section is most frequently evaluated by measuring the various voltages, and, with the power shut off, some key resistance values.

In those receivers using a single IC to provide all the amplification and control for the IF section, the alignment procedure usually gives a clue as to whether the IC itself or one of the externally mounted components is defective. Be sure to check the AGC signal as well as all other DC voltages going to the IC before deciding that it must be replaced. Many receivers use decoupling circuits, consisting of series resistors and bypass capacitors, to isolate the tuner and IF section from the chance of interference with any other section in the TV receiver. When one of these capacitors shorts out, or has excess leakage, the incorrect voltage will reach the IC. Open capacitors make it possible for various interference signals to be generated, and, in some cases, can lead to oscillations and other undesirable effects. In some instances RF chokes are wound on half-watt resistors, or else B + or bias leads pass through ferromagnetic beads that reduce the chance of interference. Be sure that all these decoupling networks are functioning properly before discarding a particular IC or some other major component.

In troubleshooting remote control systems, the most frequent problem is a weak battery in the remote transmitter. To check the transmitter operation we can use the oscilloscope to look for a decoded signal in the receiver decoder or check some test point in the receiver itself. To determine definitely whether the transmitter output or the

receiver input section is defective, we would have to have
another transmitter, known to be good, or another receiver. Troubles in the receiver and decoder portion usually require signal tracing with an oscilloscope. A voltage
and resistance check often locates the defective component, even without signal tracing.

CHAPTER 8

SYNC, DEFLECTION AND HIGH VOLTAGE CIRCUITS

In this chapter, we will look at several representative sync, deflection and high voltage circuits. Until the advent of solid state circuitry, there was little change in the design of these circuits from year to year. With the development of solid state components, many companies have changed the design of these circuits to take advantage of more reliable, more efficient components.

Figures 1.2, 2.7 and 2.8 illustrate the typical circuit functions in TVs, both color and monochrome, and monitor displays. The basic function of the sync, deflection and high-voltage circuits is to remove sync pulses from the composite video waveform, develop horizontal and vertical sweep signals that are used to drive the deflection yoke, and generate the high voltage required to drive modern display CRTs. High-voltage circuitry is, of course, not necessary for the new class of solid state display devices. Secondary outputs from these circuits control many other circuits throughout the television, including AGC, dynamic pincushion correction, convergence, noise canceling and others. Troubleshooting and adjustment of these circuits conclude this chapter.

SYNCHRONIZING CIRCUITS

We know from Chapter 3 that the composite video signal is applied to the sync amplifier and separator section. We also know that this function first removes the synchronizing pulses from the blanking pedestal and then separates the horizontal and vertical synchronizing signals from each other. The typical sync separator circuit of Figure 8.1 performs these functions in two stages. The first transistor clips the sync signals from the composite video signal. The video signal is applied through an RC network to the base of the 4464 transistor. With the emitter grounded, collector current is obtained through the voltage divider R3 and R4. As a result, only the sync pulses will reach the base of the second stage, the 4473 inverter transistor.

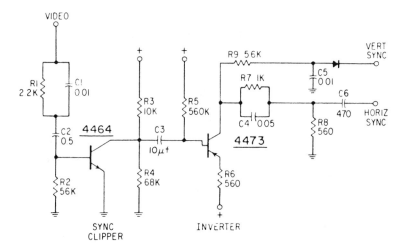

Figure 8.1: Typical Sync Separator Circuit.
Reprinted with permission of Hayden Book Company from *Fundamentals of Television* by Walter H. Buchsbaum.

This stage amplifies both horizontal and vertical sync pulses, and the actual separation is done by the differentiating network for the horizontal sync and the integrating network for the vertical sync.

Figure 8.2 shows the vertical blanking interval and the horizontal pulses that occur at that time. As a result of the integration, R9 and C5 in Figure 8.1, we see the integrated voltage in 8.2 (b), which adds up to the vertical sync pulse. The differentiation of these same horizontal pulses, R8 and C6 in Figure 8.1, is illustrated in Figure 8.2 (c). These differentiated horizontal sync pulses control the frequency of the horizontal sawtooth signal that is illustrated in 8.2 (d). A portion of the vertical sync voltage is shown in Figure 8.2 (e), and this is synchronized with the integrated vertical sync pulse of Figure 8.2 (b). The essential elements of the sync separator illustrated in Figure 8.1 are found in almost every color and monochrome TV receiver.

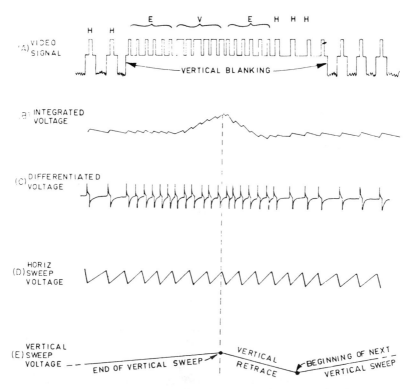

Figure 8.2: Integration and Differentiation of Horizontal Pulses During Vertical Sync Period.

Reprinted with permission of Hayden Book Company from *Fundamentals of Television* by Walter H. Buchsbaum.

Many of the circuits contain additional features, such as the noise-canceling circuit shown in Figure 8.3. This circuit uses one transistor stage, connected between the output of the first video amplifier and the input of the sync separator. When the composite video signal is free of noise, transistor Q301 in Figure 8.3 and the clamping diode D301 are both reverse biased. If noise pulses arrive that are larger than the sync pulse, they overcome the reverse bias of D301, driving it into conduction. As D301 conducts, the base voltage of the transistor also goes up, causing collector current to flow. The load resistor for the

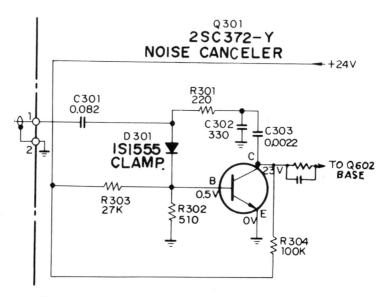

Figure 8.3: Noise Canceler—Sears, Model 562, 40960200

collector is large so that the transistor saturates quickly. This provides an effective short to the chassis for noise signals. While this particular noise-canceler circuit is typical, many variations of the same basic circuit are used in different TV receivers. In each case the principle of removing noisy signals is the same.

In most TV receivers manufactured today, the sync separation function, noise canceling, integration and differentiation are all performed within an IC. Many sync separator ICs also provide pincushion correction waveforms, and a horizontal pulse for color burst detection by the automatic color control (ACC) circuitry. The sync circuitry also usually provides an output to the horizontal automatic frequency control (AFC). The horizontal AFC circuitry generates an error voltage and corrects the frequency of the horizontal oscillator whenever it notes a difference in phase or frequency between incoming horizontal sync pulses, and the output of the horizontal oscillator.

Different manufacturers have implemented this circuitry in different fashions, even separating the different functions across two ICs.

VERTICAL DEFLECTION

Signals leaving the vertical integration network of the sync separator are passed along to the vertical deflection circuitry, eventually to drive the vertical yoke windings. Vertical sweep circuits in the U.S. and Canada operate at 60 Hz, while other countries with 50-Hz power lines use 50 Hz as vertical sweep frequency. Vertical sweep circuit problems usually revolve around raster scanning defects. These problems include loss of linearity, indicated by an unnatural stretched or squashed appearance of the picture at the top or bottom of the screen, and loss of sync, indicated by a rolling of the picture. A circuit defect is indicated if the problem cannot be corrected by adjusting the height and linearity controls, and vertical hold control.

Figure 8.4 illustrates a typical sweep circuit, beginning with the vertical sync pulse integrator, vertical oscillator, and the output stages. The integration is performed by the combination of R205 and C204, followed by R207 and the shunting capacitor C206. The 60-Hz sawtooth oscillator is composed of Q202, Q203, Q204 and Q205. This last transistor also acts as output amplifier, but a portion of its emitter signal is fed back through the vertical hold control. Components R209 and C206 set the time constant for the required charge-discharge network to generate a 60-Hz sawtooth. In many vertical sweep circuits the buffer and feedback amplifier, Q204 and Q203 respectively, are not used. These additional transistors, however, provide better linearity and stability. Note that they are also involved with the vertical size and linearity control, secondary controls usually mounted at the rear of the cabinet, as explained in Chapter 1.

The actual sawtooth current going through the deflec-

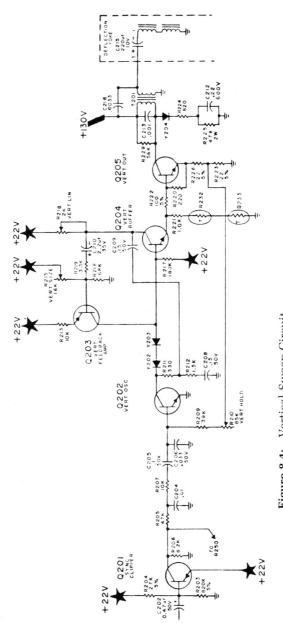

Figure 8.4: Vertical Sweep Circuit.
Reprinted with permission of Hayden Book Company from *Fundamentals of Television* by Walter H. Buchsbaum.

174

tion yoke comes from the collector of Q205 and is coupled through a transformer to the deflection yoke. Because the resistance of the deflection yoke changes as the temperatures varies, two thermistors are connected in series from the base of Q205 to ground. These thermistors are usually mounted within the deflection yoke housing, so that they sense the temperature at that point. A burnt-out thermistor is often indicated by a nonlinearity confined to a portion of the TV screen.

The reason for the interaction between the adjustment of the vertical linearity and vertical size control is apparent from Figure 8.5. The linearity control determines the collector voltage to the vertical buffer amplifier, while the size control sets the bias on the base of the feedback amplifier, with only an electrolytic coupling capacitor separating the two controls.

Many new designs implement a single IC for processing of vertical and horizontal sweep. The RCA CTC 133 is an example of a design such as this. The new breed of sweep circuit uses digital technology to process horizontal and vertical timing. This results in much more stable scanning rates, and usually eliminates the horizontal and vertical hold controls. As both horizontal and vertical frequencies are determined by a single oscillator, only one adjustment is required. See Figure 8.5 for a block diagram of the RCA deflection circuitry. We will use the CTC 133 chassis as an example of a solid state digital sweep driver throughout this chapter.

IC U400 contains an oscillator that runs at eight times the horizontal frequency. The signal passes through a divide-by-8 counter, and is sent to the horizontal amplifier and burst gate amp. At the same time, the signal is divided further and applied to the vertical blanking and amplifier circuits.

Figure 8.6 contains a simplified schematic of the vertical deflection circuitry in this RCA chassis. The sawtooth switch, Q500, turns off when it receives a pulse from the vertical amp in U400. This causes capacitor C502 to charge

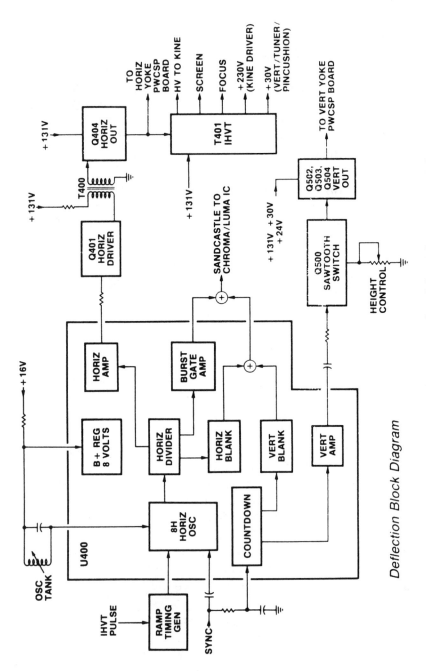

Deflection Block Diagram

Figure 8.5: This material was reproduced from the CTC 133 Color Chassis Technical Review, Copyright 1985, by RCA Corporation Technical Training, Indianapolis, IN.

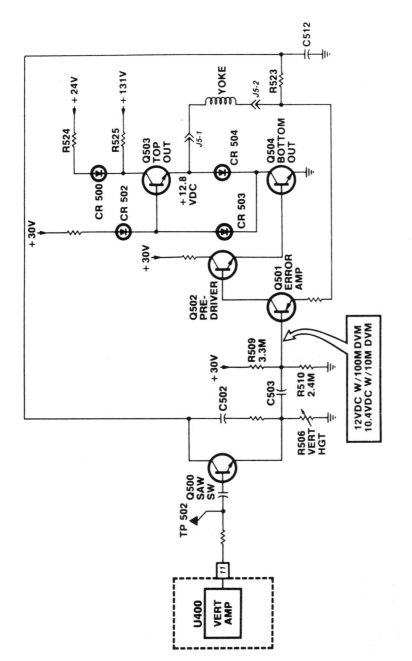

Simplified Vertical Deflection Circuit

Figure 8.6: This material was reproduced from the CTC 133 Color Chassis Technical Review, Copyright 1985, by RCA Corporation Technical Training, Indianapolis, IN.

through the vertical height control. A sawtooth-shaped waveform develops across R506 and is coupled to the error amplifier transistor Q501.

Once Q500 turns back on again, C502 discharges. The sawtooth that is generated is applied to Q502, the vertical predriver. The predriver stage feeds the sawtooth to the base of Q504, and the two vertical outputs Q504 and Q503 share yoke current. Ground return for the yoke circuit waveforms is across C512, which also provides a signal that is utilized for pincushion correction.

HORIZONTAL DEFLECTION

Signals leaving the horizontal differentiator network at the sync separator are applied to the horizontal oscillator and AFC network. The oscillator, in turn, drives the horizontal output device, which delivers horizontal scan current to the yoke, and also provides current to the high-voltage transformer (HVT) used to generate the second anode voltage at the CRT. In addition, the HVT supplies power to many other television circuits in those sets that use scan-derived power supply voltages. These types of power supplies are described in greater detail in Chapter 10.

Let's look first at a typical horizontal circuit. Figure 8.7 shows a single transistor horizontal oscillator controlled by a discrete diode-type phase detector. In this phase detector the horizontal flyback pulse is applied to one diode through C403. Its wave shape is adjusted through the R-C time constant of C404 and R407. This "feedback pulse" is compared with the horizontal sync signal that is applied through R401 and C401. When both the feedback pulse and the incoming sync pulse are exactly in phase and frequency, there will be no DC voltage across R402 and R403. When the feedback pulse is either faster or slower than the incoming sync pulse, an error voltage will be developed, either positive or negative, and this error voltage is filtered through R402 and C405. It is applied to the base of Q401 and controls the frequency of the transistor oscillator consisting of the base-emitter network of C407, L402, and C408. Adjustable coil L402 provides the horizontal hold control for coarse adjustments. The output of the collector goes to the horizontal predrive amplifier that converts the combination sinewave and pulse signal into the correct combination of pulse and sawtooth. Figure 3.11 indicates the combination of sinewave and pulse signal that would be obtainable from a horizontal oscillator like the one shown in Figure 8.7. Figure 3.10 illustrates the range of DC error voltage that is developed by the phase detector and applied to the base of the horizontal oscillator.

Individual circuits of the horizontal sweep generator section vary between different manufacturers, but some of the key elements are the same as in all TV receivers, monitors, and CRT computer displays. The block diagram of the horizontal sweep section of Figure 8.8 illustrates these key features. The output of the horizontal oscillator usually goes to a single transistor drive stage that provides the current to drive the horizontal output stage itself.

The horizontal sweep section provides the sawtooth current to the horizontal coils of the deflection yoke. Another purpose, however, is to generate the high voltage required for the CRT anode, or ultor, and that is accomplished through the high-voltage transformer, often called the flyback transformer. As illustrated in Figure 8.8, this transformer has a primary that is connected to the horizontal output stage and the deflection yoke. Two secondary windings are shown here, one to drive the high-voltage shut-down circuits and to power the scan and AC supplies, and another one to the filaments of the cathode ray tube. In many color TV receivers, the filaments of the picture tube are driven from a 60-Hz/6.3-V transformer winding that is located either on the main power transformer or on a separate filament transformer. Earlier horizontal sweep sections used a single or double loop of

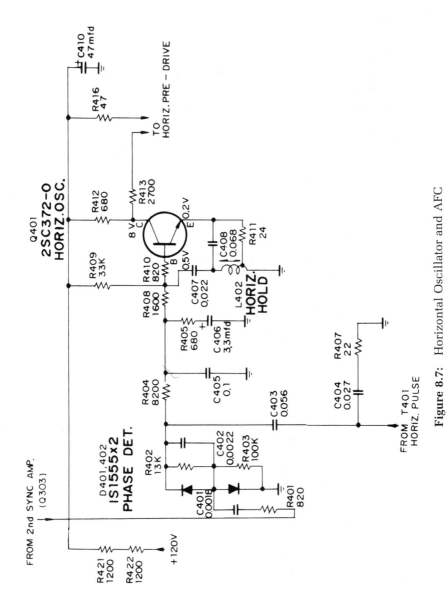

Figure 8.7: Horizontal Oscillator and AFC

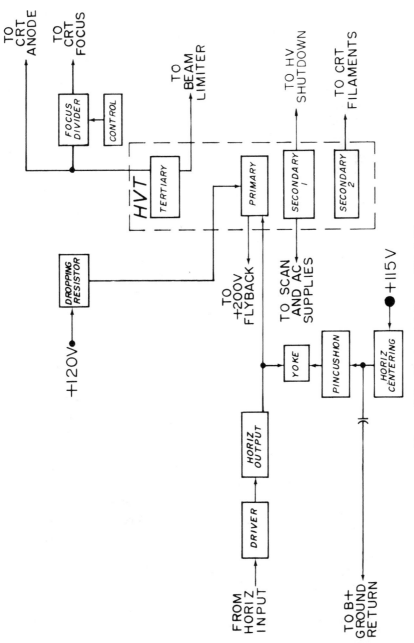

Figure 8.8: Horizontal Sweep Block Diagram.
Courtesy General Electric.

181

wire around the core of the flyback transformer as filament supply for the high-voltage rectifier vacuum tube. In recent TV sets a solid state rectifier is used and the filament winding is not needed.

The tertiary winding included in Figure 8.8 is the high-voltage section that provides the anode, or ultor, voltage and the CRT focus voltage. Note that in Figure 8.8 the low-voltage end of this tertiary, or high-voltage winding, goes to the beam limiter, or current regulator, a section mentioned earlier in this chapter.

As was noted earlier, Figure 8.5 is a block diagram of the RCA CTC 133 chassis, with digital countdown timing circuitry. A simplified diagram of the horizontal oscillator and driver circuitry is shown in Figure 8.9. The horizontal frequency is derived from the tuned circuit composed of L400 and C420. Integrated circuit U400 divides down the oscillator to 15,734 Hz for horizontal deflection. The horizontal sync signal at pin 3 of the IC is compared to a ramp voltage generated by the integrated high-voltage transformer (IHVT). An AFC correction voltage is developed within the IC, and applied to the horizontal oscillator internally.

Output of the horizontal amplifer is presented to the driver transistor Q401, which in turn, drives the horizontal output circuitry. Another unique aspect of the RCA chassis is the sandcastle output at pin 16. The video IC in this chassis requires vertical and horizontal blanking and burst gate pulses from the sweep section. To reduce the number of pins required on the ICs involved, the horizontal, vertical and burst pulses are integrated into a single pin, which is then connected to the luminance/chrominance IC in this chassis. The sandcastle output got its name because of the distinctive waveshape it displays on an oscilloscope.

The operation of the horizontal flyback section is of key importance in any kind of TV display, and for that reason a brief explanation of its fundamentals appears to be in order. As illustrated in Figure 8.10, the basic hori-

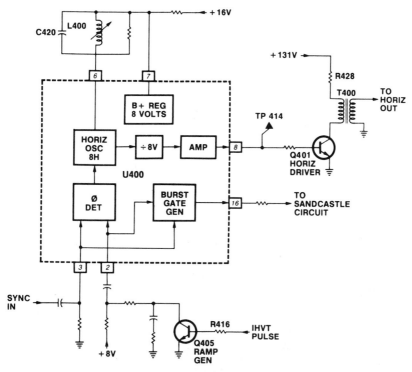

Simplified Horizontal Oscillator and Driver Circuit

Figure 8.9: This material was reproduced from the CTC 133 Color Chassis Technical Review, Copyright 1985, by RCA Corporation Technical Training, Indianapolis, IN.

zontal output circuit consists of the output transistor, the deflection yoke, a series capacitor, a shunt capacitor and a damper diode. When the electron beam is at the center of the screen, the transistor receives a pulse, turning it ON. This means that capacitor C1 is shorted and the circuit is resonant at 10 KHz and consists of the transistor, the yoke and C2. The electron beam moves to the right of the screen as energy in C2 is discharged into the yoke. This energy is in the magnetic field around the yoke, which now begins to collapse. The end of the pulse on the base of the transistor means that the transistor gets turned off and C1 is now shunted across the combination of yoke

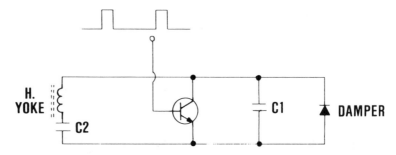

Figure 8.10:   Basic Horizontal Output Circuit

and C2; C1 changes the resonance of the LC circuit from 10 KHz to 40 KHz. The current in the yoke charges C1, and the beam rapidly moves back to the center of the screen; C2 discharges, causing current to flow through the yoke, which will move the beam from the center of the screen to the left edge. This section has built up the electromagnetic field in the yoke again, causing the damper diode to be forward biased. When the bias reaches a critical point, the diode conducts, shorting out C1 and causing the entire circuit to change its operating frequency back to 10 KHz. The current through the deflection yoke is reversed, C2 is charged again, and the electron beam is returned to the center of the screen. The next pulse starts the entire cycle again.

There are several important side effects in this system. During the retrace time, when the current is transferred from the deflection yoke into capacitor C1 and the resonant frequency is 40 KHz, a high-voltage pulse is induced in the flyback transformer. Remember that the flyback transformer primary is connected in parallel with the combination of the deflection yoke and C2 (see the block diagram of Figure 8.8). This pulse is stepped up by the high-voltage transformer winding and is then rectified by the high-voltage rectifier to provide the second anode, or ultor, voltage. The conduction of the damper diode is used to provide the B+ boost power. This circuit is quite economical because both the flyback pulse and the current through the damper diode are used to generate different voltages that are required elsewhere in the TV set.

A typical horizontal flyback circuit, including the horizontal driver and output stage, is shown in Figure 8.11. Note that there is a coupling transformer between the collector circuit of the horizontal driver and the base of the horizontal output transistor. The horizontal deflection coils are connected in series with a linearity coil and with the pin-cushion transformer. Capacitor C1707 corresponds to C2 in Figure 8.10, and the combination of C1701 and C1703 corresponds to C1 in the basic horizontal output circuit of Figure 8.10. The damper diode is Y1701, completing the key elements of the basic horizontal output circuit.

This G.E. flyback circuit uses three rectifier diodes, distributed, as illustrated, in the high-voltage section to rectify the second anode and the focus voltage. In other flyback circuits a single high-voltage coil is used, and several rectifiers then provide the high voltage. In this particular system, Y1703 is a voltage boost diode that increases the potential across C1705 to provide the master screen control voltage that is higher than +125 V DC.

The voltage regulation portion and the low end of the high-voltage winding are not shown in Figure 8.11, but Figure 8.12 shows a simplified high-voltage regulator circuit in which the low end of the high-voltage winding goes to the "beam limiter" circuit. Component C1 is a filter capacitor, R1 is an isolating resistor, and the combination of R2, R3 and R4 sets the base and collector voltage for the regulating transistor. Note that the brightness control has an effect on collector current, and, within limitations, also controls the total electron beam current in the CRT. The three diodes in the transistor circuit assure that the range of the base and collector current is limited to the correct values. There are a number of variations of the circuit found in different manufacturers'

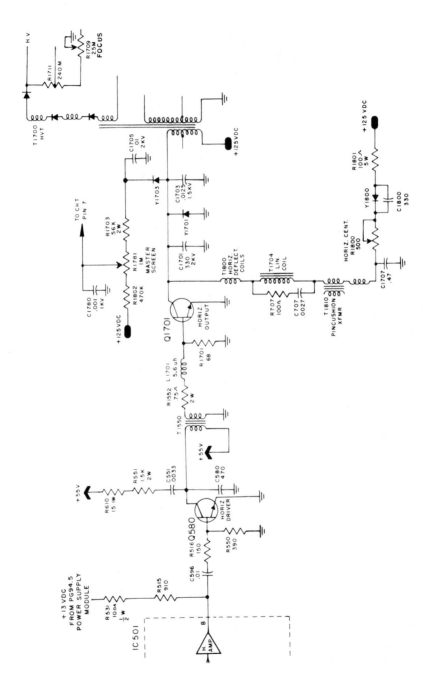

Figure 8.11: Horizontal Flyback Circuit.
Courtesy General Electric.

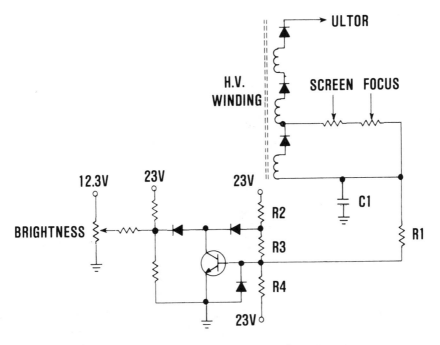

Figure 8.12:   Simplified HV Regulator Circuit

receivers, and some of them provide shut-down of the high voltage when excessive current, due to arcing or other defects, is drawn.

In some color TV receivers the high-voltage regulator also reduces the danger of excessive X-ray radiation by limiting the maximum voltage. At the nominal 25 KV, which is used in most color TV receivers, only a very limited number of "soft" X-rays are emitted. Like all radiation, the intensity is reduced in proportion to the square of the distance. Proper shielding of the high-voltage section normally prevents this kind of radiation from being harmful to either the viewer or the service technician. Manufacturer's instructions about avoiding the danger of X-ray radiation should be followed closely in all instances.

HIGH-VOLTAGE PRECAUTIONS

As mentioned above, X-ray radiation is not a really serious problem in high-voltage work, but precautions against electric shock are essential whenever you service any high-voltage circuitry. The high voltage is generated in the flyback circuit and depends on the horizontal oscillator for its source. When the set is turned off, the oscillator is also turned off, but the filter capacitors used for focus, screen, and the ultor itself still remain charged for a period of time. While a shock from these capacitors is not lethal, the strong jolt you may receive can cause you to strike other objects or fall to the ground, resulting in potentially serious injuries. Even though the circuit diagram does not contain a high-voltage capacitor, the capacitance between the second anode coating inside the picture tube and the grounded outer coating, the chassis or shield, is large enough to store a noticeable charge. For this reason we urge you to always discharge the high-voltage capacitance with a grounded clip-lead connected to a screwdriver that is then touched to the second anode cap terminal or some readily accessible high-voltage point.

Many service technicians check the presence of high voltage by using a well-insulated screwdriver that is held near a high-voltage point. Drawing an arc from the high-voltage connector at the picture tube is one way to make sure that the second anode voltage is present there, but it is not good practice because it overloads the high-voltage supply itself. The best method to check for high voltage is to use a commercial high-voltage probe connected to a volt-ohmmeter on the proper scale. This not only establishes the presence of high voltage but also permits you to measure it under different settings of the brightness control. You can check the operation of the regulator circuit in this manner.

High-voltage components, including the flyback transformer and rectifiers, are often enclosed in a metal shield can. The two most frequent defects are arcing or corona.

Arcing can occur either because dirt has accumulated and forms a low-resistance path between a high-voltage point and ground, or because sharp points shorten the path. Arcing is more likely to occur when humidity is high, at high altitudes where the air is thin, and when age has reduced the effectiveness of the insulation. The remedy to arcing consists of cleaning, drying, and applying better insulation. Corona is essentially a continuous high-voltage discharge into the surrounding air. In most instances, the origin of corona is a sharp point rather than a smooth large surface. Corona appears as a purplish glow surrounding the sharp point, and often is only visible in relative darkness. In most cases of corona, a fine hissing sound is heard and the characteristic odor of ozone is noticeable. Corona reduces the available high voltage for the picture tube because it draws current off into the air. Persistent corona will usually lead to arcing.

Both of these defects can be easily repaired by first observing their location and then, with the TV set shut down and all high-voltage capacitors discharged, giving the entire high-voltage section a thorough cleaning. Sharp points should be smoothed out by careful filing and should then be covered by "corona dope" or some other insulating material specifically made for this purpose.

When replacing any component in the high-voltage shielded cage, smooth points, rounded solder joints, and careful cleaning of all wire clippings and dirt are essential to avoid the effects of corona and arcing.

PINCUSHION CORRECTION

The pincushioning effect is usually not important in CRT computer displays or monochrome TV receivers, but appears most frequently in color TV receivers, particularly of the large-screen type. As described in Chapter 6, the pincushioning is due to the use of highly efficient deflection yokes and affects both vertical and horizontal deflection. Different manufacturers use somewhat different circuits, but the basic pincushion correction circuit of Figure 8.13 is typical of almost all of them. The key element in this circuit is the pincushion transformer that couples a portion of the horizontal sawtooth current into the vertical output circuit and a small portion of the vertical sawtooth into the horizontal circuit. In this manner both vertical and horizontal deflection currents are modified at the time period when the electron beam is at the extreme four corners of the screen. The action of the pincushioning circuit has been compared to the effect of the horizontal and vertical dynamic convergence circuit in Delta-type color picture tubes.

The latest model 27- to 40- inch large screen CRTs require extra circuitry for raster shaping. The RCA CTC 133 uses a 27-inch flat face CRT, dubbed the COTY–29 Square Planar CRT. Figure 8.14 contains diagrams representing the shape and distortions in both the standard and square planar CRT.

The very flat surface of the CRT causes a crosshatch pattern to alternately compress, spread out, compress and

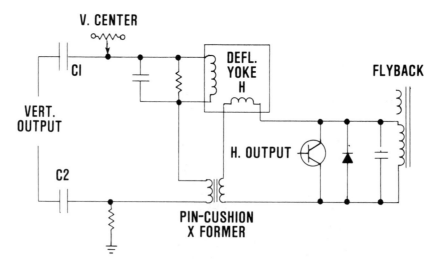

Figure 8.13:   Basic Pincushion Correction Circuit

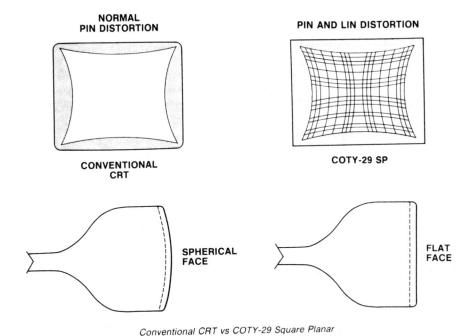

Conventional CRT vs COTY-29 Square Planar

Figure 8.14: This material was reproduced from the CTC 133 Color Chassis Technical Review, Copyright 1985, by RCA Corporation Technical Training, Indianapolis, IN.

spread out across the face of the CRT. This distortion has been dubbed "gull distortion" because a horizontal line resembles the flapping wings of a seagull when this circuit is misadjusted.

Both pincushion distortion and gull distortion is a factor of the distance the electron beam must travel at a fixed angle of deflection. Extra circuitry is provided in the 27-inch receiver that compensates for gull wing distortion. In the RCA chassis, if the circuitry is suspected of causing a problem, it may be bypassed by connecting the yoke windings directly to the chassis, bypassing the gull wing correction circuitry.

Pincushion correction circuits hardly ever require troubleshooting because the key element, the pincushion transformer, handles only small amounts of current and is a highly reliable device. If the pincushion transformer were to open, both vertical and horizontal deflection circuits would be inoperative. A short circuit in a pincushion transformer, or in any of the resistor, capacitor or diode networks that are associated with it, would cause a noticeable pincushioning effect in the picture.

TROUBLESHOOTING THE SYNC, DEFLECTION AND HV SECTION

The symptom-function method described in Chapter 1 is the most effective way to locate trouble in the sync or in the vertical or horizontal section. If there is no vertical deflection, the picture will appear as a horizontal line. Because some color TV receivers have a service switch that collapses the vertical sweep for a certain adjustment procedure, be sure to check that switch before assuming a defect in the vertical deflection system. Other problems in the vertical deflection section are usually due to vertical nonlinearity. If the range of adjustment is insufficient, then a circuit problem exists in the vertical height, linearity and output section. Vertical linearity can be determined by using a dot or grid test pattern or by simply observing an off-the-air picture and determining whether round objects are indeed round. Remember that the components least likely to be defective are the deflection yoke and the vertical output transformer. Potentiometers, capacitors and transistors are more likely culprits.

When neither vertical nor horizontal locking can be established, the sync pulses are missing. This can be due either to a defect in the sync separator or to a misalignment of the tuner or IF section. If the picture cannot be synchronized vertically or horizontally on any channel, regardless of the adjustment of the fine tuning control, the sync separator or the clipper is the most likely suspect. Verification of this can be made only by signal tracing with the oscilloscope. We can check the appearance of the composite video signal at the output of the video detector and the first video amplifier, and at the input of the sync separator. If neither vertical nor horizontal sync signals appear at the output of the separator, that circuit is defective. If only horizontal or only vertical sync signals appear, the defect is either in the integrator or the differentiator leading from the sync separator to the respective sweep oscillator.

Defects in the horizontal sweep section are more difficult to locate, particularly if the horizontal oscillator either does not function or operates at a frequency that is considerably different from the correct 15,750 Hz. When two pictures are vertically squeezed together and appear one above the other, it is obvious that the vertical oscillator frequency is approximately 120 Hz. Similarly, when several pictures appear squeezed side by side on the screen, the horizontal oscillator frequency is two or three times what it should be. If the horizontal oscillator frequency is considerably lower than 15,750 Hz, the flyback section will not operate properly and no high voltage will be obtained.

Lack of high voltage can be caused by a number of different types of defects. The horizontal oscillator may not oscillate because of a defective transistor, a shorted capacitor or some other component defect. Even if the horizontal oscillator works correctly, a defect in the driver stage or the output stage will result in a lack of high voltage. Finally, a defect in the flyback transformer, the damping diode or any of the components associated with the circuits can also result in a loss of high voltage. For this reason, the use of the oscilloscope in troubleshooting the horizontal flyback section is of great help. Be sure, however, to never use the oscilloscope probe on any point that might have a voltage in excess of a few hundred volts. High-voltage rectifier diodes can be tested—with the power off—by measuring forward and backward resistances. In troubleshooting the flyback transformer itself, use the oscilloscope only on the low-voltage terminals and use the high-voltage probe of the VOM on the high-voltage winding. Flyback transformers can fail because of defective insulation, overheating or cracking of the ferrite core. These defects do not usually show on DC measurements, and most service technicians will simply replace the flyback transformer if they can obtain the correct signals in a low-voltage winding and nothing out of the high-voltage. Flyback transformers can be replaced only with an exact duplicate.

Other problems relating to the horizontal section include those relating to scan-derived power supplies. Televisions that contain scan-derived power supplies invariably have an automatic shut-down sequence that takes effect when there is an overload condition on the horizontal output stage. This is because a short in the power supply output could cause the HVT or horizontal output device to be destroyed. There are many different techniques that are recommended when shut-down occurs. Many manufacturers suggest putting a 100-watt bulb in series with the AC line while troubleshooting. Alternatively, a variable AC power supply could be used to slowly bring up the TV, and allow testing at a reduced voltage. The theory is that a short that draws excessive current at 120 volts may not trip the shut-down circuitry at approximately 60 volts (the voltage that appears at the TV set when the bulb is in series with the chassis). When troubleshooting high-voltage circuitry, be sure to follow manufacturers' recommendations, especially as regarding the scan-derived power supply outputs. Be sure to use only exact replacement components when the schematic or service literature calls for it.

Note in passing that it is good practice to "look for the obvious and simple things first." For example, a scan-derived power supply that won't come out of shut-down tends to have a formidable aspect, just because of its intricate circuitry. If approached in the same manner that relatively simple circuitry is approached, the fault is sometimes obvious. As an illustration, a widely used type of scan-derived power supply would not come out of shut-down, and had excessive B+ voltage from the unregu-lated section. This excessive output was an immediate clue to the trouble.

When the schematic was inspected, it was obvious that the unregulated section had lost its load, with the result that the output voltage increased. The only way that its load could be lost was for a PC conductor to have burned open. A quick check with a voltmeter showed that although excessive B+ voltage was being applied to the input end of the conductor, there was no voltage at the output end. Then, a Zener diode connected to a point along the conductor was found to be short-circuited.

400   450   500   550   600   650   700

◄────── ULTRAVIOLET   INFRARED ──────►

MILLIMICRONS

Figure 4.1:   VISIBLE SPECTRUM.
Color TV Servicing, 3rd Ed., Walter H. Buchsbaum. Prentice-Hall, Inc. Copyright 1975.

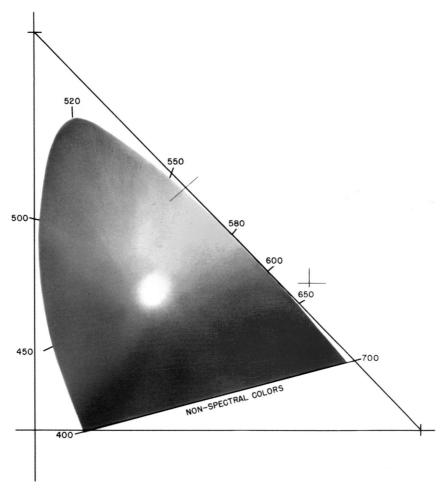

Figure 4.2:   COLOR DIAGRAM.
Color TV Servicing, 3rd Ed., Walter H. Buchsbaum. Prentice-Hall, Inc. Copyright 1975.

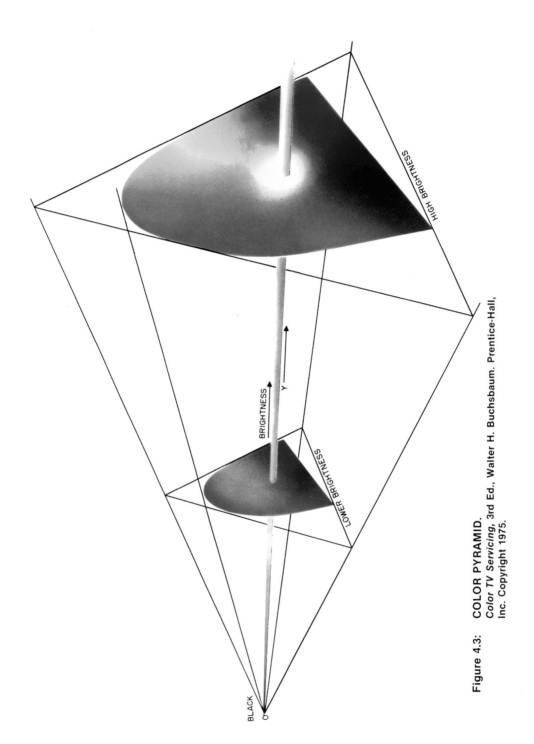

BLACK

O

BRIGHTNESS

Y

LOWER BRIGHTNESS

HIGH BRIGHTNESS

Figure 4.3:   COLOR PYRAMID.
Color TV Servicing, 3rd Ed., Walter H. Buchsbaum. Prentice-Hall,
Inc. Copyright 1975.

Figure 6.11: POOR RED PURITY.
Color TV Servicing, 3rd Ed., Walter H. Buchsbaum. Prentice-Hall,
Inc. Copyright 1975.

Figure 6.12: CROSSHATCH PATTERN, BADLY MISCONVERGED.
Color TV Servicing, 3rd Ed., Walter H. Buchsbaum. Prentice-Hall,
Inc. Copyright 1975.

Figure 6.13:
GOOD CONVERGENCE.
Color TV Servicing, 3rd Ed.,
Walter H. Buchsbaum.
Prentice-Hall, Inc.
Copyright 1975.

Figure 6.14:
HORIZONTAL
CONVERGENCE OFF.
Color TV Servicing, 3rd Ed.,
Walter H. Buchsbaum.
Prentice-Hall, Inc.
Copyright 1975.

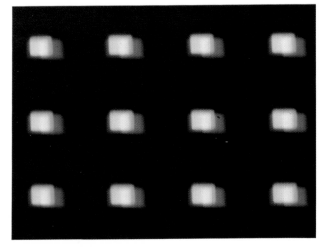

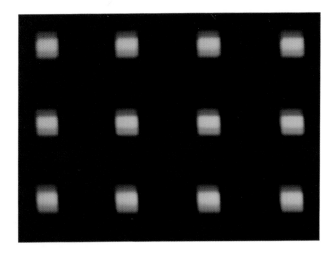

Figure 6.15:
R-G VERTICAL
CONVERGENCE OFF.
Color TV Servicing, 3rd Ed.,
Walter H. Buchsbaum.
Prentice-Hall, Inc.
Copyright 1975

Figure 13.2: TINTED MONOCHROME PICTURE.
Color TV Servicing, 3rd Ed., Walter H. Buchsbaum. Prentice-Hall,
Inc. Copyright 1975.

Figure 13.3: POOR PURITY, MONOCHROME.
Color TV Servicing, 3rd Ed., Walter H. Buchsbaum. Prentice-Hall,
Inc. Copyright 1975.

Figure 14.2: WEAK COLORS.
Color TV Servicing, 3rd Ed., Walter H. Buchsbaum. Prentice-Hall, Inc. Copyright 1975.

Figure 14.3: LOSS OF COLOR SYNC.
Color TV Servicing, 3rd Ed., Walter H. Buchsbaum. Prentice-Hall, Inc. Copyright 1975.

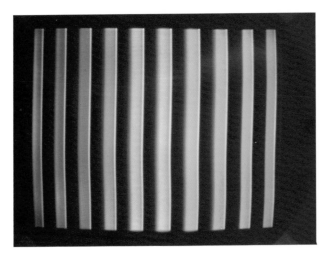

Figure 14.4:
GOOD PICTURE.
Color TV Servicing, 3rd Ed.,
Walter H. Buchsbaum.
Prentice-Hall, Inc.
Copyright 1975.

Figure 14.5:
BLUE MISSING.
Color TV Servicing, 3rd Ed.,
Walter H. Buchsbaum.
Prentice-Hall, Inc.
Copyright 1975.

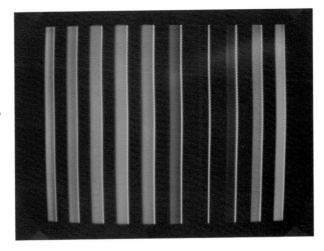

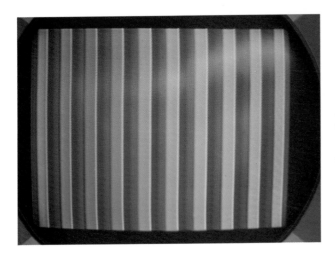

Figure 14.6:
EXCESSIVE BRIGHTNESS.
Color TV Servicing, 3rd Ed.,
Walter H. Buchsbaum.
Prentice-Hall, Inc.
Copyright 1975.

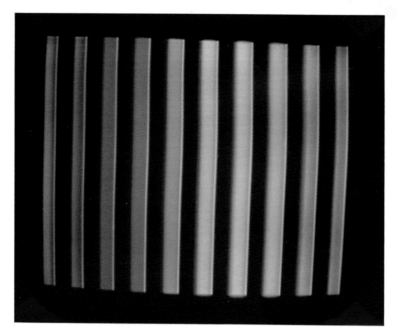

Figure 14.7: HUES WRONG.
Color TV Servicing, 3rd Ed., Walter H. Buchsbaum. Prentice-Hall, Inc. Copyright 1975.

Figure 15.3: 900 KHz BEAT INTERFERENCE.
Color TV Servicing, 3rd Ed., Walter H. Buchsbaum. Prentice-Hall, Inc. Copyright 1975

CHAPTER 9

COLOR CIRCUITS

The functional descriptions of the various parts of a color television receiver, theory of color television and functions of color circuits have been discussed in chapters 1, 4 and 5. This chapter will describe the operation of various production model circuits, how they are adjusted and techniques for troubleshooting.

CIRCUIT FUNCTIONS

The composite video signal contains video, color, sound and sync components. It is the function of the first video stage to deliver the appropriate portions of the composite signal to their respective destinations. Figure 9.1 contains a block diagram that represents the operation of a typical color section. The chroma bandpass amplifier (also known as the 3.58-MHz amplifier) processes the color information. A horizontal keying pulse delivers a horizontal sync pulse that contains the eight-cycle color burst reference signals. If no burst signal is present, the color killer circuitry turns off the chroma bandpass amplifier, so that color noise is not transmitted to the color demodulator circuitry.

The sync burst is also used to lock in the 3.58-MHz reference oscillator, which is then used to synchronously demodulate the chroma information by using the **I** and **Q** vectors. This process was discussed in greater detail in Chapter 4. The matrix circuitry then either feeds the grids of the CRT with R–Y, B–Y and G–Y signals, or it feeds separate Red, Green and Blue video driver transistors, which also receive luminance information. The resultant output then drives the CRT cathodes with Red, Green and Blue signals.

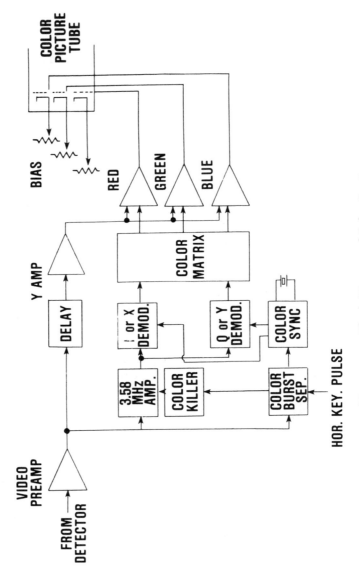

Figure 9.1: Block Diagram of Color Section

200

VIDEO AND COLOR SEPARATION

In current production models, there are two methods of
separating the color information from the luminance, or
monochrome portion, of the signal. Until recently, this
separation was achieved by simple bandpass filtering,
which stripped off video information above 3 MHz, and
processed it through color circuitry. Newer designs often
implement comb filter technology to provide a better quality picture after separation of chroma and luminance. To
understand this process, we must take a closer look at
how video information and color information are interleaved in the transmission system.

Figure 9.2 contains a diagram of video signals. Figure
9.2A demonstrates how video information in a monochrome signal is concentrated at 15,734-Hz intervals (the
horizontal scan rates). To ensure compatibility with

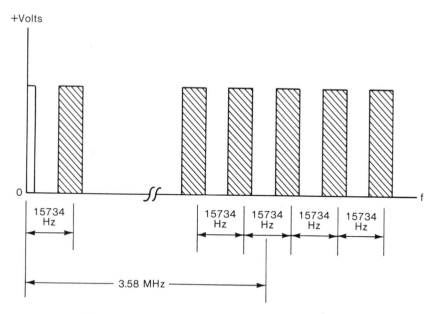

Figure 9.2A: Video Bandspread.
Luminance signals are concentrated 15,734 Hz. apart.

monochrome television and to maintain the same bandwidth, the color information was interleaved within the
empty areas above 2.0 MHz. This is demonstrated in Figure 9.2B.

Figure 9.3 shows how using a bandpass filter at the
color bandpass input removes video outside the bandpass, but still contains luminance information that is not
affected. A notch filter is used at the input of the video
amplifier stage to remove chroma information, as shown
in Figure 9.4. This is done to remove the chrominance
from the video signal, which would otherwise cause an
interference pattern to appear in the video. Stripping the
video above 3 MHz results in the loss of high-frequency
video information. While this process results in acceptable response and detail up to 3 MHz, a better technique
would result in sharper pictures and more detail.

The comb filter circuitry found in current designs
provides the technique for separation of chroma and lu-

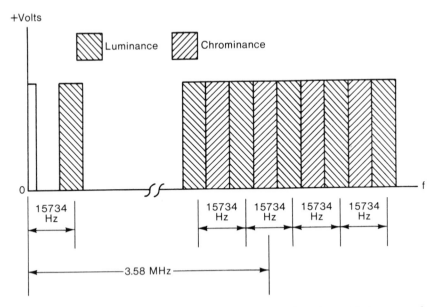

Figure 9.2B: Chrominance information is interleaved between each
luminance carrier.

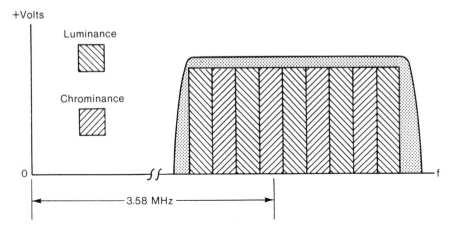

Figure 9.3: Bandpass Filter.
Using a bandpass filter to remove chroma fails to remove all luminance
information.

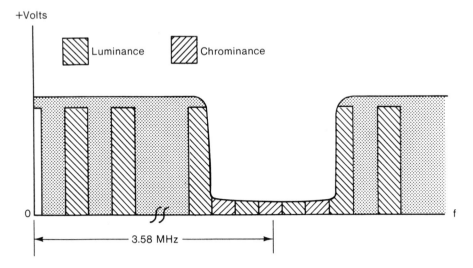

Figure 9.4: Notch Filter.
A notch filter removes the chrominance information and also results
in the removal of some luminance information.

minance with improved frequency response and picture quality. Comb filters have no effect on the frequency response from 0 to 2 MHz, then comb every 15,734 Hz to the outer band of 4.5 MHz. The output of the two stages are shown in Figure 9.5A and B. The filter is named because it "combs" the band, stripping out only the chroma or luminance information. The stripping action causes no video information to be lost in the process, greatly enhancing the picture quality.

Though comb filtering techniques have been known for years, only recently have they been practical for implementation in television circuitry. Methods differ from one manufacturer to another, however all operate in a similar fashion, so we will look at the comb filter circuitry that is used in the CTC 101 series chassis. Figure 9.6 contains a diagram of a typical comb filter circuit in an RCA chassis. A charge-coupled device (CCD) IC is used to delay the video signal processing. The CCD device is

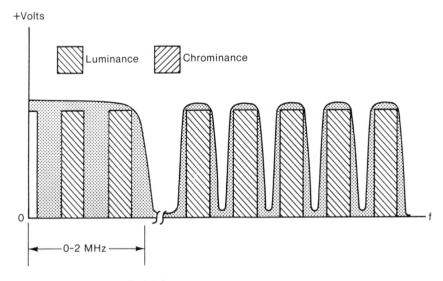

Figure 9.5A: Ideal Filters.
The ideal luminance filter would be flat to 2 MHz., then comb every 15,734 Hz.

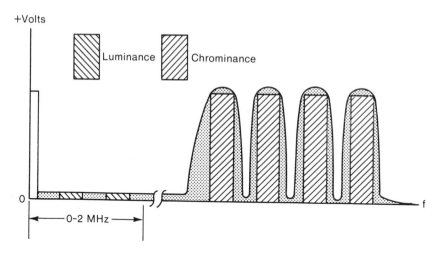

Figure 9.5B: The ideal chroma filter would have zero response to about 2 MHz., then comb every 15,734 Hz.

also known as a "bucket brigade" IC because it samples video, and passes it internally from one storage cell in the IC to another, similar to the operation of a firemans' bucket brigade. The time delay to transfer through the CCD is enough to delay processing of the video signal. The clock rate of the 3.58-MHz oscillator is tripped to 10.74 MHz to provide the proper sampling rate.

The actual filtering is achieved by the low-pass and band-pass filters in the diagram. As some low-frequency video information is lost in the filtering process, a dynamic vertical detail processor is used to restore low-frequency response to normal. Low-frequency video is recombined with combed video, restoring maximum detail at low frequencies. Outputs of the comb filter travel to the video amplifier and chroma bandpass amplifier.

In older designs, the filtering of 3.58-MHz chroma information is accomplished directly by the bandpass amplifier. Figure 9.7 illustrates the principles of the color bandpass amplifier. The input signal contains the composite video signal with a bandwidth of up to 4 MHz, and the 3.58-MHz color subcarrier. The input resonant circuit,

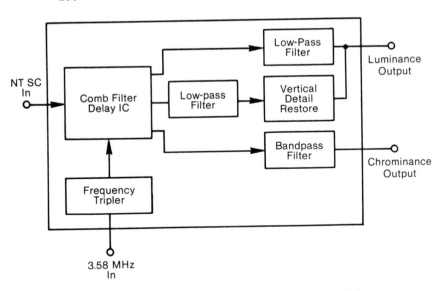

Figure 9.6: RCA design comb filter module

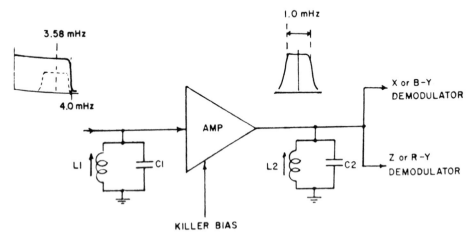

Figure 9.7: Color Bandpass Amplifier Functions.
Color TV Servicing, 3rd Ed., Walter H. Buchsbaum. Prentice-Hall, Inc.

consisting of L1 and C1, and the output resonant circuit, consisting of L2 and C2, generate the 1.0-MHz bandwidth. A picture of a typical bandpass response was shown in Figure 5.6. The output of the bandpass amplifier is then supplied to the **I** and **Q** and **X** and **Z**, or B–Y and R–Y demodulators. Note that the color killer bias is applied to the amplifier in Figure 9.7. When monochrome pictures are received, the color killer detects the absence of the 3.58-MHz color burst, and generates a bias voltage that cuts off the bandpass amplifier.

COLOR DEMODULATOR

The color demodulator functions illustrated in Figure 9.8 are identical to both demodulators. The only difference between them is the phase angle of the color sync signal that is applied to the demodulator. Note that the 3.58-MHz subcarrier is applied, together with the 3.58-MHz reference signal, and the video output requires a low-pass filter. The reason for this is that the video signal is band-pass limited and the 3.58-MHz subcarrier and reference signal must be eliminated in order not to generate interference on the screen.

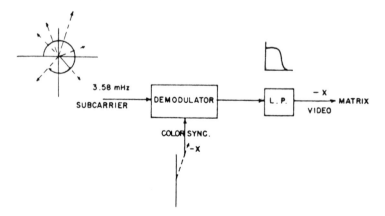

Figure 9.8: Color Demodulator Functions.
Color TV Servicing, 3rd Ed., Walter H. Buchsbaum. Prentice-Hall, Inc.

Without going into the theory of synchronous phase and amplitude demodulation, we can get an idea of the operation of the demodulator from the simplified sketch of vector and sinewave addition in Figure 9.9. In the upper portion of this illustration we have shown four separate instances of the continuously rotating vector diagrams and their sinewave equivalents. Farthest left, the reference burst is at 270° with the color subcarrier at approximately 110°. The vector labeled **R** is the result of the addition of the burst and the subcarrier. Just below the vector diagram, the sinewave equivalent of these three signals is indicated. Point 1 is the instant where the color burst is at its zero or reference point, the subcarrier is on a positive cycle and the resultant signal **R** intersects. This point 1 is plotted again in Figure 9.8(b), which shows the

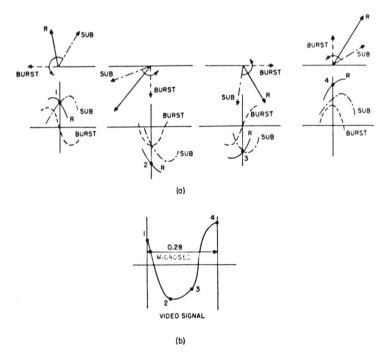

Figure 9.9: Vector and Sine Wave Addition.
Color TV Servicing, 3rd Ed., Walter H. Buchsbaum. Prentice-Hall, Inc.

video signal resulting from the four examples of sinewave and vector addition. In the second example in Figure 9.9(a), the color burst is at the 180° position with the subcarrier at the approximately 250° position. Note that the resultant signal **R** will be below the baseline. The third example shows the burst at the 90° position with the subcarrier at approximately 190° and the resultant **R** again lying in the negative portion of the cycle. The illustration of the vectors and sinewave addition of Figure 9.9(a) in the upper right, illustrates the burst at zero and the subcarrier at approximately 60°. Note that the resultant **R** will be on the positive side. The entire sequence of these four instantaneous vector additions takes only 0.28 s. In essence, the demodulator circuit generates a video signal from the burst reference and subcarrier in exactly the same way as illustrated for a short portion in Figure 9.9.

ACTUAL COLOR CIRCUITS

Modern color television chassis design dictates the use of specialized integrated circuits for chroma functions. Many custom-designed ICs from different manufacturers design the chroma functions into one or more ICs. Specialized ICs provide color synchronization, bandpass amplification, demodulation and matrixing. Auxiliary functions include automatic color correction (ACC), flesh-tone correction, vertical interval reference (VIR) color control and other circuitry. In many chassis, such as the RCA CTC133, chroma and luminance processing is done in one IC, the Luma/Chroma processor. The ICs that do these jobs are often proprietary to a particular TV manufacturer, and when a defective IC is suspected, replacement of the IC must be with an original equipment replacement part, or authorized substitute. Representative examples of ICs in production televisions of different manufacture are described in the following paragraphs.

The typical color sync and killer IC and its internal

circuits, as shown in Figure 9.10, is used in the Sears model 562.40270300 and similar receivers. This IC contains a power supply regulator to assure proper DC voltages for all circuits within the IC. In this particular system the color burst itself has been removed from the horizontal sync pulse before it is applied to pin 8 of the IC. It goes through one stage of amplification and is then applied to the automatic frequency and phase control (AFPC) detector. Note that this circuit is connected to a balanced R-C

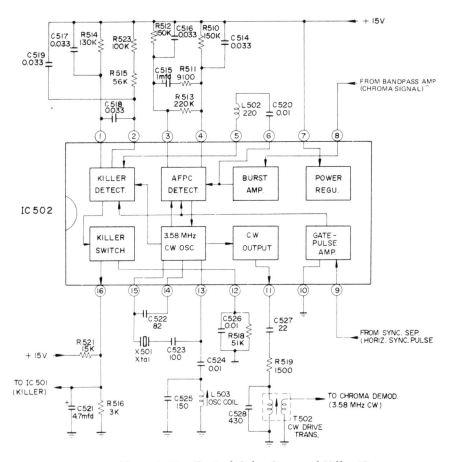

Figure 9.10: Typical Color Sync and Killer IC

network through pins 3 and 4. The AFPC detector also receives a keying pulse from the gate pulse amplifier so that it operates only during that period of time when the color burst itself is present. It compares a signal from the 3.58-MHz oscillator, which is crystal controlled and fine tuned by the oscillator coil, with the color burst it receives. If there is a phase or frequency difference, an error voltage is sent back to the oscillator.

The burst amplifier output also goes through a phase shifting network external to the IC before it is applied to the killer detector section. This circuit receives a horizontal keying pulse from the gate pulse amplifier as well as a signal from the 3.58-MHz oscillator. During the period of the color burst, the killer detector compares the signals from the oscillator with the phase-shifted color burst. When both the phase-shifted color burst and the oscillator output are detected, no signal goes to the killer switch. If the color burst is absent during monochrome transmission, then the killer detector section sends a DC signal to the killer switch and that stage then generates the cut-off bias for the bandpass amplifier that is on another IC.

The color sync or reference signal goes from the oscillator to an output amplifier and through a tuned transformer to the color demodulator. Phase shifting between the two reference signals takes place at the input to the color or chroma demodulator.

A combination of discrete circuits and ICs is used in the Hitachi GTX chassis, and the circuits are shown in Figure 9.11. In this system the three cathodes of the color picture tube are connected to three transistors, one for each color signal. The brightness or Y signal is obtained from the video detector and goes through a delay line, DL301, to the video preamplifier Q301. The video amplifier itself is on the IC and its output, not shown in Figure 9.11, goes to the RGB matrix. Transistor Q302 acts essentially as a DC level control, in conjunction with a "subbright" and brightness potentiometer, and controls

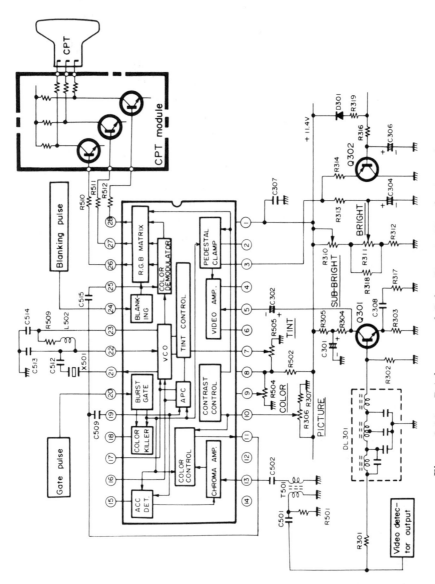

Figure 9.11: Brightness and Color Circuit, Hitachi GTX Chassis. Courtesy Hitachi Ltd.

212

the pedestal clamping level, a function contained on the IC.

The integrated circuit of Figure 9.11 contains the color sync section that consists of the automatic phase control (APC) and the 3.58-MHz oscillator, labeled VCO in this circuit. An external crystal is used. The keying pulse is applied to the burst gate that also controls the color killer circuit, and, through it, the color control, the automatic color control (ACC) detector, and the chroma amplifier. The functions labeled "contrast control," "color control" and "tint control" are essentially DC bias amplifiers that are connected to external potentiometers that adjust the respective functions. For all its apparent sophistication the brightness and color circuit of Figure 9.11 performs the same functions as shown in the block diagram of Figure 9.1.

Figure 9.12 is a simplified block diagram of the luma/chroma circuitry in the RCA CTC133 color chassis. Detected composite video is applied to the comb filter circuit, which is very similar to the filter described earlier in this chapter. Output of the comb filter is both color, which is applied to the chroma peaker, and video, processed through the vertical restoration circuitry. Video is applied to the luma core and delay lines. The luma core functions reduce noise in dark scenes, and produce horizontal peaking. The major luma/chroma processor circuitry drives the CRT, and provides automatic Kine Bias. The majority of the signal processing circuitry in the CTC133 chassis is accomplished with a few special purpose ICs.

We will look at color signal processing in the CTC133 chassis. See Figure 9.13 for a simplified circuit diagram. A standard chroma bandpass amplifier is used to amplify chroma, with an ACC circuit monitoring amplifier gain, adjusting color level as required. The keyed amplifier is used to separate burst from chroma information. The burst signal is used to control the color killer and ACC circuits, while the chroma signal is passed along to the second

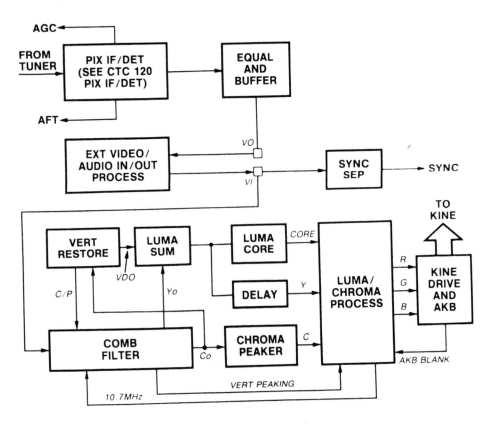

Simplified Signal Processing

Figure 9.12: This material was reproduced from the CTC 133 Color Chassis Technical Review, Copyright 1985, by RCA Corporation Technical Training, Indianapolis, IN.

chroma amplifier. The color and picture controls affect the gain of the second chroma amplifier, and the killer amplifier cuts off the second chroma amplifier if no color burst is present.

Color burst is applied to the automatic frequency/phase control (AFPC) circuit. The AFPC circuit compares the frequency and phase of the color burst to an internally generated VCO circuit. The VCO output is applied to the hue control circuit, which then can be adjusted via the tint control for proper color display. This signal and the

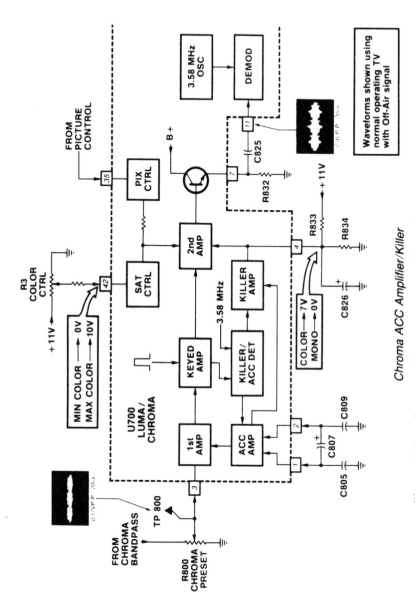

Figure 9.13: This material was reproduced from the CTC 133 Color Chassis Technical Review, Copyright 1985, by RCA Corporation Technical Training, Indianapolis, IN.

Chroma ACC Amplifier/Killer

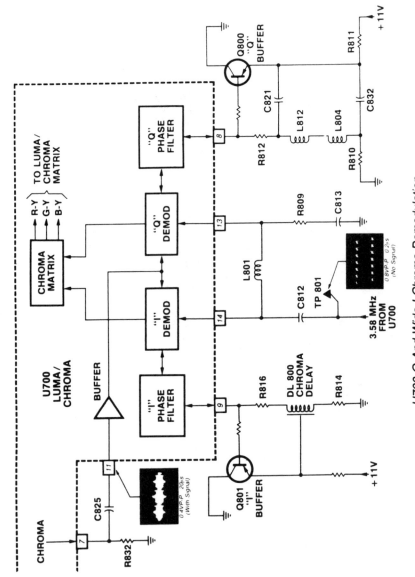

Figure 9.14: This material was reproduced from the CTC 133 Color Chassis Technical Review, Copyright 1985, by RCA Corporation Technical Training, Indianapolis, IN.

chroma signal are processed by a fleshtone correction circuit, amplified and coupled to the demodulator circuits.

The CTC 131/132/133 chassis series use new demodulation techniques that process luminance from 0 to 4.2 MHz, and full chrominance information. This signal-processing refinement comprises use of the comb filter and other sophisticated techniques to decode the **Q** and **I** signals. Because of the extended frequency response of the **I** demodulator, RCA uses the term "wide **I**" to identify the improved circuitry. Wide **I** demodulation provides fast enough response to eliminate errors in color display that would be apparent in standard chroma demodulators.

Figure 9.14 demonstrates a simplified schematic of the **Q** and Wide **I** chroma demodulators. The chrominance signal is coupled from the IC pin 7 chroma output into the IC again at pin 11. Chroma **Q** and wide **I** signals are applied to the appropriate demodulators. The external circuitry at pins 8 and 9 are external filters that obtain the required bandwidth and minimum phase distortion. The output of the **Q** and **I** demodulators is applied to the chroma matrix circuitry, which, in turn, feeds R–Y, B–Y and G–Y to the luma/chroma matrix for CRT display.

AUTOMATIC COLOR CIRCUITS

One of the simplest automatic color correction or control circuits uses two sets of color controls, one accessible from the front panel and the other preset under a secondary panel or at the rear. When the automatic control switch is activated, sometimes combined with an indicator light, the hidden controls, brightness, contrast, intensity and tint take over, and when the automatic indicator is deactivated, the viewer can adjust these four parameters from front panel controls. In many color sets the basic automatic color control (ACC) circuit operates in the same general manner as an automatic gain control (AGC) except that it affects the amplitude of the color signal only. A

number of different circuits have been developed to provide correction of the actual color in the color TV receiver
and thereby allow the viewer to switch channels without
having to readjust any of the color controls. The two most
widely used methods of automatic color correction are
described below.

VERTICAL INTERVAL REFERENCE (VIR)

Stations transmit two types of test and reference signals
during the vertical blanking. The so-called vertical interval test signals (VITS) are not fully standardized and vary
between different networks and different stations, but they
use the 16th, 17th and 18th line during the vertical blanking interval. The 19th line of this vertical blanking period
is used for the VIR signal, a standarized test signal transmitted by the majority of color TV stations. Figure 9.15
shows the horizontal pulse that occurs during the 19th
line, starting at the top of the vertical scan. Note that there
is the standard 8-cycle 3.58-MHz color burst, followed by
the pulse itself, on the top of which there is a 24 μs long
burst of the same 3.58-MHz color reference signal. Following this is a luminance reference signal, which is 12
μs long. The two portions, the 24 μs long color reference
signal and the luminance reference signal, are used to
automatically correct the tint phase and color saturation
distortion due to the transmission system between the
studio and the TV receiver. Figure 9.16 shows the IC and
its associated discrete transistors that perform the VIR
correction. The VIR switch must be on and sync signals
must be received through the base of Q1603. The following functions are performed in the sequence indicated.

During each vertical blanking interval, the VIR recognizer section has to recognize the start of the vertical
blanking section and then count to the 19th line to know
that this is the instant when the VIR signal occurs. The
presence of the VIR signal, the 3.58-MHz burst of 24 μs,

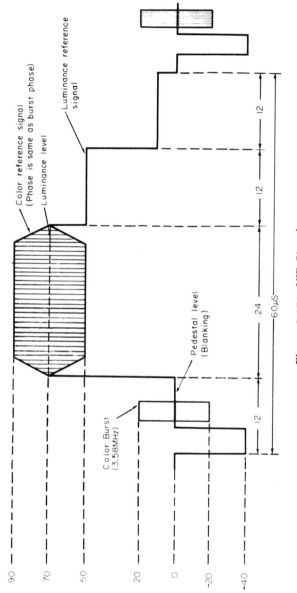

Figure 9.15: VIR Signal.
Courtesy Hitachi Ltd.

219

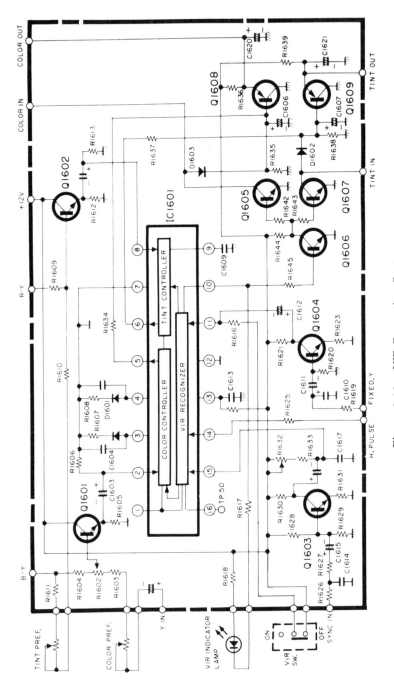

Figure 9.16: VIR Correction System.
Courtesy Hitachi Ltd.

220

followed by the luminance reference signal, must be detected and indicated on the VIR lamp. Next, the VIR recognizer section provides the color reference signal to the tint controller and the luminance reference, the 50 percent amplitude portion, to the color controller. Two external potentiometers permit the viewer to indicate the preferred tint and preferred color (intensity) setting. The actual performance of the color amplitude control and the tint control is accomplished by two sets of transistors. Note the terminal "color in" which leads to Q1605 and the terminal "color out" that leads to Q1608. The gain between these two stages is controlled by the color controller output, just as the tint controller acts on the signal between Q1607 and 1609. This VIR correction system is used in the Hitachi NP9X chassis, and somewhat different systems are used in G.E., RCA and other manufacturers' receivers. The basic functions of detecting the 19th line and indicating the presence of the VIR signal, controlling color and tint according to the VIR signals themselves, are the same for all VIR circuits.

FLESH TONE CORRECTION

It is difficult to tell, in a color picture, whether the blue of the sky is close to reality or whether the green of the trees indeed appears the same way in nature, but it is not difficult to detect flesh tones that are unnatural. For this reason a number of late-model color TV receivers now have automatic flesh tone correction circuits. These circuits are able to prevent the change of flesh tones to an unnatural yellow or magenta when channels or programs are changed. Figure 9.12 (a) shows the vector presentation of the normal color reference burst, the I and Q, and the color difference vectors. The area of flesh tones is indicated by the shaded ellipse surrounding a portion of the positive I vector. The width of that ellipse is denoted in the adjacent vector diagram by + or − a small amount, delta, of the **Q** signal.

A simplified block diagram of Hitachi's flesh tone correction system, used in their model NP9X series of color TV receivers, is shown in Figure 9.17 (b). Although only the red and blue difference signals are shown, the green color difference signal is also supplied to the **Q** signal composing circuit. This circuit consists of a diode, three resistors and a capacitor and reconstitutes a small amount of **Q** signal from the three color difference signals. The reverse amplifier and feedback circuit then supply a negative amount of the respective color difference signal so

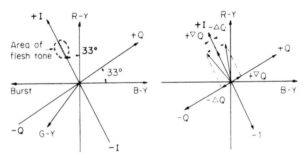

(a) FLESH TONE VECTOR PRESENTATION

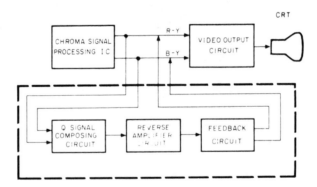

(b) FLESH TONE CORRECTION SYSTEM

Figure 9.17:   Courtesy of Hitachi Ltd.

that, in effect, the area of flesh tone variation has been decreased.

COLOR CIRCUIT ADJUSTMENT

In most modern color TV receivers the number of service adjustments is quite small. The many automatic features and the widespread use of integrated circuits have reduced the number of service adjustments. Looking at the block diagram of a typical color circuit shown in Figure 9.1, we can see the need to adjust the bandpass response of the 3.58-MHz color amplifier at very rare occasions. A coarse adjustment of the L-C network, which is part of the color sync section, the 3.58-MHz oscillator, may be necessary when major parts in that circuit have been replaced. There is no adjustment in the demodulators, the color matrix usually operates with fixed values and the remaining adjustments involve the color signal amplitudes and the DC bias voltage in the color picture tube.

A) COLOR BANDPASS ADJUSTMENTS

The best method of checking and aligning the color bandpass amplifier response is to use the sweep generator setup shown in Figure 7.16 for the RF and IF alignment. The sweep generator should be able to provide a signal ranging from approximately 10 KHz to 5 or 6 MHz. The sweep generator is connected to the output of the video preamp of Figure 9.1, and the detector probe is connected to the output of the 3.58-MHz amplifier. A typical bandpass response, as illustrated in Figure 5.6, should then be observed on the oscilloscope. Appropriate adjustments on the L-C networks will provide the desired bandpass response.

B) OVERALL COLOR ADJUSTMENTS

The most convenient and widely used method of checking
and touching up whatever adjustments can be made in
the color signal section uses a color bar generator. Figure
9.18 illustrates the connection of the color bar generator
and oscilloscope, and Figure 9.19 shows the correct color
bar display that should appear on the TV screen. Note
that bars 2 and 8 represent the **I** and **Q** signals respectively.
Bars 3, 6 and 10 represent the primary colors. We can
evaluate the adjustment of all the color controls and the
performance of all color circuits by observing the color
test pattern on the screen and by tracing the waveforms
through the various sections of the color TV receiver. The
color bar waveforms of Figure 9.20, for example, represent
the correct output for the R–Y and B–Y demodulators.
Note that the R–Y demodulator output has bar 3, pure
red, as the greatest amplitude. The B–Y demodulator output, by comparison, has bar 6, pure blue, as maximum
amplitude. At the instant of bar 6, there will be practically
no output at the R–Y demodulator, just as the B–Y demodulator has minimum output at bar 3, the pure red.

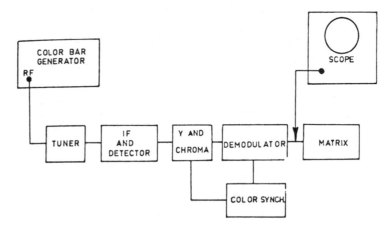

Figure 9.18: Connection of Color Bar Generator.
Color TV Servicing, 3rd Ed., Walter H. Buchsbaum. Prentice-Hall, Inc.

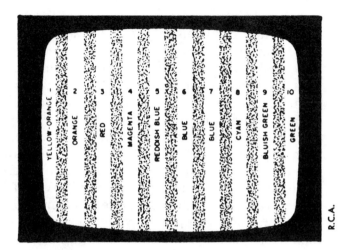

Figure 9.19: Correct Color Bar Pattern.
Color TV Servicing, 3rd Ed., Walter H. Buchsbaum. Prentice-Hall, Inc.

C) COLOR TEMPERATURE ADJUSTMENTS

This adjustment sets the correct background color on the TV screen when no picture is being received. Most color TV receivers have a service switch at the rear of the set that collapses the vertical sweep so that a single horizontal line is produced. The brightness and contrast controls should be preset to approximately midrange, and the color bias controls and screen controls, as well as the color drive controls, should be turned to minimum. When the service

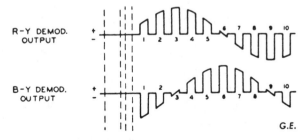

Figure 9.20: Color Bar Waveforms.
Color TV Servicing, 3rd Ed., Walter H. Buchsbaum. Prentice-Hall, Inc.

switch is in the service position, one of the screen controls, either red, green or blue, is advanced to produce a thin horizontal line at the center of the screen. Depending on the color of the line produced, the remaining bias controls are adjusted to produce a horizontal white line. For optimum adjustments, one of the three bias controls should remain at minimum, with the other two adjusted to produce pure white. Next, the service switch is set to the normal position, and a black and white picture is produced by shorting an appropriate test point to ground or by setting the color killer bias to cut off. With the brightness and contrast controls set close to maximum, the color drive controls are adjusted to produce a "warm white" picture. The shorted test point or cut-off color killer bias is removed and normal color pictures should now be observed.

Only generalized color adjustments can be presented here, and the actual manufacturer's data should be followed closely, whenever available. The overall principles of using a sweep generator for bandpass alignment, a color bar generator for test and adjustment of the color circuits and, finally, the service switch for adjustment of the picture are presented in more detail in every manufacturer's service manual.

TROUBLESHOOTING

Color defects are such an important subject for the service technician that all of Chapter 14 is devoted to this topic. In that chapter, reference is made to the full-color illustrations in this book because the approach is based on the symptom-function method discussed in Chapter 1. The methodical, step-by-step technique used in Chapter 14 locates color defects to a particular circuit function, while Chapter 13 does the same for monochrome defects. In the preceding paragraphs we have covered detailed color circuits, and the following troubleshooting hints are limited to particular circuit elements. We suggest to the reader that he look over Chapter 14 first and then use the troubleshooting hints below.

Loss of all color is most frequently due to a defect in the 3.58-MHz amplifier, the color killer, the color burst separator or the color sync section. Here are the most likely defects in those sections:

A) 3.58-MHz AMPLIFIER

If discrete transistor or IC amplifiers are used, these semi-conductors and the B+ voltages to them should be checked. If the amplifier is part of a complete color IC, check the external components, such as the L-C bandpass networks. If they appear good, the entire IC may have to be replaced.

B) COLOR KILLER

In discrete circuits, the transistors and diodes are the most likely culprits. Check the voltages. If the killer is part of an IC, the entire IC will have to be replaced.

C) COLOR BURST SEPARATOR

If made up of discrete transistors, try replacing them, but use the oscilloscope first to check that the proper sync and keying pulses are applied. Check the R-C network that shapes the keying pulse. The same applies to sets where the burst separator is part of a color IC. Replacement of that IC may be necessary.

D) COLOR SYNC SECTION

Use the oscilloscope to check that proper color reference bursts and oscillator feedback signals are applied to the automatic phase detector (APC). Check the output of the oscillator itself. Depending on the results, discrete transistors or ICs may have to be replaced. The crystal itself and the L-C network are rarely defective.

Wrong colors can be due to defects in external control circuits or in discrete transistors or diodes. The symptom function method used in Chapter 14 will show you what defects are due to one of the demodulators, the matrixing section or the color video circuits. In each case transistors cause the most frequent failures, while ICs, in general, appear less likely to become defective. Before replacing an IC it is always good practice to check all voltages and measure the external resistors.

Modern TV receivers use printed circuit boards to mount the components of the color circuits. You should look for such mechanical defects as solder bridging, broken conductors, and cold solder joints before going through the tedious task of replacing an IC. Connectors, connecting wires and cables are another source of intermittent or open connections.

Tuned amplifiers such as a 3.58-MHz amplifier outwardly have no direct relationship to a basic audio amplifier. However, we will see that a tuned amplifier operated at its resonant (peak) frequency is actually identical to a basic audio amplifier. In other words, a tuned tank (collector load) is purely resistive at its resonant frequency. Accordingly, the L and C components can be disregarded in analysis of its normal characteristics. For example, the Pi-R H-parameter verification test provided in troubleshooting program 1 of the appendix has the same application in a tuned amplifier as in a basic audio amplifier, provided that the tuned amplifier is operated at its resonant frequency.

CHAPTER 10

AUDIO AND POWER SUPPLY CIRCUITS

Audio and power supply circuitry have usually been simple circuits with few components, and little likelihood of problems. Since the advent of switch mode power supplies, stereo audio, scan-rectified power circuitry and other advances, these circuits are no longer simple in many cases. In this chapter you will look at the operation of typical audio circuits, both monophonic and stereo. Power supplies are covered in the second half of the chapter. Audio and power supply circuit troubleshooting, and possible defects in these circuits, are also discussed.

AUDIO CIRCUITS

The audio section of any TV receiver, whether stereo or monophonic, accepts a composite video signal, which includes the 4.5-MHz intercarrier audio signal that is decoded, amplified and applied to the loudspeaker. In addition, in stereo televisions, the audio circuitry splits stereo signals into two channels, and optionally provides a second audio program channel. Monophonic transmission is covered first, then a section describes transmission and reception of stereo signals.

Figure 10.1 illustrates, in simplified form, the signals you will find in the audio section of any monophonic TV receiver. The composite video signal contains video, sync and blanking pulses, as well as the heterodyne products of the video IF and audio IF carriers. Standard transmission protocol demands that these two signals be 4.5 MHz apart. The audio IF carrier is frequency modulated with a maximum deviation of ± 25 KHz. When the intercarrier 4.5 MHz is amplified by itself, it is limited in amplitude so that a frequency modulated, constant amplitude sinewave signal is obtained. This FM signal is then demodulated to produce the actual audio signal.

A variety of FM demodulators or detectors have been used in TV receivers over the years. Early TV receivers used a double diode, center-tapped transformer circuit

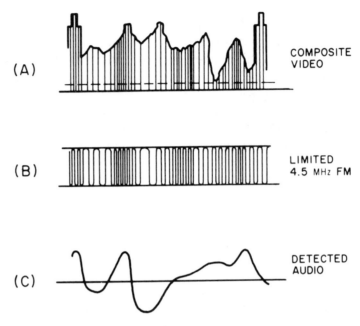

(A)   COMPOSITE
                                                       VIDEO

(B)   LIMITED
                                                       4.5 MHz FM

(C)   DETECTED
                                                       AUDIO

Figure 10.1: FM Audio Waveforms.
Reprinted with permission of Hayden Book Company from *Fundamentals of Television* by Walter H. Buchsbaum.

called either a discriminator or a ratio detector. This circuit required tuning the primary transformer for maximum and tuning the secondary for balance. As we shall see in the following paragraphs, modern TV receivers use a somewhat simpler phase shift-type detector. Regardless of the type of circuit used, the frequency response must be a balanced curve as illustrated in Figure 10.2. Although the maximum deviation of a standard television audio signal is only ±25 KHz, the typical response curve shown in Figure 10.2 shows the peaks separated by 100 KHz, and an absolutely flat portion of the curve can be expected over the range of + and − 50 KHz, providing some tolerance in the alignment. When correctly aligned, the zero crossing of this curve is at precisely 4.5 MHz and any frequencies above this point produce a positive voltage output and any frequencies below that point a negative

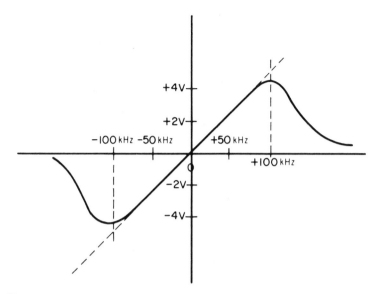

Figure 10.2: FM Detector Response Curve.
Reprinted with permission of Hayden Book Company from *Fundamentals of Television* by Walter H. Buchsbaum.

voltage output. As explained later under "Audio Adjustment," it is possible to actually observe this kind of response curve on the oscilloscope or measure it by using a VOM.

Almost all monophonic TV receivers use a single integrated circuit to perform the audio detection and amplification function. Figure 10.3 shows a typical audio IC with all of the important functions. At the input, labeled 1 through 3, there is usually a tuned circuit, sharply resonant at 4.5 MHz. Some receivers have a special ceramic filter that provides the required sharp response curve centered at 4.5 MHz. In the IC shown in Figure 10.3, there is a special active filter interposed between the limiter and the detector. This filter provides, again, a 4.5-MHz response. The resonant circuit, consisting of L188 and C188, is tuned exactly for 4.5 MHz and provides the phase shift necessary to the FM detector to generate the response curve of Figure 10.2. The output of the detector goes to

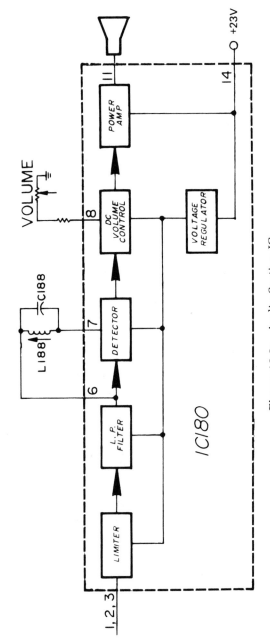

Figure 10.3: Audio Section IC. Courtesy General Electric.

the audio power amplifier through the DC volume control portion that permits locating the volume control on the front panel of the TV receiver without affecting the audio directly. In this particular IC, the +23 V power supply source is applied directly to the power amplifier stage but goes through a voltage regulator for the other stages.

In many TV receivers the audio output from the IC does not drive the speaker directly. ICs are generally limited in their power dissipation characteristic and require external heat sinks if they are to dissipate more than 200 milliwatts. For this reason separate, discrete transistor stages are used for the audio output amplifier. In some recent TV receivers, efforts have been made to improve the quality of the audio reproduction by using several speakers and a push pull transistor audio amplifier as output. In TV receivers that are combined with AM/FM stereo and audio systems, the output of the IC is usually sent to the input of the stereo audio system, although it may provide the output only in monophonic, not stereo, format.

Figure 10.4 shows the audio IC used in several different RCA chassis. It provides the same essential functions as are illustrated in Figure 10.3, with some modifications. The two input leads to the 4.5 MHz IF amplifier and limiter stage permit a nongrounded, balanced input from a 4.5-MHz resonant circuit. The FM detector, again, requires an external L-C network, connected to pins 10 and 11, to perform the FM demodulation. The electronic attenuator with its output to the volume control performs the same function as the DC volume control section of Figure 10.3. In the RCA version, however, the attenuated audio output and the input to the power amplifier are brought out separately so that they can be connected to an external tone control and de-emphasis compensation network. While the audio section of Figure 10.3 provided the power directly to the power amplifier and used the voltage regulator for all other stages, in the RCA version the audio power amplifier current is con-

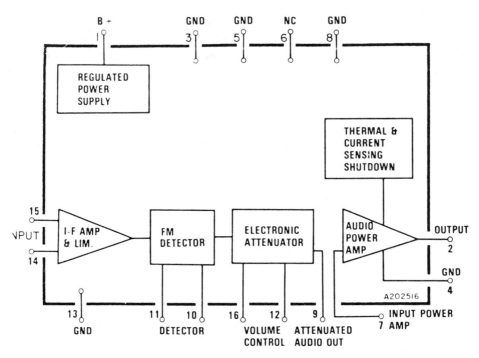

Figure 10.4: Audio IC for RCA Models.
Courtesy RCA Consumer Electronics.

trolled by a thermal and current sensing shutdown circuit. This circuit protects the IC in case the audio power amplifier either draws too much current or gets too hot. When troubleshooting the loss of audio output, the presence or absence of this feature is an important factor in determining where the trouble actually lies.

MTS STEREO CIRCUITS

Many current production televisions now contain circuitry that will detect, decode and reproduce audio in full stereo. In addition, a separate audio program channel is available in sets so equipped, for simultaneous broadcast of the program in a foreign language, or for other purposes.

The new format approved for TV stereo is very similar to the existing FM broadcast band stereo format. We will look at the new technology (and standards), then see how it is implemented in current-model televisions. In the section on audio troubleshooting, common problems will be covered.

The simplest method for sending stereo in an existing TV signal would have been to modulate the standard audio carrier with one channel, and create a new subcarrier for the other channel. This approach was ruled out, however, because people with monophonic receivers would then be missing one channel of audio information during stereo broadcasts. As a result, the format of FM stereo broadcasting was applied with several differences. Basically, here is how the current system works.

- A monophonic signal is generated by summing the information in the left and right channels. This signal is then applied to the normal audio subcarrier. This signal is referred to as the L+R signal.
- Another signal is generated by subtracting the information in the right channel from the left channel audio. This L−R signal is then used to amplitude modulate a subcarrier that is located above the normal audio signal. The subcarrier is then suppressed at the transmitter, and only the amplitude-modulated sidebands remain in the transmitted signal.
- A pilot carrier of constant amplitude is then sent at ½ the frequency of the original L−R subcarrier. The pilot signal has two purposes. It is used to restore the L−R subcarrier at the receiver, and is also used to determine the presence of a stereo broadcast.
- Another subcarrier is also provided above the L−R signal which can be used to carry a separate audio program. This signal is referred to as the S.A.P. carrier, is FM modulated, and is transmitted either independently or in addition to a stereo transmission.

When the L−R sidebands are demodulated, the L−R signal is then algebraically added to the L+R signal in a matrix. The addition process is illustrated in the following formulas:

$$\text{left channel} = (L+R) + (L-R) = 2L + R - R = 2L$$
$$\text{right channel} = (L+R) - (L-R) = 2R + L - L = 2R$$

Refer to figure 10.5 for an illustration of the composite stereo signal distribution. The L+R signal is FM modulated with a band spread of 50 Hz to 15 KHz. The L−R suppressed subcarrier is at 31.5 KHz, and the AM sidebands range from 16.5 KHz to 46.5 KHz. The reason for 50 KHz deviation of the L−R signal is to provide enhanced signal/noise ratio. The pilot signal is at the horizontal frequency of 15,734 Hz, and the S.A.P. carrier is located at 78.6 KHz, and has a bandspread of 65 KHz to 95 KHz. A telemetry signal is available at approximately 102 KHz. This FM signal is used for secondary commu-

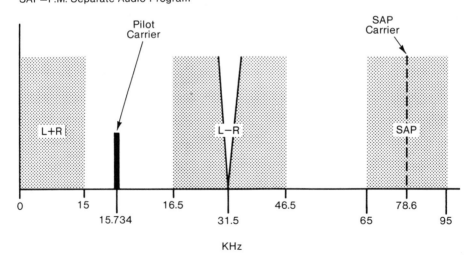

Figure 10.5: Composite Stereo Signal Distribution

nication, however it is not receivable by consumer stereo decoder circuitry.

Many televisions currently being manufactured contain stereo decoder circuitry, and many monophonic televisions also contain a stereo ready connector on the rear panel for connection to a multichannel TV sound adaptor. The adaptor receives undetected audio from the television, and decodes the stereo or S.A.P information contained on the audio signal. Whether the decoder is built in or added on, the decoding process is identical. Of course, to take advantage of the stereo audio present in a stereo adaptor, the adaptor must be connected to auxiliary inputs on a stereo amplifier. Most stereo TVs contain a stereo amplifier, often the amplifiers and speakers that are built in are adequate, but sound quality is improved by routing audio to a high-quality stereo amplifier and speaker system.

The $L-R$ signal is AM, therefore it is susceptible to extraneous noise. To provide a better signal-to-noise ratio, the DBX system of dynamic noise suppression is applied at the transmitter and receiver for the $L-R$ signal. In addition, the DBX circuitry is used to reduce noise in the monophonic S.A.P. signal.

Figure 10.6 contains a block diagram of a typical stereo decoder. Low-pass filters separate $L+R$ and $L-R$ signals for processing. The $L-R$ decoder recovers $L-R$ audio and routes it to the DBX noise-reduction circuitry. The matrix circuit separates the left and right channel information and presents it to the audio input selection circuitry.

S.A.P. frequencies are separated by a bandpass filter, decoded and processed through the DBX circuitry. Input selection circuitry then determines whether mono, stereo, or S.A.P. signals reach the audio amplifiers.

DBX noise suppression is by far the most complex component in the stereo specification. Fortunately for the service technician, the DBX circuitry is all contained within a single IC. A simplified description of the process, how-

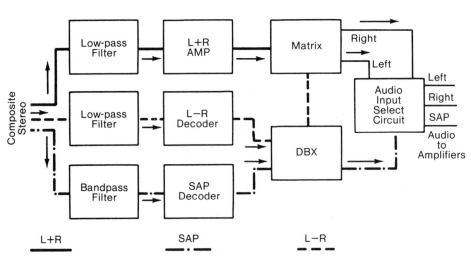

Figure 10.6: Basic Stereo Decoder

ever, is in order so that the process can be understood by the technician.

DBX noise reduction is based upon automatic compression and expansion of the audio signal. High frequencies are pre-emphasized, just as they are in standard FM transmissions. In addition, large audio levels are compressed at the transmitter, while low levels are expanded. Compressing the large signals results in a decrease in S/N ratio however, since large-level signals already have a high S/N ratio, the reduction is acceptable. Low-level signals are expanded, thus increasing their low S/N ratio. The overall S/N ratio is improved and better quality sound reproduction results.

TV AUDIO ADJUSTMENTS

The intercarrier audio signal frequency is determined quite accurately by the TV transmitter because the audio FM carrier is placed exactly 4.5 MHz above the video RF carrier. When the 4.5-MHz intercarrier signal is obtained at the detector, its amplitude, but not its frequency, is determined by the alignment of the tuner and the IF section. If we are reasonably sure that this alignment is correct, only two or three adjustments of the 4.5-MHz signal are necessary. Remember that, unless a SAW filter is used, specific audio traps in the IF section must be tuned to the 41.25-MHz IF audio signal. If, for example, one of the adjacent channel traps is misaligned and also set to the 41.25-MHz signal, excessive attenuation of the audio IF signal may occur, resulting in insufficient amplitude of the 4.5-MHz intercarrier FM signal. Manufacturers' instructions for checking the amplitude of the 4.5-MHz intercarrier signal usually indicate the specific test points for this purpose.

Most service technicians use an "off-the-air" signal for the 4.5-MHz adjustments. With a strong local channel tuned in, the antenna signal is attenuated, either by removing one or both antenna leads and substituting a short piece of wire, or by using a suitable RF attenuator, until a hiss or buzz is heard in the sound. First the FM detector coil is tuned for best sound and then other 4.5-MHz-tuned circuits are adjusted for the strongest, buzz-free audio signal. Of course, if the sound is unclear and contains hissing with the normal antenna, the adjustments of the FM detector coil and the other tuned circuits are made at that point.

Some TV sweep generators provide a 4.5 MHz, crystal-controlled signal that can be connected to the output of the video detector and that can be used for the alignment of the 4.5-MHz resonant circuits. If that signal is frequency modulated, an oscilloscope can be connected to the output of the FM detector or to a suitable test point brought out from the audio IC, and the actual FM detector response curve illustrated in Figure 10.2 can be observed. In most instances, however, an unmodulated 4.5-MHz signal is available. In that case the output of the FM detector or the output of the electronic attenuator or DC volume control can be connected to a VOM. The FM detector-tuned circuit is then adjusted for zero output at exactly 4.5 MHz, with its positive or negative DC voltages measured as the signal generator is varied above and below that frequency.

Stereo audio circuits have very few adjustments and vary from one manufacturer to another. An audio separation adjustment is commonly found, which should be adjusted to manufacturers' specifications, that provides maximum channel separation between left and right. Some circuits may have a frequency adjustment on their PLL pilot carrier circuitry that must be adjusted with a frequency counter. There may also be a level adjustment that controls audio levels into the DBX circuitry. Use an oscilloscope to adjust this control to the proper amplitude.

TROUBLESHOOTING TV AUDIO CIRCUITS

Audio defects are invariably indicated by the sound, or lack of it, coming from the speaker. If no sound at all can be heard, shorting the volume control to ground usually provides an indication of whether the defect is before that point or between that point and the speaker. Shorting the volume control to ground should produce a click. If no click is heard, we can try shorting the input to the audio amplifier itself to ground, and, failing to hear a click at that point, we would check the power supply voltage to the output amplifier. In most TV receivers the loudspeaker is mounted at the front and is connected to the output amplifier, with or without coupling transformer, through a short cable and plug/jack arrangement. Intermittent contacts, broken or partly broken wires, in that area, often cause total loss of sound.

If instant shorting of the volume control to ground produces a click, this indicates that, at least to some extent, the audio portion is working. The most likely defect now is in the stages between the video detector and the FM detector. This assumes that a good picture is received.

If the picture itself is distorted, weak, or out of sync, the problem may be in the antenna or RF tuner. If good pictures are received on several channels but no sound, the defect must be either in the 41.25-MHz sound trap in the IF section or in the 4.5-MHz chain in the audio section.

Because most modern TV sets use a single IC for the audio section, troubleshooting is usually limited to voltage and resistance measurements of the external components, and, when these test good, the IC has to be replaced. Because replacing an IC always requires an exact duplicate and entails a fair amount of work, many service technicians use a 4.5-MHz signal generator to inject a signal at the output of the video detector and then try to trace it through with the oscilloscope to see if, by chance, the defect lies in some part other than the IC.

Distorted sound is very often due to a misalignment somewhere in the RF, IF or 4.5-MHz intercarrier section. To establish where the problem lies, vary the fine tuning control, or, where available, the internal AFT (automatic fine tuning) voltage to see if good audio can be obtained, regardless of picture quality. If that is possible, then RF or IF misalignment is at fault. Leaky coupling capacitors in the audio circuits can also cause distorted sound. Although loudspeakers are among the most reliable components of TV receivers, age, excessive moisture or heat, or simple mechanical failure can cause the loudspeaker voice coil to rub, the cone of the loudspeaker to become stiff, brittle or even cracked, and all of these defects will cause poor sound. In replacing the loudspeaker it may be desirable to get an exact duplicate, but, if the voice coil impedance and the mounting size matches, almost any speaker will do.

Stereo decoder circuitry is very reliable; however, problems could include lack of stereo reception, lack of SAP reception, excessive noise level, lack of audio or distorted sound. Possible defects will be covered separately.

No Stereo. This could be caused by a loss of the L − R signal; check the stereo decoder and DBX circuitry.

No SAP reception. Check the SAP decoder and DBX circuitry for defects.

Excessive noise level. Check for defects in the DBX circuitry. Noise generated by defective transistors or ICs in the audio circuitry could also cause this problem.

No audio in a monaural broadcast accompanied by distorted stereo sound. This defect could be caused by a loss of the L + R signal, which would cause a loss of monophonic audio. During a stereo broadcast, the L − R amplifier could still be functional. Distortion would result, however, because during times of identical signals in the left and right channel, the L − R signal falls to zero, causing no output at that instant. The resultant waveform would be intermittent and distorted.

Audio power amplifiers usually have push-pull circuitry in which a pair of transistors are operated in complementary-symmetry, and ordinarily in the class AB mode. In other words, each of the transistors conducts for slightly more than one-half cycle and is cut off for almost one half cycle. From the viewpoint of basic circuit analysis, this mode of operation is quite comparable to that of a simple class A single-transistor amplifier. Accordingly, troubleshooting program 1 in the appendix may be used to compute the normal characteristics of a class AB complementary-symmetry audio output stage.

POWER SUPPLY CIRCUITS

In vacuum tube TV receivers, the power supply consisted primarily of a large transformer, vacuum tube rectifiers, a filter choke and a number of filter capacitors. The transformer also contained windings for the 6.3V CRT filament and filament supply voltages for all the other vacuum tubes. In current TV receivers, power supplies range from the simple circuit of Figure 10.7 to much more complex power supplies. New designs in power supplies include scan-derived voltage sources, switch mode power units and others. Even with all the complexities, the basic function of all power supplies remains the same, which is to utilize the 120 V AC power from the wall socket to generate the DC voltages required in the TV receiver. Battery-operated receivers are designed to operate directly from DC sources such as dry cell and automotive batteries. These units typically have simpler power supply requirements, due to the fact that DC is provided directly from the battery.

The circuit of Figure 10.7 is typical of the power supply of many monochrome, small-screen receivers. The combination of R1, C1, −R2, −C2 and R3, helps to reduce the various undesirable effects common on many commercial powerlines. The fuse and the ON/OFF switch are essential in protecting the rest of the receiver. In this circuit a bridge rectifier consisting of four diodes, each shunted by a 680-PF capacitor, changes the AC line voltage to a pulsating 120 Hz DC which is filtered by the combination of R4, C7 and C8. The shunt capacitor across each diode is used to reduce diode noise. Note that the input of the AC line cord is separated from the chassis ground by a 1-meg resistor, R3, and a 680-PF capacitor, C1. The DC output, +140 V, is referenced to ground at the grounded junction of the diode bridge rectifier. The power supply in Figure 10.5 does not contain any regulation, and its 140 V output will vary according to the line voltage, except-for the effects on filter capacitors C7 and C8.

The power supply circuit of Figure 10.8 is used in some Sears color TV receivers and is considerably more complex because it contains a DC regulation circuit. Many older-model televisions contain an AC interlock as illustrated in Figure 10.8 at the plug and jack B801. This interlock is opened when the back of the set is removed.

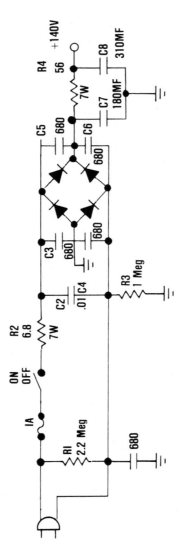

Figure 10.7: Power Supply for RCA Monochrome TV Set

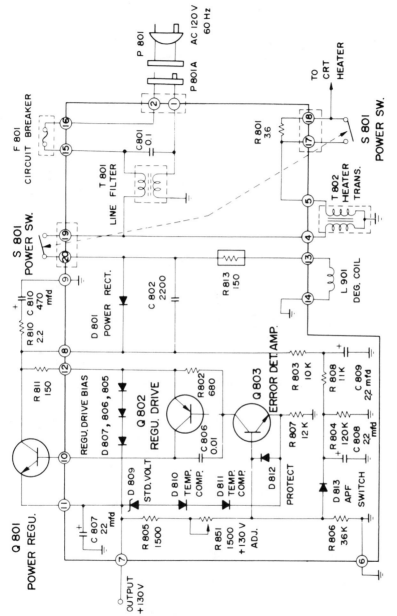

Figure 10.8: Power Supply of Sears Model 562.40270300. Courtesy Sears.

247

Should the consumer decide to open the back of the receiver, he will find it impossible to apply power to the television since the interlock cord remains with the back when it is removed. Service technicians routinely carry jumper cords that allow them to bypass the interlock. There are two types of interlock cords, polarized and nonpolar. The two types are not interchangeable, so both types must be available. The difference between them is in the size of the interlock connector pins. On a polarized cord, one pin is larger than the other, while on a nonpolar type, both pins are the same diameter. Polarized types must be used for "hot chassis" televisions (those that have one side of the metal chassis tied to the AC mains). Newer-model televisions no longer contain an AC interlock, but bear the prominent warning "No User Serviceable Components Inside, Refer Servicing to Qualified Personnel."

Figure 10.8 shows a circuit breaker, F801, instead of a fuse and an inductive line filter which returns one side of the powerline to chassis ground. A single power rectifier is used and its output, filtered by R810 and C810, goes to the collector of the power-regulating transistor 801. A small portion of the DC voltage goes to the base of the error-detecting amplifier which also receives a portion of the 130-V DC regulated output. Screwdriver adjustment of the potentiometer R851 permits the service technician to set the exact value of the 130-V output. The emitter of the error-detecting amplifier receives its exact voltage through a Zener diode D809 which is followed by two temperature-compensating diodes and, finally, the 12-K resistor, R807, to ground. Another transistor, Q802, is used as intermediary gain stage between the error-detecting amplifier and the power regulator. It receives the error-detecting amplifier collector output on its base and then controls the gain of the power regulator. Transistor Q802 applies its output between the collector and base of the power regulator transistor and thereby controls its gain. This transistor, Q801, is of the power type, mounted on a suitable heat sink and able to dissipate considerable thermal energy. The power supply shown in Figure 10.8 also contains two other elements found in most color TV receivers. A degaussing coil, L901, is connected to the AC side of the power rectifier through the temperature-sensitive resistor R813. The filaments of the color picture tube are on whenever the AC plug is connected to a wall socket, but filament power is reduced because R801, a 3.6-ohm resistor, is in series between the heater transformer and the CRT filaments. When the power switch is turned on, the resistor is shorted and full filament power is applied.

Many recent color TV receivers utilize some of the power generated as part of the flyback circuit to provide DC voltage for some receiver sections. The block diagram of Figure 10.9 illustrates the power supply of the G.E. 19 EC chassis and is typical of many recent color TV receivers. The 120-V AC goes through a circuit breaker, line filter, heater transformer and degaussing coil arrangement like that of Figure 10.8. A bridge rectifier, followed by two filter capacitors and a choke coil, provides the positive 120 V to the sweep or deflection circuits. A preregulator and regulator (PSR and REG) control the current through the negative (ground) leg which also contains the over-current sensor. Except for the + 120 V to the sweep section, all other sections of the receiver are operated by power derived from the high-voltage transformer (HVT). This includes the horizontal oscillator that obtains its power from the HVT. To make sure that the horizontal oscillator starts, however, a special start-up SCR controls + 47 V going to the sweep circuit to start the horizontal oscillator. After the start-up period, the + 47 V is supplied, through a diode, from the HVT.

The HV shut-down circuit receives + 47 V through the start-up SCR and/or from the HVT. It also receives a special beam-current limiting signal that will cause the + 13 V to the horizontal oscillator to be shut down when the beam current limit is exceeded. In some G.E. chassis, the conventional solid-state regulator provides the + 15- and + 20-V bus, but in the EC-P models a special ferro

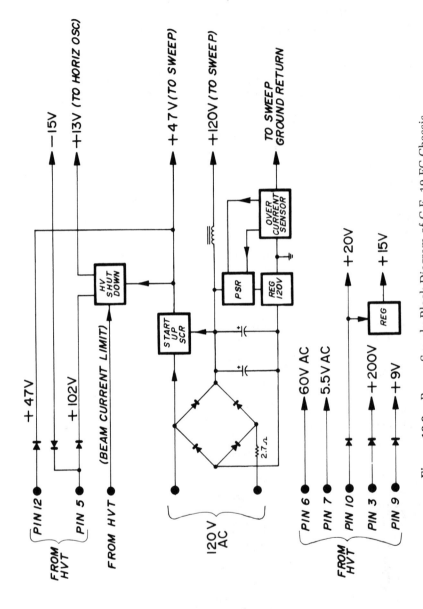

Figure 10.9: Power Supply Block Diagram of G.E. 19 EC Chassis. Courtesy of General Electric.

250

resonant saturable reactor provides a constant output voltage, regardless of changes in input voltage. This circuit uses the 15,750-Hz pulses from the HVT that are then rectified and filtered. Because of the high frequency, the saturable reactor and all other components are relatively small.

Some circuit detail of the block diagram of Figure 10.9 is shown in Figure 10.10. Note that the +120 V goes through voltage divider R907 and R911 and series resistor R909 to provide the +47 V DC to the start-up circuit. Regulation of the +120-V source is provided by the PSR module that contains a transistor, a Zener diode, and two series diodes. These three diodes set the voltage level of the emitter, while the base voltage is derived from the +120 V DC in combination with a filter and rectified DC signal from the emitter of the horizontal output transistor. The collector of the PSR transistor drives the base of the 120-V regulator. This transistor is a power transistor, mounted on a heat sink and protected by a ½-amp fuse and two 15-watt resistors going from the emitter to ground. In effect, these two resistors are in the ground return circuit and assist the two 220-MF capacitors in filtering the +120V DC.

Many of the recent color TV receivers that use complex power supplies such as the one shown in Figure 10.9 employ circuits similar to those described above. Minor variations do not generally affect the overall performance, nor do they affect the troubleshooting.

With so many new video devices such as VCRs, video games, computers and video disk systems, it is popular to provide connections on standard televisions to allow direct hook-up of these video accessories to the TV so it may be used as a monitor. This necessitates that the television have a "cold" chassis, so that interconnection of external video sources that are also tied to the AC line does not create a shock hazard for the consumer. Early televisions were isolated from the AC mains with expensive, bulky 60-Hz power transformers. With today's modern,

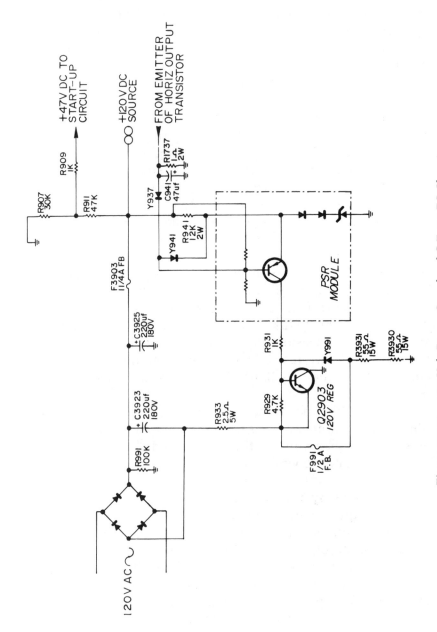

Figure 10.10: 120-Volt Power Supply of G.E. 19 EC Chassis. Courtesy General Electric.

inexpensive televisions, this technique is not acceptable. Many manufacturers are using switching-mode power supplies that provide isolation, are lower in cost, lighter, smaller and better regulated than older designs.

In some chassis, the manufacturer elected to use optoisolators and transformers at the video jacks, and still used a hot chassis design. In more elaborate receivers with multiple input and output connections, this method is inefficient. Switching power supplies provide the required isolation for many of these models, and provide all the advantages described above. Figure 10.11 contains a block diagram of the switching regulator power supply in the RCA CTC 133 chassis. Remote control televisions require a standby power supply that maintains power to the remote receiver in the television so that the remote unit can turn the receiver on and off. The CTC 133 is turned on and off via U101, an optoisolator that connects to the local ON/OFF switch, the remote ON/OFF switch in the tuner, and the high voltage shutdown/X-ray protection circuits. This power supply, as are many switching supplies, has a hot ground assembly, so be careful when working in this area. Alternating current is applied directly to the bridge rectifier, which provides 150 volts Raw B+ to T101 and the start-up supply. Eleven volts DC from the start-up supply is enough to start U100 working when signalled by the ON/OFF optoisolator. The overcurrent protection circuit can also shut down U100 if too much current should happen to flow through the power MOSFET Q100; U100 provides a pulse-width modulated signal to Q100, driving it on and off, which causes current pulses to flow through T101. The pulses are transformer coupled to the main power supply rectifiers in the TV, providing 131V, -24V, $+24$V, $+16$V and $+5$V to the external television circuits. Power is maintained to the set via the run supply feedback winding on T101. The run supply delivers 12 V to the regulator IC and B+ trim network, a precision voltage divider that generates a regulator reference

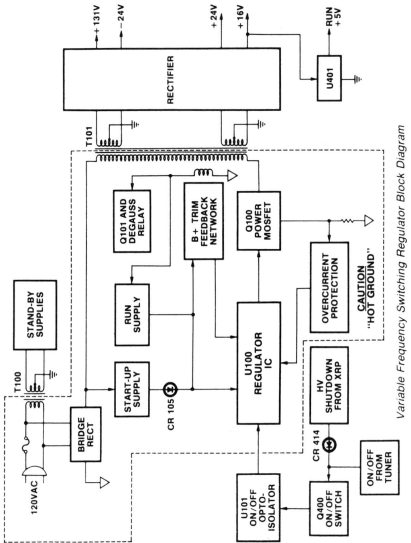

Figure 10.11: This material was reproduced from the CTC 133 Color Chassis Technical Review, Copyright 1985, by RCA Corporation Technical Training, Indianapolis, IN.

Variable Frequency Switching Regulator Block Diagram

source voltage. The Run supply also delivers +5V from the 16V supply via U401.

The CTC 133 chassis uses a power MOSFET, rather than a bipolar switching transistor because they are better suited for critical switching applications. They are capable of operating with less drive, at higher frequencies using simpler circuits than bipolar devices. In addition, they are more reliable and have very high-speed switching times. These advantages outweigh the fact that the MOSFET devices are more costly than their similarly rated bipolar cousins. In the CTC 133, Q100 operates as a simple switch. The most common mode of failure for Q100 will be a short between drain, gate and source.

As with all televisions with hot chassis connections, always use an isolation transformer when servicing. Not using an isolation transformer could result in damage to the equipment, the receiver, or injury to the technician.

TROUBLESHOOTING TV POWER SUPPLIES

Caution: Most inexpensive monochrome and color TV receivers are not isolated from the power line. In addition, even cold chassis models have hot chassis characteristics. This means that you can receive a severe electric shock if one part of your body is grounded and the other comes in contact with the "hot" side of the 120-V AC line. To avoid this danger, use an isolating transformer between the AC power line and the AC side of the receiver under test.

Most power supply troubles can be readily located with voltmeter tests. Defective components can usually be isolated with ohmmeter tests. When troubleshooting a modern color TV receiver, however, we have to consider that many of the voltages normally associated with the primary power supply really come from the high-voltage transformer section and the actual defects may not be read-

ily apparent. It is possible, for example, that loss of the
5.5-V AC in Figure 10.9 is due to a short in the socket of
the pilot lamp that is illuminated by that voltage. It is
also possible that this voltage, derived from the high-voltage
transformer (HVT), is missing because of a defect in the
particular winding or bleeder circuit of the HVT portion
itself. A defect in the high-voltage shut-down circuit could
be interpreted as excessive beam current in the CRT. A
defective diode in any of the regulators could cause poor
or no regulation of certain key voltages that would then
affect the performance of the TV tuner, the IF section, the
color section or some other portion of the TV receiver. In
order to troubleshoot this type of power supply defect,
the manufacturer's service information, at least in block
diagram form, should be carefully consulted.

When troubleshooting color TV receiver power supplies with the power on, it is good practice to use only
one hand in order to avoid accidental electric shocks. The
ground side of the meter should remain connected to the
proper ground while only the probe side of the meter is
moved from point to point. Whenever it is necessary to
switch leads or to move both sides of the meter leads at
the same time, the power to the TV receiver should be
disconnected.

When the power supply defect is manifest by a blown
fuse or circuit breaker, the first step is usually to replace
the fuse or reset the circuit breaker, in the hope that a
momentary condition or simply old age caused this defect. If the fuse blows again, or the circuit breaker drops
out again, we must suspect a defect farther down in the
power supply section. Do not turn power on again, but
proceed with a visual inspection of the power supply
module or DC board, looking for charred components. The
next step will be to test first the AC and then the DC side
of the power supply. Remember, when the ohmmeter is
connected across properly operating filter capacitors, there
will be an instantaneous indication of low resistance that
will then increase as the capacitor is charged up. If the

ohmmeter connected across the filter capacitor shows a constant resistance of less than 100 ohms, the filter capacitor is probably defective, or else some other component is shorted across it. In most TV receivers the connections to the power supply can be interrupted by means of plugs and jacks. Open these plugs and jacks to help you determine if a short circuit is within the power supply board or elsewhere. If no short is apparent with the plugs disconnected, but a short does appear when the plug is again connected, the defect is apparently in the particular section supplied through that particular plug. The most likely trouble in this case is a bypass or filter capacitor at the remote section that is supplied by the power supply.

MOST LIKELY POWER SUPPLY DEFECTS

Even in early vacuum tube receivers, the filter capacitors were the most likely defect, with the vacuum tube rectifiers the second likely source of trouble. In modern TV receivers the most likely defects appear in the following order:

> shorted filter capacitors
> leaky filter capacitors
> defective power regulator transistors
> defective circuit breakers
> open rectifier diodes
> open series power resistors
> defective IC regulators
> defective power switches
> defective high-voltage flyback transformer
> cable connectors and wires.

CHAPTER 11

ANTENNAS AND DISTRIBUTING SYSTEMS

TV antennas, transmission lines and the many types of television distribution systems could be the subject of an entire book. In this chapter we will discuss antenna fundamentals, and some of the most frequent reception problems that are due to the antenna and its location. The same approach will be taken for transmission lines and TV distributions systems. Many accessories are used to provide signals to your television receiver. Antenna couplers, master antenna systems, pay TV devices, cable TV, satellite television and direct broadcast satellite systems will be discussed briefly. At the end of this chapter, you will find some very useful tips on installing a new television receiver, and on assisting the customer in obtaining the best possible reception.

TV ANTENNAS

All TV antennas are in some way based on the dipole principle illustrated in Figure 11.1. Note that the dipole consists of two equal rods, each being as long as one quarter of the wavelength of the signal to be received. At the center of the two rods, where the antenna lead-in or transmission line is connected, the current is maximum and the voltage minimum. Simple dipoles are most efficient and operate according to antenna theory only at a single, resonant frequency. Since TV channels cover a broad band, it is necessary to make some modification in the dipole antenna, as well as to accept some deterioration of performance at the upper and lower frequencies from the resonant frequency.

The maximum signal reception—or transmission pattern of a dipole—is shown in Figure 11.2. The two circles indicate that signals of equal strength will be received from the front and from the back of the antenna. For TV reception, this type of directivity is undesirable, since it would permit the reception of reflected signals as well as direct signals. For this reason, reflectors are usually

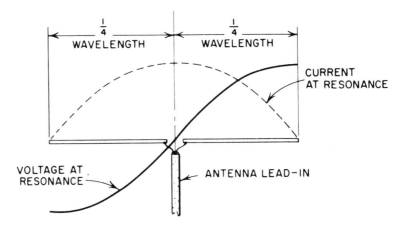

Figure 11.1: Dipole Antenna Principles.
Reprinted with permission of Hayden Book Company from *Fundamentals of Television* by Walter H. Buchsbaum.

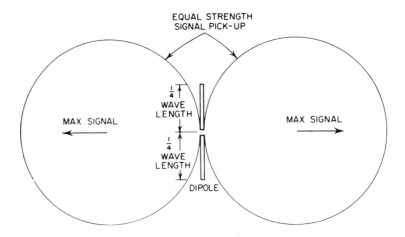

Figure 11.2: Dipole Directivity Pattern.
Reprinted with permission of Hayden Book Company from *Fundamentals of Television* by Walter H. Buchsbaum.

used together with any kind of TV antenna. Figure 11.3 shows the change in directivity pattern when a dipole antenna is spaced one-quarter wavelength away from a reflecting wall. Now the maximum signal is received from only one direction, with increased sensitivity, as indicated by the teardrop-shaped directivity pattern.

Practical TV antennas cannot use a reflecting wall, nor can the one-quarter wavelength spacing be assured for all channels. For that reason, a combination of reflecting rods and so-called directors is used to give the dipole antenna more directivity. Directing elements (straight rods that are shorter than the dipole) and reflecting elements (which are usually longer than the dipole) are spaced somewhat less than one-quarter wavelength away from the dipole itself, and an array of these elements make up the popular Yagi antenna illustrated in Figure 11.4. The arrow indicates direction of maximum sensitivity, and Yagi antennas have a narrow directivity pattern that increases in sharpness and sensitivity of gain as more and more director elements are added. The Yagi antenna shown in Figure 11.4 makes

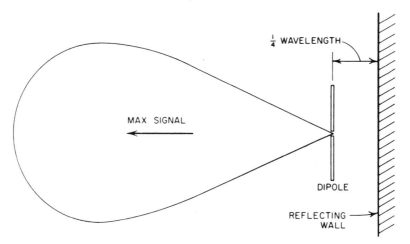

Figure 11.3: Directivity of Dipole with Reflector.
Reprinted with permission of Hayden Book Company from *Fundamentals of Television* by Walter H. Buchsbaum.

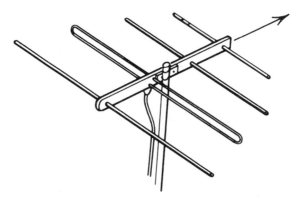

Figure 11.4: Basic Yagi Antenna.
Reprinted with permission of Hayden Book Company from *Fundamentals of Television* by Walter H. Buchsbaum.

use of a special type of dipole, the folded dipole, which provides a better bandwidth and can be designed to match a 300-ohm, twin-lead transmission line. Broadband Yagi antennas, covering channels 2 through 6 as well as 7 through 13, are commercially available. By using many elements tuned to different wavelengths in the desired VHF band, these antennas are, in effect, a combination of several basic Yagis, interleaved in one plane and mounted on a single assembly.

Most of the commercially available TV antennas are classified for reception in one of three areas: (1) local—15 to 20 miles; (2) suburban or mid-distance—20 to 30 miles; or (3) fringe—up to the point where the curvature of the earth limits reception. Cost and complexity increase according to the sensitivity and directivity, and fringe area antennas are the most complex and expensive.

One of the most widely used antennas for midrange and fringe areas is the log periodic antenna shown in Figure 11.5. The horizontal plane view is shown in Figure 11.5 (a) and a top view of the antenna, together with the equivalent L-C networks, is shown in (b). This antenna is based on a formula using a ratio of the natural logarithm that results in a scale factor T, whose common values

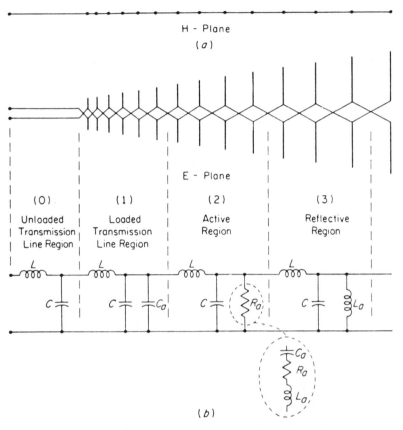

Figure 11.5: Log Periodic Antenna and Equivalent Circuit.
Complete Handbook of Practical Electronic Reference Data, Walter H.
Buchsbaum. Prentice-Hall, Inc.

range from 2 to 6. This scale factor determines both the
spacing and the length of the individual dipoles and results in an antenna that covers an extremely wide frequency band, with constant radiation resistance, constant
beam pattern, and constant gain over the TV band. In
effect, several adjacent dipoles in a log periodic array will
be close enough in length to resonate at any given channel,
and the other dipoles, which make up the reflective region,

provide a very sensitive, high-gain, narrow beam. The basic log periodic antenna is available in many varieties, including V shaped dipole elements, with the open end of the V directed towards the TV station. Several log periodic antennas can be used in arrays to result in a narrow vertical beam pattern.

When the basic dipole is changed from a rod to a triangle or a cone, the bandwidth of the antenna increases; this principle is frequently used in UHF antennas. These so-called "bow tie" antennas are simply broadband dipoles. When used as UHF antennas without reflectors, they are able to pick up UHF stations or UHF interference from both directions. In many commercial TV antennas, bow tie UHF elements are used in conjunction with the VHF elements that then provide the reflection in order to give the UHF antenna the desired directivity.

Most quality commercial antennas are available with specifications as to gain, directivity, bandwidth and characteristic impedance. This characteristic impedance depends on the point of connection to the transmission line. It is absolutely essential that the characteristic impedance of the transmission line be matched as closely as possible to the impedance of the antenna. The overwhelming majority of TV antennas provide a 300-ohm impedance, suitable for direct connection to the familiar ribbon-like, twin-lead, 300-ohm TV transmission line. When your TV installation requires the use of a coaxial cable in conjunction with a 300-ohm antenna, a matching device of some sort is essential. This matching device should transform the 300-ohm impedance to 50 or 75 ohms, standard values for coaxial cable, but it must also provide a transformation between the balanced 300-ohm antenna to the unbalanced, grounded 50- to 75-ohm coaxial cable. Such matching devices are often called baluns, an abbreviation to indicate their function. Commercially available baluns are recommended in every case since they are properly designed and tested for broadband operation and for weatherproofing as well.

ANTENNA PROBLEMS

For the service technician, antenna problems fall into three categories. The first is the location of the antenna with respect to all the TV transmitters in the area. Clearly, it would be best if all TV transmitters were located in a single place and the antenna could be mounted so that it is within line of sight of all transmitters. If two stations to be received are separated from each other, we will aim the antenna to a point between them, hoping that the directivity pattern will be sufficiently wide to receive both of them. In many instances, however, several antennas must be used, each aimed at one TV station, and their signals must then be combined. Antenna combiners for exterior use are commercially available and are highly recommended in such installations. Antenna rotators are essentially mast-mounted, geared-down motors that are controlled remotely. In some locations rotators are the best solution to this type of problem.

RF signals travel in straight lines and are reflected by tall buildings, mountains and other solid obstacles. This phenomenon causes the second (and usually the worst) problem for the installing service technician. The so-called "ghost" on the screen is the result of reception of a strong, usually direct path signal, together with a somewhat weaker reflected signal. Because the reflected signal arrives at the TV antenna microseconds later, it is displayed to the right of the direct path signal. In instances where the direct path signal is weaker and the reflected signal is stronger, the ghost will appear stronger than the first signal. Most ghost problems that are due to location require complex and expensive solutions. Ghosts are usually most pronounced on a specific channel, and a separate Yagi antenna, tuned to that channel only, may be required to receive the best possible signal, regardless of how this would affect the other channels. Ghosts, however, can also occur due to transmission line problems, and this difficulty will be discussed later in this chapter.

The third antenna problem the service technician encounters most frequently is due to the physical condition of the antenna elements and connections. Wind, rain, snow and air pollution will cause any antenna to deteriorate in its electrical and mechanical performance. In most parts of the U.S., the useful life of even the best-made antenna that is mounted outside is no more than five years. When reception is clearly deteriorated, pictures are noisy or full of "snow" and reception tends to be intermittent, the only remedy is to replace the antenna, its mounting structure and the transmission line. In many instances, it is easy to convince the set owner of the necessity for this by disconnecting the transmission line from the TV receiver and connecting a simple rabbit's ear indoor antenna instead. The indoor antenna frequently gives a good or better result than the corroded aging outdoor installation. In areas where rabbit ears are unsatisfactory, show the set owner a picture on a new portable connected to his antenna. This will verify his need for a new system.

TRANSMISSION LINES

Earlier in this chapter, we have spoken of the characteristic impedance of transmission lines, and this concept is illustrated in Figure 11.6. The characteristic impedance, Z, of a two-wire transmission line depends on the diameter, d, of the conductors and the distance between them, D. The equation given in Figure 6(a) is based on a transmission line that uses free air as dielectric between the two conductors. When polyethylene or some other plastic dielectric is used, the constant 276 is changed, reducing the spacing between the two wires somewhat. Practically all commercially available TV twin-lead transmission lines have a characteristic impedance of 300 ohms. The characteristic impedance of a coaxial transmission line depends on a constant, 138, and the log of the ratio

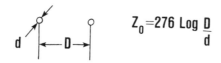

$$Z_0 = 276 \ \text{Log} \ \frac{D}{d}$$

(a) TWO WIRE TRANSMISSION LINE

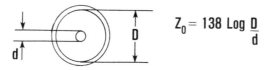

$$Z_0 = 138 \ \text{Log} \ \frac{D}{d}$$

(b) COAXIAL TRANSMISSION LINE

Figure 11.6: Transmission Line Fundamentals

between the diameter of the inner conductor and the inside diameter of the outer shield, as illustrated in Figure 11.6 (b). Coax transmission lines used in TV systems generally have a characteristic impedance of 75 ohms. Many coax cables used for a variety of other purposes have a characteristic impedance of 50 ohms, however, and the service technician installing a new coax transmission line must make sure that it is of the proper type. Coax cables usually have a number such as RG-58/U. This particular coax cable has a characteristic impedance of 50 ohms, but the popular RG-59/U has a characteristic impedance of 75 ohms. Both appear very similar and the best way to tell the difference between them is to read the type number on the cable itself. RG-59U should be used in new installations.

Aside from mechanical defects, the main electrical problems that occur in TV installations concerning transmission lines are the result of excessive voltage standing wave ratios (VSWR). This phenomenon has been extensively researched and described in the literature, and consists, in essence, of reflections of the signal that tend to reinforce each other and cause the appearance of ghosts on the TV screen. The principle of maximum power transfer, one of the basics of all electrical networks, states that maximum power is transferred when the source impedance is exactly the same as the load impedance. In a TV antenna and transmission line system, the characteristic impedance at the antenna, the characteristic impedance of the transmission line and the characteristic impedance of the terminals of the VHF or UHF tuner of the TV set itself must all be properly matched. Earlier in this chapter, we discussed the impedance-matching problem between the antenna and the transmission line at the antenna terminals. If an impedance mismatch exists at the tuner, then some of the RF energy will be reflected back to the antenna, and this will result in a high VSWR.

If you have used a 75-ohm coax cable from the antenna to the TV receiver that has a 300-ohm tuner input terminal, you must use another impedance-matching device, this time of the indoor type, to convert the 75-ohm unbalanced into a 300-ohm balanced impedance. A 300-ohm to 75-ohm resistive matching pad is shown in Figure 11.7 (a). If the resistance values are changed, this same arrangement can be used to match 300 ohms to 50 ohms. One of the drawbacks of a resistive pad, however, is that it will result in some attenuation, due to the losses in the resistance. When the signals from the antenna are sufficiently strong, these losses may not be important and the resistive pad can be used. Commercially available matching pads use broadband resonant networks and operate with considerably less attenuation. Some attenuation, usually stated as insertion loss, will occur with any type of matching pad.

When ghosts or reflections appear on the screen in an installation that uses 300-ohm twin lead as transmission line, one simple way to check that these problems are not due to VSWR is to grasp the transmission line approximately 12 inches away from the termination, and move your hand along the line towards the antenna while

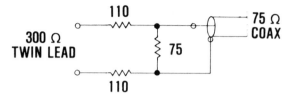

(a) 300 TO 75 Ω MATCHING PAD

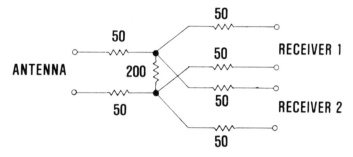

(b) RESISTANCE ANTENNA SPLITTER

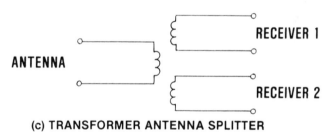

(c) TRANSFORMER ANTENNA SPLITTER

Figure 11.7: Transmission Line Pad and Antenna Splitters

watching the screen. If this seems to have an effect on the
ghost, the problem may be in the transmission line itself.
Some service technicians try to solve this kind of problem
by cutting the transmission line, about six inches at a time,
hoping to reach a resonant point at which they then connect the transmission line to the TV tuner, minimizing
the VSWR problem. Wrapping aluminum foil about eight
inches wide around the transmission line, and moving it
along for best reception, minimum VSWR, is another ap-

proach favored by some service technicians. Occasionally, the appearance of VSWR is caused not by impedance mismatch, but because the reflected signal on a particular channel is so strong that it is picked up by the transmission line itself. Substituting a coax cable for the twin lead will usually eliminate that problem.

GROUND AND LIGHTNING ARRESTORS

A TV antenna mounted on top of a house or on a tall tower can attract lightning. To reduce the danger of damage caused by lightning, commercially available lightning arrestors should be used as part of any TV antenna installation. In some areas, there are local ordinances requiring adequate grounding systems. For practical considerations, however, even a top-notch lightning arrestor system may not prevent damage to the television or other associated equipment in every case. This should not preclude their use, however, because lightning arrestors can be very effective in preventing damage when lightning strikes nearby objects.

Lightning ordinarily is attracted to the highest grounded point, or at least to the highest point that has minimum resistance to ground. When lightning arrestors are used, good grounds are essential for their operation. In many installations that use approved lightning arrestors, the effectiveness of these devices is greatly reduced because the ground path itself contains considerable resistance. If your antenna installation is sufficiently elaborate to use a metal tower and guy wires, or if it is considerably higher than surrounding structures, be especially sure to use a heavy ground cable. Keep the path from antenna to ground as short as possible. Number 10 or Number 8 aluminium wire is recommended. Use at least a six-foot copper ground rod. Drive it as far into the ground as possible, and if possible, moisten the ground around the rod with salt water. The salt will soak into the ground, improving the effectiveness of the grounding system by lowering the effective resistance.

TV DISTRIBUTION SYSTEMS

Many American homes now have two or more TV receivers operating from a single antenna. If we were simply to connect two or three receivers, in parallel, across a single transmission line, we would create an immediate impedance mismatch. In addition, it is likely that one TV set would interfere with the other due to radiation from the local oscillator. A variety of antenna splitters, or antenna couplers, are on the market and should be used whenever more than one TV set is connected to one transmission line/antenna system. Figure 11.7 (b) shows a resistance antenna splitter for two receivers and Figure 11.7 (c) shows a transformer type of antenna splitter. The resistance antenna splitter provides some isolation and a minimum of impedance mismatch but also includes considerable insertion loss or reduction in signal. With a properly designed broadband RF transformer, the impedance mismatch as well as the insertion loss can be greatly reduced, and for that reason we recommend the use of commercially available, transformer-type antenna splitters whenever possible. While only a two-way splitter is shown in Figure 11.7, these devices are also available for up to four TV sets. When more TV receivers than four are to be connected to a single antenna, some amplification is usually required; this leads to the master antenna system illustrated in Figure 11.8.

Master antennas are used in most modern apartment buildings where it would not be practical to have separate antenna installations on the roof for each apartment. The block diagram of Figure 11.8 shows a typical installation. Three separate antennas are shown here, but this depends, of course, on the local conditions. Because so many tenants are served by the antenna installation, every effort is

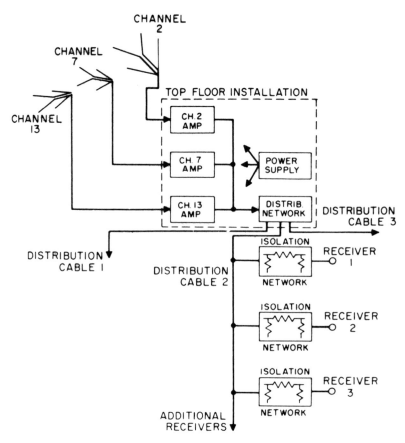

Figure 11.8: Typical Master Antenna System.
Reprinted with permission of Hayden Book Company from *Fundamentals of Television* by Walter H. Buchsbaum.

made to provide the best possible signals from every channel that can be received in that area. The amplifiers, together with the power supply and distribution network, are located as close to the antennas as possible, usually in a weatherproof cabinet on the roof, or somewhere close to the top floor. Master antenna systems require careful design and are usually installed by specialized companies who purchase all of the required amplifiers, splitters, isolation networks, terminations and distribution cables. The individual isolating networks at each apartment are designed to provide at least 10 db or more insertion loss. This can be tolerated because the RF signals have been amplified sufficiently, and this insertion loss is necessary to avoid interference or impedance mismatch for the remainder of the distribution cable.

PAY-TV SYSTEMS

A number of different systems exist throughout the United States in which the viewer pays for seeing special TV programs. In hotels and motels, a master antenna system is augmented by transmitting special programs, usually videotape or film, on some unused channels. In one type of system the viewer phones a special operator who then activates the desired program to that particular room. The nominal charge for this service is then added to the hotel bill. In some other systems, a special unscrambler or code converter has to be activated. The basic system of a master antenna and distribution amplifier remains, with the special channels added on.

The most widely used pay-TV systems for the individual home use a standard UHF channel over which the programs are transmitted in a special format that does not permit the ordinary home receiver to receive them properly. In most of these systems, the horizontal sync pulses and the audio signal are encoded in a special way. Without a decoder, for which rental is charged, the set owner will get only what appears like interference on that channel. A monthly rental for the decoder covers the cost of all programs one wishes to see. The detailed methods of encoding the horizontal sync pulses and the audio vary slightly between different pay-TV systems, but, in each case, the decoder is connected between the antenna and the TV receiver. The decoder switches between normal reception, directly from the antenna, and the processing of the special cable pay-TV signal through the decoder.

In essence, the decoder contains an RF receiver for the particular UHF channel, amplifies and detects the video and audio signal, decodes the sync and audio into a normal composite video and audio signal, and then modulates the RF carrier again so that a normal UHF TV signal can appear at the antenna terminals of the receiver. Such decoders are rented on a monthly basis and remain the property of the pay-TV company. When a defect occurs in the decoder, only the pay-TV company can repair it. Whenever a TV receiver operates satisfactorily on the normal channels but fails to receive the pay-TV signal, we can assume that the decoder is defective.

Another popular form of pay TV is in use in the microwave frequency band. These systems are similar in nature to satellite receiving systems discussed later in this chapter, except that the transmitter is earth bound, and is located within the community.

The systems are characterized by a small dish antenna (one to two feet in diameter), and a microwave receiver that is installed near the customer's TV. Connection of the TV to this system is usually made by a coaxial cable to the TV antenna input. In many cases, the customer must connect his TV antenna to the microwave receiver, and the receiver to the TV. When watching normal local programs, the microwave receiver is off, and automatically connects the antenna "straight through" to the TV. When watching the pay channel, the customer turns his TV to a specified unused channel (usually 3 or 4), and watches the program, which the receiver has converted from microwave frequencies to video and sound, and then remodulates the signals onto the unused channel.

CABLE TV

In a basic cable TV system, illustrated in Figure 11.9, the output of the master antenna, TV channels received locally and programs from local studios are added to the

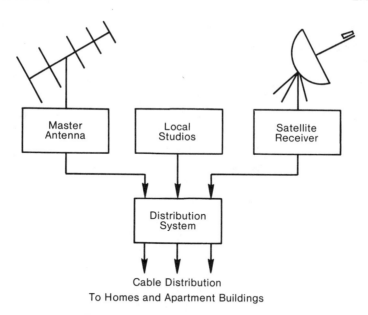

Figure 11.9: Basic Cable TV System

distribution system itself. In addition, cable companies use a satellite receiving setup to bring cable customers a large selection of premium movie, entertainment and sports channels, super-stations and a large variety of programming that is regional or specialized in nature.

A cable distribution system is basically the same as that used in a master antenna system except that the length of the cable runs and the number of tap-offs is usually much larger. A typical master antenna installation in an apartment complex may have several hundred subscribers, while cable TV systems may have a hundred thousand subscribers.

All the channels that can be received by the VHF and UHF tuners can be received by cable subscribers. In most instances the so-called midband and super-band frequencies are supplied on the cable. Some TVs are capable of receiving these "cable only" channels. A listing of these channels and a brief description is found in Chapter 7.

Most cable systems operate on a "tier" system of service. All subscribers receive basic service, which includes all local channels, and some super-stations. Extra services cost more, and are usually scrambled, requiring the cable customer to obtain a decoder to view these "premium" channels. The decoder is provided by the cable company, and thus the company knows which customers to bill for the premium service.

Troubleshooting the TV tuner and IF section in a receiver connected to a cable or master antenna system sometimes presents problems because it is difficult to determine whether the signal is lost in the master antenna, cable system or TV tuner. If local stations can be received, it is easy to determine where the problem is, but in some locations a rabbit's ear antenna simply will not pick up any signals. One way to determine whether the master antenna or cable TV system is at fault makes use of another receiver, known to be good, to determine if the trouble lies in the TV tuner, or in the particular cable TV tap-off. A short circuit in the isolating network shown in Figure 11.8 would show the same symptoms as if all the channel amplifiers or the particular distribution amplifier for this cable were defective. Some service technicians working in areas served by master TV antennas or cable systems carry a small portable TV set just for that purpose. If their TV set receives usable signals at a particular tap-off, the trouble is definitely in the TV set, and if not, the cable TV or master antenna TV company has to be notified that their equipment is defective.

SATELLITE RECEIVING SYSTEMS

A growing phenomenon in this decade is the installation of home satellite receiving systems. These Television Receive Only (TVRO) systems are comprised of an antenna, microwave amplifier, down conversion assembly and receiver. The systems are very popular in rural areas where a large variety of television programming has never been available before. The antennas are aimed at communications satellites, and are tuned directly to programming that was meant primarily for distribution to cable companies. In addition to cable programming, all the television networks are using satellites to distribute programming to their affiliates via satellite. There are also a growing number of programmers who are providing programming meant to be received only by people with TVRO equipment. These TVRO systems differ substantially from the proposed direct broadcast satellite systems that are discussed in a later section.

The number of TVRO earth stations is over three million at this writing, and is growing rapidly at present. The only dark cloud in the skies for this medium is the announcement that many programmers will be scrambling their transmissions, so that only paying subscribers will have access to their programming. On the bright side, those who are scrambling their signals are making provisions for TVRO owners to obtain decoders either through cable company outlets or directly from the program supplier. Further, there are many advertiser-supported programmers who have no desire to scramble, as it would decrease the size of their available audience. If all noncommercial premium channels were to scramble their signals tomorrow, there would still be over 70 available channels, with more being added every day.

Television technicians need to be aware of the mechanics of satellite reception, and typical problems that might be encountered by the servicer. There are complex and highly technical principles and circuitry involved, but there are many problems that may be diagnosed and repaired by the television technician, simply and easily.

To understand how the TVRO system works, we need to look at some basic principles and background on the satellite program distribution system. The development of satellites and the current state of the art were foretold by Arthur C. Clarke, a science fiction writer, over 40 years ago. Clarke realized that the height of a satellite above the earth determined its speed, and he theorized that if a satellite were placed in an orbit at some critical height over the equator, the forward speed of the satellite around the earth would equal the speed of earth rotation. What this means is that the rapidly moving satellite seems to be hanging in a stationary position above the earth, which is rotating below.

A satellite that appears stationary is required to eliminate costly "tracking" hardware that allow an antenna to follow the path of a moving satellite across the sky. In addition with nongeosynchronous satellites, 24-hour operation would not be possible as the moving satellite must spend some time "behind the earth" and inaccessable to a given location.

Television networks and cable programming distribution companies soon embraced this technology as they could transmit their signal from its origination to the satellite. This "uplink" signal is then retransmitted by a very low power transponder in the satellite back to earth. The coverage area provided by these satellites covers the entire U.S., and the satellite radiation pattern (often called its footprint) is strongest at the center of the U.S., and gets weaker at each coast, and in the upper midwest. Cable companies and network affiliates need to put up a receiving system to receive this "downlink" signal.

Even though satellite distribution is expensive, and requires expensive transmission and reception equipment, and renting time on a satellite is very expensive, the whole process is much cheaper than providing and maintaining hundreds of terrestrial microwave links from one community to another so that all distribution points can receive programming from a single source.

There are two frequency bands in use today by satellite programmers; the C band is the older, and is found in a spectrum around 4 gigahertz. The 12-gigahertz Ku band is also being used now that technology has improved the quality of Ku band equipment. Ku band has two advantages over C band; there is less terrestrial interference from competing microwave services, and the smaller wavelength means that antennas can be much smaller and still provide equivalent gain. This notwithstanding, at present, there are very few services on Ku band, and nearly all home systems currently being installed are C band. Persons making new installations should keep compatibility with Ku band in mind, as dual receiving systems are becoming available. In addition, Ku band is the one that will probably be chosen when Direct Broadcast systems are implemented.

There are many aspects of satellite reception that we could discuss, but with limited space, we are going to concentrate on home TVRO receivers and their typical problems. Each satellite has 24 transponders (older models have 12), and TVRO equipment must be able to find a given satellite, distinguish between channels, and reject interference from adjacent satellites and terrestrial interference sources.

A home system consists of six basic components, and each component needs to be compatible with the other for maximum performance from a TVRO installation. The six components are:

1. dish antenna
2. motor-drive assembly (or manual drive assembly)
3. feedhorn assembly
4. low-noise amplifier
5. down converter
6. receiver

We will look at how each item works, and each section will discuss principles and problems that the technician might encounter in an installed system. In addition, maintenance, where required, will be noted to keep the system operating at maximum efficiency. There is not room here to provide a complete discussion of TVRO system installation. There are many entire books written on TVRO installation.

THE SATELLITE DISH

The dish is actually a high-powered reflector of microwave energy. The curve of the dish is a parabola that "captures" microwave energy and reflects it to the focal point of the system. The very small amount of microwave energy that falls upon the surface of the dish is reflected into the feedhorn assembly at the focal point. Figure 11.10 demonstrates this process.

In theory, the basic structure of a dish assembly is not really very sophisticated. In practice, however, there is a lot of support hardware involved. For example, the feedhorn must be centered exactly at the focal point. In addition, some transponders are horizontally polarized, while others are vertically polarized. This requires some method of rotating the pickup element in the feedhorn for proper polarization. Some means must also be provided for aiming the dish directly at the satellite. We will look at problems involving the feedhorn in the next section. This section will concern itself with the dish and tracking assemblies for aiming the dish.

Inexpensive dish systems have a fixed position that is aimed at a given satellite and bolted down. These are, as you might expect, the simplest to maintain. Their major limitation is the maximum reception of only the 24 transponders on that particular satellite. These systems are typically found in commercial service where only one or two transponders are accessed for programming. Once installed, these systems give very little trouble.

Home systems typically have either a manual or motorized method of aiming the dish to move from one satellite to another. This allows a much greater choice of programming, of course. There are special considerations to mounting a dish that is expected to track the belt of

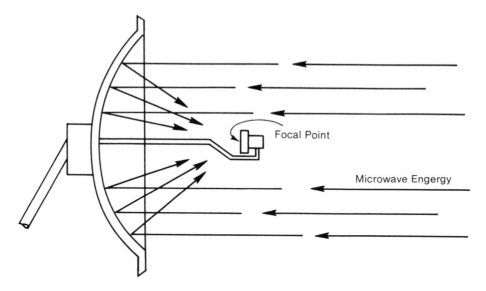

Figure 11.10: Satellite Reception

satellites that ring the equator. There are a few problems the technician should be aware of about dish installation that could affect reception on the dish at a later date.

There are two major styles of dish-mounting assemblies, Az-El mounts and polar mounts. By far, the polar mount is the most popular, as it is the easiest to adjust. It is also probably the most difficult to install. Az-El mounts are named because they are adjusted in two steps, azimuth and elevation. The satellite belt rings the equator, and if they could be seen by an observer in the northern hemisphere, the satellites would appear to be low on the east and west horizons, and higher in altitude as the angle approaches south. Once the dish is mounted on the Az-El mount, it is simply adjusted to the correct azimuth and elevation and tightened down.

A polar mount adjusts azimuth and elevation in one step. As the satellite is moved from east to west (azimuth), the elevation automatically changes in the right proportion. This makes installation more difficult, as the support that holds the dish must remain precisely vertical, thus the requirement that the dish be held down with a substantial amount of concrete. The polar mount is used almost universally in systems that are designed to move from one satellite to another. Installation is tricky, as once a satellite is found, the mount must be adjusted so that the dish will find all the other satellites on precisely the same arc.

Troubleshooting

One common service problem with this system is that the mast may drift off vertical due to changes in the earth. This is more noticeable in systems that use a concrete pad that sits on the surface of the ground. Pole mounts that do not reach below the frost line may also have this problem. Systems that are installed properly, with a large concrete support structure, seldom have trouble. If the mast is not vertical, there will be an inaccuracy in the path of the dish across the sky, and some satellites will not provide the strongest signals.

Dish antennas may be damaged by hail, or other large projectiles that cause dents in the surface. Denting of the dish assembly causes a decrease in the performance of the system due to irregularities in the curve of the parabola.

MANUAL DRIVE SYSTEMS

The manually adjusted polar mount is usually a simple worm gear assembly with a hand crank that turns the gear, which repositions the dish. These systems are relatively unpopular because of the inconvenience of having to go outside to adjust the antenna position and change satellites. They are, however, inexpensive and easy to maintain, with only lubrication of the gear system required in most cases.

Troubleshooting

Service problems are limited to lack of lubrication, binding due to bent or misaligned components (often caused by high-wind load on the dish itself), or other problems causing breakage of mechanical components.

THE MOTOR DRIVE ASSEMBLY

The motorized mount assembly is more complicated, in that a motor and a remote antenna positioner (often called the controller) are required. Since the system is designed to be adjusted from inside, cabling for operating the motor, both control and power, must be provided. In addition, some means of feedback must be provided to let the controller know when the dish has achieved the desired position. The automatic positioner hardware is far more complex and expensive than the manual assembly. See Figure 11.11.

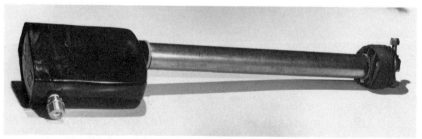

Figure 11.11A: Actuator and Drive Assembly.
Ball-screw linear actuator jack with 18-inch stroke for use with Satscan™ drive controller unit.
Photograph courtesy Channel Master Division of Avnet, Inc.

Figure 11.11B: Antenna Drive.
Channel Master programmable Satscan™ antenna drive is micropro-
cessor controlled and has infrared remote control.
Photograph courtesy Channel Master Division of Avnet, Inc.

Troubleshooting

Service problems include all of the problems that may
afflict a manually operated system, and also problems related with the feedback sensors inside the motorized dish
assembly. Also, open cables, bad connections, and other
problems are occasionally found. Though many antenna
positioners are electronic, they occasionally develop
problems. There is often a thermal cutout on the power

supply to prevent either the power supply or dish actuator motor from overheating. Fuse failures can be caused by internal shorts in the controller, or by binding or freeze-up of the actuator tubes.

Another problem that can occur with automatic positioners is the failure of automatic limit switches or devices. The motorized assembly usually contains limit switches that are designed to shut off the motor when either end of the arc is reached. A failure in these switches can cause much physical damage to the system, even damage to the dish itself if it happens to come into contact with the ground or other obstacles. Sluggish motor movement can be caused by dirty actuator tubes, or improper mounting angle of the actuator. A rarer occurrence in already-existing installations is the use of inadequate wire guage for the length of run. This problem might appear in winter, when the assembly is generally harder to move. Motor movement in only one direction can be caused by improper end limit setting, or controller electronics failure.

If the motor oscillates, check the feedback or gain adjustment in the controller unit.

If the satellite positioning readout is incorrect, check that all clamps and other parts are where they belong. Also check the feedback circuit components at the dish site for looseness or defects. In magnetic switch feedback systems, check for proper rotation of the magnets. Another problem might be a bad battery in the controller memory circuit.

THE FEEDHORN ASSEMBLY

At the focal point of the dish, an antenna system is required to collect the signal reflected there from the dish. The feedhorn serves this function, and also separates vertical and horizontal polarized transponders. Figure 11.12 contains a photo of a feedhorn. To conserve spectrum,

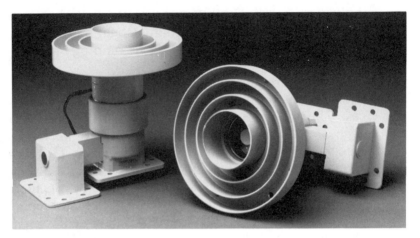

Figure 11.12:   Feedhorn Assembly.
Sidewinder™ feedhorn assembly with solid-state polarity switching
and skew-adjustment from Chaparral Communications.
Photograph courtesy of Chaparral Communications Corp.; San Jose,
CA.

twelve channels are horizontally polarized, while the other
twelve are polarized vertically. On some satellites, the
even channels are horizontal, while the odd transponders
are vertical. On other satellites, the opposite configuration
is found.

The feedhorn selects horizontal or vertical polarization by one of three methods. The first method, and by
far the most popular, is by a small motor that mechanically rotates the small hook-shaped probe located in the
mouth of the feedhorn. This motor is often called the
Polarotor. Though Polarotor is a trade name belonging to
Chaparral Communications, the term is often used by
technicians throughout the industry to describe the motor
assembly.

The second method for changing polarity is by electronically rotating the signal using an electromagnetic ferrite device. This method is less efficient, and has some
loss, but has the advantage of being all solid state, and
not requiring another motor assembly in the system.

The third method, used by relatively few manufacturers is to use dual probes, and switch electronically between them. There are also some efficiency compromises with this setup, and it requires a dual cable run (one for each polarity), but the major advantage with this system is that it is possible for a multiple receiver system to view any transponder, with any other transponder accessible simultaneously available to another receiver. With either of the other systems, multiple receivers are limited to reception of odd or even transponders only.

The feedhorn must be properly positioned at the focal point of the dish parabola. There are two basic styles of feedhorn mount. The first is a single pole mounted at the center of the dish, with the feedhorn at the end. This support section is often called a "button hook" mount. The other style is a three- or four-support rod assembly that holds the feedhorn at the focal point. See Figure 11.13

Figure 11.13A: Buttonhook and Support-Rod Feed Mounts.
Channel Master five-foot portable mesh dish antenna with button hook style LNA mount.
Photograph courtesy Channel Master Division of Avnet, Inc.

Figure 11.13B: Channel Master six-foot fiberglass dish with quad-rapod LNA mount.
Photograph courtesy Channel Master Division of Avnet, Inc.

for examples of both styles. The support structure needs to be installed at the precise focal point, or snowy, "sparkly" pictures will result. The feedhorn must be centered, and on the same plane as the dish. It is recommended that guy wires be attached to buttonhook mounts for greatest stability.

Troubleshooting

Problems with the feedhorn assembly usually revolve around the polarization control motor, or problems with the probe assembly itself. If only one polarization is received clearly, check for frozen motor parts, an open motor, power supply or cabling. Poor performance on one polarity can be caused by improper skew settings on the receiver. The receiver unit has been assigned to control the servo units on motorized control units. Skew is a fine tuning adjustment that adjusts the position of the probe in small steps for precise positioning.

Hum bars can be caused by a polarization control that continues to run against its end stop, or by defects in the power supply or improper gauge of control wires.

Poor performance or a gradual decline in performance of the system might be caused by a shifting of the feedhorn from the exact focal point. Foreign matter such as spider webs or moisture in the waveguide can cause degradation of the video. Install a weather cover to prevent this problem from reoccurring. Moisture may be found between the feedhorn and LNA. Be sure there is a gasket between the units, and the flange is clean and dry when they are reinstalled, and be sure all bolts are fastened securely to prevent degradation of waveguide performance in this critical area.

THE LNA

At the back of the feedhorn, the low noise amplifier (LNA) can be found. See Figure 11.14. The LNA is primarily a preamplifier that amplifies the signal that the feedhorn is delivering. Though there are two specifications of importance for choosing an LNA, the one of most importance is the noise temperature. LNA assemblies can be purchased with noise temperatures in the range of 60 to 120 degrees Kelvin. The 60k units are the most expensive, and have the best performance. The advantage of a lower noise

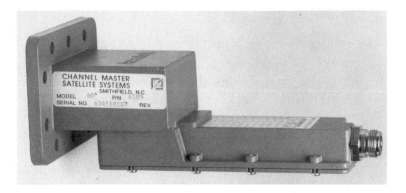

Figure 11.14: An 80-degree LNA assembly.
Photograph courtesy Channel Master Division of Avnet, Inc.

temperature is that the system will deliver a clearer picture for a given size dish. There are obviously financial
and aesthetic tradeoffs to be made in that spending more
on a lower noise temperature LNA will reduce the size,
expense and performance requirements of the dish. As a
practical matter, 100k LNA assemblies are adequate with
eight foot dishes in the central U.S. At the coasts, and in
the northern U.S., where the satellite footprint is weaker,
it is more common to find 80k, or even 60k units on eight-
foot dishes.

Troubleshooting

Many problems with the LNA assembly are related to bad
connections and cabling problems. Be sure to check the
N connectors thoroughly. Basically LNA assemblies are
not field serviceable, so double-check connections first.
Typical LNA units draw about 100 ma, so a quick current
check might be performed. If current draw is about normal, you can probably assume the LNA is OK, and look
for problems in the feedhorn or down converter. Check
with the manufacturer's specifications of the LNA for exact current requirements if in doubt.

THE DOWN CONVERTER

In many systems, the LNA is physically attached to the down converter assembly, as these two units often work together. Even though the down converter is mounted at the LNA, it is actually part of the receiver. Its purpose is to change the operating frequency of 4 Ghz to a much lower IF, as low-loss transmission line for 4 Ghz is very expensive. There are two major types of down converter units available, the single conversion unit, and the block conversion unit. See Figure 11.15. There are other variations that are also found, as well.

The single-conversion unit has been around the longest. The standard down converter is a single-conversion mixer that generates an IF frequency of 70 Mhz, which is transmitted by coax to the receiver unit. This eliminates long runs of 4 Ghz signals. The major disadvantage of a single conversion down converter is that it is impossible to view different transponders on the same satellite with different receivers, as only one transponder frequency is being converted to 70 Mhz at a time.

The block down converter, on the other hand, translates the entire satellite transponder bandwidth, thus allowing multiple receivers to be tuned to any given vertical or horizontal transponder. The block down converter (BDC) converts the range of transponder frequencies from 4 Ghz to either approximately 400-Mhz or 900-Mhz frequencies, depending upon the brand.

The BDC receiver then selects from the desired transponder. The only problem with this setup is that if the polarotor is tuned to the vertically polarized transponders, all receivers must receive only vertically polarized stations. This lets any receiver in the system tune either the even or odd transponders only.

One company overcomes this problem by using two pickups, one horizontal and one vertical. A special dual coaxial cable carries both vertical and horizontal block down converted signals to the receivers in the system,

Figure 11.15: A 70-MHz down converter assembly.
Photograph courtesy Channel Master Division of Avnet, Inc.

and allows any receiver to view any transponder, regard-less of polarity. The BDC, when combined and sold with an LNA assembly, is often called an LNB unit.

Troubleshooting

As the down converter is typically considered to be part of the receiver, troubleshooting these assemblies is cov-ered under receivers.

THE RECEIVER

The receiver units vary in complexity from simple con-tinuous-tuning models to microprocessor-controlled dig-ital tuning with automatic selection of transponder polarity, audio frequency subcarrier, stereo or mono selection, pa-rental lockout on certain transponders and many other features. Many later-model receivers have motor-drive

Figure 11.16: A microprocessor-based, remote control satellite receiver with built-in actuator electronics.
Photograph courtesy of Chaparral Communications Corp.; San Jose, CA.

control circuitry built in, so that a single remote control unit, for example, can be used to select the satellite and tune transponders. See Figure 11.16.

Nearly all receivers generate NTSC composite video, and feed it to an RF modulator for display on the television channel 3 or 4. Televisions with monitor inputs can be driven directly from the video output jack on most satellite receivers. Another output that is found on the back of most receivers is a baseband output. This jack is connected to descramblers and other accessories that need the presence of the entire bandwidth of the transponder selected, rather than filtered video such as is found on the video output jack.

Many receivers also have a 70-Mhz input and output pair that are normally connected "straight through." If terrestrial interference is a problem, open the connections between the 70-Mhz jacks, and install a TI filter in the line.

The audio systems on satellite receivers range from simple monophonic audio that modulates the internal RF modulator for distribution to the TV set to dual channel stereo receivers. Satellite transponders have the ability to carry audio on several different subcarriers. The two most commonly used carriers are 6.2 and 6.8 Mhz. This necessitates a tunable audio receiver. Most transponders use 6.8 Mhz, but enough use 6.2 Mhz to make things difficult.

Stereo reception is implemented in several ways, though most receivers that are stereo equipped have only two formats. There are left and right audio jacks at the receiver rear panel for driving the auxiliary input of a stereo system. Discrete stereo reception is received by tuning one audio subcarrier control to the left channel subcarrier and tuning the other to the right channel subcarrier. Usually, on discrete stereo stations, 6.2 Mhz is left channel and 6.8 Mhz is right channel.

Matrix stereo is tuned in a similar manner, but one transponder contains a L + R signal, while the other contains a L − R signal. The matrix circuitry in the receiver then decodes the two signals, and delivers stereo to the audio jacks. The system is similar to the matrix found in FM and MTS stereo systems in the broadcast industry.

Troubleshooting

This section is not meant to be a complete guide to bench service of satellite receiver units, as there are many complex circuits involved. If you want to begin repairing satellite receiver units, I recommend *Troubleshooting & Repairing Satellite TV Systems* by Richard Maddox, copyright 1985, by Tab Books.

Commonly found field serviceable problems in the receiver and down converter can be traced to power supply troubles in many cases. The receiver also supplies power to the polarotor in many systems. Simple checks of the system you can make are the fuses, or for B+ on filter capacitors in the unit. Inspect for opens or shorts in the assembly.

DIRECT BROADCAST SATELLITE

The direct broadcast satellite system is not the same system that we discussed under home satellite reception systems. While the home TVRO systems were designed to operate on the C band, and receive programming meant for cable and commercial subscribers, the DBS system was designed with the home TVRO system in mind. Essentially, DBS is oriented toward 12-Ghz service so that homeowners can be supplied signal with very small dishes. It is envisioned to be a pay service, with scrambled programming.

The future of DBS service is uncertain at this time with the proliferation of C band services that are unscrambled. Three major company efforts at developing a DBS market have ended in bankruptcy, and at present, there are no such systems in operation on 12 Ghz. DBS is also essentially being implemented on C band with the arrival of a very few broadcasters who are providing commercially supported and noncommercial scrambled programming for the TVRO owner. At present, most of these systems are in operation for only a few hours a day.

With the high interest in C band, and a large user base, DBS will have to wait until premium channel providers scramble their signals, thus making a pay service competitive with the current cable pay services. The advent of dual-band C and Ku receivers will also help the DBS market.

Principles and equipment for DBS are similar to C band, with the exception of the higher frequencies involved. The major advantage of Ku band, especially in urban areas is the lack of telephone transmission interference. The major competitor to DBS in urban areas is the large user base of cable system companies. A DBS service must be as versatile as cable TV before a large urban user base can be expected.

COMMON SCRAMBLING SYSTEMS

As most companies who provide premium programming
for cable services are now scrambling, the TV technician
will be running into satellite TV decoders. There are currently two major systems in use. The most commonly
found unit is the Orion descrambler, which is rented or
purchased from a programming supplier. This relatively
simple decoder unit is in use on many home TVRO-ori-
ented broadcasts, and is also used for DBS service.

As the industry is maturing, premium programmers
who want to provide service to home TVRO stations without alienating their cable company sponsors realized that
TVRO owners would not buy several different decoders,
and have one for each service. As a result, a standard
decoder system is developing.

The VideoCipher by M/A Com Corporation is currently being used by HBO, and several other cable companies are either using or testing it with their premium
channel programming. The unique aspect of these decoders is that they are addressable individually by the uplink
signal, and will allow unscrambling of signals on a subscription basis for many services simultaneously. They
have the ability to selectively maintain a scrambled picture for regions that might have a special events blackout,
such as a local football game. The VideoCipher also allows
pay per view descrambling of only selected events, so a
TVRO owner does not have to pay for a month of unscrambled service, should he desire to only view a single
program, or only a few per month.

The system is very sophisticated, and operates by
modifying the synchronization circuitry. The sound channels (it allows stereo broadcasts) are digitally encoded and
transmitted during the horizontal retrace intervals, so normal sound channels are available for simultaneous transmission of alternate sound programming.

In practice, a TVRO owner will purchase a decoder

from the nearest cable company, a satellite equipment retailer or from the premium programming provider directly. He will provide all the subscription services he desires to receive with the correct address of his decoder unit. Upon payment of the monthly fee, his descrambler will be activated from the uplink signal, thus allowing him to receive unscrambled programming. Should he wish to discontinue service, his decoder address is removed from the uplink signal, and the VideoCipher fails to descramble. Special programming such as pay per view movies and sporting events can be ordered in a similar manner, and charged to a special account or to a major credit card.

In principle, the system is efficient, secure, and usable by many services simultaneously. Testing, so far, has found there are problems with the installation of the units on certain receivers. Some receivers do not provide a wide-enough bandpass for the addressing information to reach the descrambler, and since the descrambler cannot receive its own address, it fails to descramble the picture.

Another problem that has occurred is that many receiver units do not have the appropriate connections to accept the descrambler. The descrambler must be connected to a baseband output; a video output connection will not suffice. Skeptics argue that the system will work adequately with only the very small audience of TVRO owners currently in place, however they feel the system will bog down as millions of DBS 12-Ghz systems are installed, and the uplink signals must transmit many addresses. Even when sending hundreds of addresses per minute, addressing millions of descramblers will take some time, and as the system bogs down, scramblers will fail to keep the programming unscrambled. (This is not normally a problem unless the VideoCipher loses power, and must wait to be addressed again after power is restored.)

The scrambling situation will remain, and become a part of satellite TV. It must be looked upon as a new market for programming, as TVRO owners rightfully should pay for the programming they receive, if it is not commercially supported.

TV INSTALLATION TECHNIQUE

A complete TV installation includes the selection and installation of the antenna, the transmission line and the final installation of the TV receiver. Detailed antenna installation and selection procedures could be the subject of an entire book, but the following paragraphs will prove helpful.

SELECTING THE ANTENNA

The simplest way to choose an antenna is to look at the antenna used in the immediate vicinity of your installation. If they are all 14-element log periodic antennas, all pointing in the same direction, the chances are good that this type of antenna is best suited for this location. In some instances you are replacing a previous antenna and can get some guidance from the set owner as to how his reception has been. Consider the possibility, however, that new TV channels, particularly in the UHF band, may have made their appearance, and since the old antenna could not receive them, the set owner may not be aware of their existence. When installing an antenna in a completely new TV location, many service organizations install intermediate range antennas temporarily until they can determine what the local signals are like. It is not a good idea to install a fringe area antenna in what is really a local or metropolitan area. If the distance from the transmitter is anywhere between 20 and 40 miles, and if there are no obstructing mountains or other structures between the sight and the transmitter, an intermediate type of antenna should be satisfactory.

The height of the antenna deserves some consideration. The higher the antenna has to be, the more complex and expensive the installation. One of the least complex installations is the one where the antenna can be located in the attic. This eliminates the purchase of a sturdy mast, mounting hardware for it, corrosion by weather and other problems. Unfortunately, some roofs are covered with sheet metal that makes the antenna ineffective.

The weaker the signal, the higher the antenna may have to be. This is particularly true of fringe area installations. In some areas antennas are mounted on towers on nearby hills with transmission lines as long as a mile or more. Preamplifiers are sometimes required, increasing the cost and complexity of the installation even more. Remember that stacking antennas increases the gain but not in a linear fashion. An array of two identical antennas does not double the signal strength, nor do four antennas quadruple the signal strength. As more and more elements are added, the improvement becomes less.

When two or more stations are located in different directions from the site of the new installation, an antenna rotator may be necessary. Space in this book does not permit us to give detailed instructions on installation and servicing of antenna rotators, but the manufacturers' data provided with each unit contains this information.

One of the best sources for suggestions as to the type of antenna most suitable to a specific location would be your local electronics distributor, because he knows what kind of antennas are usually bought.

TRANSMISSION LINE INSTALLATION

The most widely used and least expensive TV transmission line is the flat, ribbon-like, 300-ohm twin lead. This type of transmission line works very well, particularly in the absence of strong interference. To reduce or minimize some outside interference many technicians tend to twist the 300-ohm transmission line between stand-offs. If the interference is serious, a coaxial cable will have to be used. In installing 300-ohm twin lead, it is important that the transmission line be supported at 6- to 10-foot intervals. Specially insulated twin lead stand-offs are available from local electronic distributors to keep the twin lead securely in place. Twin lead should not be taped to the metal mast. Before the transmission line enters the house, it should form a "drip loop" so that rainwater will run down and drip off rather than flow along the twin lead into the opening. Inside the house the transmission line can be fastened against wood or plaster but should not be taped or screwed against metal surfaces. The path from the antenna to the TV set location should be carefully chosen to keep the transmission line as short as possible and to keep the number of bends and twists to a minimum.

The installation of coax cable should follow the same guidelines as for twin lead, except that it is possible to bring coax cable in direct contact with metal surfaces and the exterior walls and mouldings. In connecting to the antenna, be sure to provide the required impedance matching devices as described earlier in this chapter.

LOCATION IN THE HOME

Most set owners already know where they want to locate the TV receiver. The service technician, however, has to point out certain limitations. It is very poor practice to locate the TV receiver next to an active radiator or air-conditioner. A window sill is also a poor location for a TV receiver. In general, TV receivers should be located near an AC outlet and not too far from a wall. In viewing TV, a completely darkened room will result, in most cases, in eyestrain. When a room contains colored lights, there will be a tendency to misadjust the color controls on a color TV receiver, resulting in wrong colors. The ideal location for a TV set is in a corner, providing the best viewing area for the largest number of people, and with a low-level light on top of or behind the TV receiver.

Neither extreme brightness nor total darkness is recommended for good TV viewing. Some common-sense considerations should also be used in locating the TV set. It
should not be located where people can trip over the
power cord or over the transmission line, or where people
can easily bump into the TV set. A TV set should never
be pushed up against drapes or pillows which would ham-
per the flow of cooling air at the rear of the cabinet. For
that same reason, locating it above a radiator or other
source of heat is also not recommended.

OPERATING TESTS

Before instructing the owner in the use of the set, the
service technician should make sure that good pictures
are received on all channels, that all the front panel controls work properly, that the screen is clean and that nearby
lights do not cast a strong reflection on the screen itself.
Be sure to switch to all channels and check that the color
killer works properly on monochrome as well as on color.
Only when the service technician is sure that the TV receiver functions reliably on all channels should the owner
be notified that the installation is ready.

INSTRUCTING THE OWNER

The ultimate aim of any TV installation is to satisfy the
customer. Instructing the owner and his family is as important as the purely technical parts of the installation.
Sometimes a considerable amount of tact and courtesy is
required to avoid offending or slighting the customer. Any
effort expended in this final step of any good installation
will be returned many times in future business relations.
Here are some of the points that experienced service technicians make when instructing the owner:

1. Explain the different sets of controls. Only the front
   panel controls should be used by the customer. Point

out and explain the function of each of the front panel controls.

2. Emphasize that any of the secondary or tertiary controls should be adjusted only by the service technician and that some of them require the use of special test equipment. Point out that misadjustment of these controls may require a service call and repeat that such service calls cannot be made without an extra charge because they are not covered by the service warranty.

3. Demonstrate the operation of the ON/OFF switch, volume control and all other front panel controls. Turn the receiver off and ask the customer to tune in all available channels under your supervision.

4. Make a special effort to explain the chroma (intensity) control and the tint control. Make sure the customer also understands the automatic features of the receiver.

5. After the explanation is completed, ask members of the customer's family to tune in every station while you are there, point out mistakes and show the correct setting for each control. Before leaving, be sure to ask if there are any questions. Leaving the company's or your own card completes the installation.

CHAPTER 12

TV ACCESSORY PROBLEMS

Over fifty million TV sets are in homes all over the country, and many of them are used for more than receiving TV broadcasts. This chapter deals with these special applications of the TV receiver. These applications invariably involve some accessory, such as video recorders, TV games or personal computers. In other words, the TV receiver is connected to another device and utilized as a monitor or computer CRT display. It may not be obvious why there should be any problem in such applications, and, in general, most TV receivers work quite satisfactorily with all accessories. When problems arise, however, it is often difficult to determine whether the defect is in the TV set or in the accessory.

All commercial video cassette recorders (VCR) or video disc players, as well as TV games and personal computers, can be connected to any monochrome or TV receiver through the antenna terminals. This means that these devices must provide a standard TV signal, just like that transmitted from a TV station. If the TV receiver works correctly with a signal from a TV station, there appears to be no reason why it should not work correctly with an identical signal originating in the device connected only a few feet away. It doesn't always work out, however.

VIDEO CASSETTE RECORDER CONNECTION

The increasing popularity of videocassette recorders (VCR) has also brought new problems to the TV set owner. There are three cassette formats to choose from, VHS, Beta and 8mm. VHS is the most popular, while Beta has a smaller cassette, and is generally thought to have slightly better picture quality. The 8mm format was designed for portable camera-recorder combinations, though there are VHS and Beta cam-corders available as well. Fortunately for the TV set owner, VCR hookup is identical for each of the three VCR types. Modern VCRs have all the proper switching required to connect to any TV set; however, the owner must learn how to use each of the controls on the VCR, in addition to remembering those of the color TV receiver. When setting the VCR timer to record a program at a certain time, we have to set the antenna switch so that the signal will be received by the VCR instead of going directly to the TV set. It is also essential that the desired channel be correctly tuned in on the VCR. This means that, some time before the actual recording, both the VCR and the TV set must be turned on and the VCR tuned to the desired station, while we check the picture and sound on the TV set.

In addition to these operational problems, malfunctions and defects can occur in the video cassette recorder as well as in the TV set, and it is sometimes difficult to decide just where the problem is. Figure 12.1 shows a block diagram of the VCR connection. Note that in the switch position illustrated, the VCR receives the selected station from the antenna. The transmitted signal passes through a tuner and IF amplifier and then goes to the video recorder/playback section. In order to monitor what is being recorded, the TV tuner must receive the composite video signal, together with the audio signal, in the standard broadcast format. This is accomplished via the RF modulator which operates on an unused channel. There is an internal switch that selects one of two possible frequencies. In other words, the tuner in the VCR may be set to channel 73 while the tuner in the TV set selects either channel 3 or 4. When the VCR is not in use, the antenna switch is connected in such a way that the signals from the antenna pass directly to the tuner in the TV set.

The third position of the switch passes the TV signals through a 1:2 splitter so that the videocassette recorder can receive one channel while the TV set can receive, independently, any other channel. Of course, when the TV set is connected to the antenna directly, or though the coupler, the RF modulator should be shut down to avoid radiating any potential interfering signal into the TV set tuner.

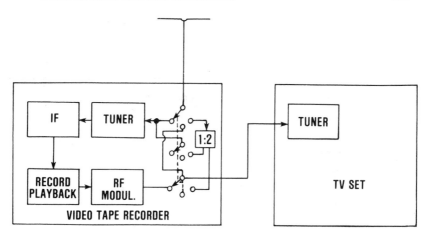

Figure 12.1: Videocassette Recorder Connection

Figure 12.2 shows a block diagram of the functions generally provided in the RF modulator itself. In most TV accessory devices, the RF oscillator can be switched to operate either on channel 3 or 4, although in some, other VHF channels can be selected. Some VCRs do not use RF oscillators but obtain the desired RF frequency by multiplication from a crystal-controlled source, such as a 4.5-MHz or a 3.58-MHz oscillator.

Note that the audio signal goes to a 4.5-MHz FM modulator that assures that the audio signal will be 4.5 MHz above the RF carrier, as required for standard TV broadcast reception. Sync, video and color information are applied to the color modulator, which contains a 3.58-MHz crystal-controlled oscillator and a phase-amplitude modulator to generate the color subcarrier. This subcarrier, together with the composite video signal, the Y or brightness signal in color transmission, is applied to the RF modulator itself, which generates the RF transmission signal. As was explained in Chapter 2, one part of the double sideband that results from modulating the RF carrier is suppressed and this function is performed in the output filter.

Although we have shown the antenna switch of Fig-

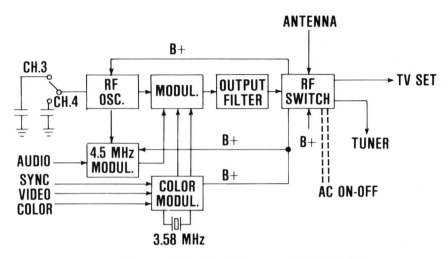

Figure 12.2: Block Diagram of RF Modulator

ure 12.1 to be a simple three-position switch, the actual functions performed by the RF switch module of Figure 12.2 are more complex. When the VCR is set to record, a portion of the antenna signal must go to its internal tuner. When the VCR is set for playback or when the TV set is used to monitor the recording, the antenna must be connected to the internal tuner but the output of the RF modulator must be connected to the TV set. On the other hand, when the VCR is used for recording and the TV set is used for viewing an off-the-air broadcast, the RF switch must connect the TV set as well as the internal tuner to the antenna and must remove B+ power from the RF oscillator, the 4.5-MHz modulator and the color modulator. This assures that no interfering signals will reach the TV set tuner.

The block diagram of the RF modulator shown in Figure 12.2 is essentially the same for all TV accessories. Only the RF switch has different functions, because TV games and personal computers don't need a signal from the antenna. For TV games, the RF switch will also contain the AC ON/OFF switch. In some TV games, the AC

ON/OFF switch drives a relay that automatically connects the antenna leads directly to the TV set whenever power is turned off.

TYPICAL VIDEOCASSETTE RECORDER CONNECTION PROBLEMS

The most obvious way of determining whether a defect is located in the TV set or in the VCR is to operate the TV set from an "off-the-air" station and compare the results with the results obtained when the VCR is in the monitor or playback mode. In many instances, this will show where the defect lies. Unfortunately, however, the VCR RF output is always on an unused TV channel. This means that we have no way of evaluating the performance of the TV set on that particular channel.

A quick way to make sure that the channel from the VCR RF modulator is working correctly would be to tune the TV receiver to that channel and then adjust the fine tuning, or automatic fine tuning (AFT) voltage, over its entire range to see which point gives best reception of that channel. If the best reception is still not very good, the fault can be either in the circuits of the RF modulator, illustrated in Figure 12.2, or in the RF alignment of the TV tuner for the particular channel transmitted by the RF modulator. The best solution to this problem is to use a TV sweep generator and oscilloscope to align the TV tuner and RF circuits of the TV set, as described in Chapter 7. Once we are certain that the TV set is properly aligned for the channel on which the RF modulator transmits, we can begin to troubleshoot the RF modulator itself.

Even if the RF modulator operates correctly, troubles in other parts of the VCR may prevent you from receiving a good picture on the TV set. Assume, for example, that the tuner on the VCR is noisy or misaligned. The IF section may be misadjusted and not have sufficient gain. In addition to these electronic troubles, the tape itself, the tape transport, and the recording and playback mechanism may all have defects that prevent you from getting a good picture.

One of the major VCR connection problems occurs for those TV set owners who are also cable TV subscribers. Even if you have a cable-ready TV and cable-ready VCR, not all cable companies have equipment that makes VCR hookup easy. The problem is magnified when premium movie channels are also part of the system. Figure 12.3 demonstrates three possible connection techniques. Figure 12.3A is the simplest method, and is probably the method used by most cable companies if you let them install the system. Its major advantage is that all channels, including premium channels, may be recorded or viewed. The major disadvantage of this hookup is that the ability to watch one channel while recording another is lost. Both the recorder and TV must be set to the cable box output channel at all times.

Figure 12.3B demonstrates a more versatile hookup, but requires some extra hardware. A two-way splitter is installed in the cable line, which allows signals to travel to an A–B switch to select either the VCR or TV. The major advantage of this hookup is that the ability to record one channel, even if it is a premium channel, while watching another is allowed in most cases. This method works

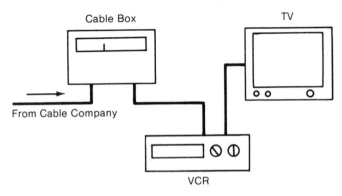

Figure 12.3A: Cable-VCR Hookups

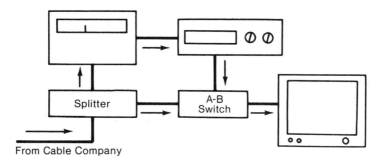

Figure 12.3B

especially well if your TV set contains a cable-ready tuner.
If your TV is not so equipped, you will only be able to
watch cable channels 2 through 13 directly, though any
cable channel may be viewed while watching through the
VCR tuner. Also, since the descrambler is in the VCR line,
you must view premium channels through the VCR line.
The major disadvantage of this method of connection is
that when you use the timer to record cable channels, you
lose the versatility of being able to record more than one
channel without resetting the cable box. This means that
all programs recorded while you are away must be on the
same cable channel.

Figure 12.3C demonstrates the most versatile hookup,
but requires both a cable-ready VCR and cable-ready TV.
The major advantage of this hookup is that you may watch
any channel while recording any other channel, and timer
recording can occur on multiple channels. The major disadvantage of this hookup is that premium channels may
not be available due to the requirement of an in-line descrambler.

Another solution, though more expensive, is to purchase a video switching unit. These units range in price
from $25.00 to well over $100.00, and allow you to select
many options for VCR, cable, video disk, TV game, computer and so on. A video switcher can even let you record
the output of your computer onto video tape. If you are
using your VCR to make home movies, your home com-

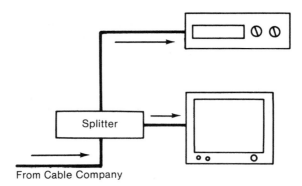

From Cable Company

Figure 12.3C

puter can become an inexpensive video titler, help you make animated graphics or do other special effects. There are so many types of switching units, and so many different combinations, there is not room here to discuss the possible connections.

TYPICAL TV GAME CONNECTION PROBLEMS

As illustrated in the block diagram of Figure 12.3, the antenna switch for a TV game connection to the TV set is much simpler than that of a videocassette recorder. In many instances when the TV game is turned on, the antenna is automatically disconnected and the TV set is connected to the RF modulator. In most respects the RF modulator shown in Figure 12.2 will be identical to that used in TV games. Some of the connections, such as an audio input, may not be used and the game may not provide color, but the general principles are the same. The antenna switch is always linked with the game power switch, and the RF modulator is therefore shut off whenever the TV set receives off the-air broadcasts. Like the VCR, however, the TV game also transmits the RF-modulated output on an unused TV channel. The problem of determining whether the modulator or the tuner in the TV set is defective and the test method to use are the same as described above.

When the TV game pattern appears on the TV screen, we know that the TV tuner and the entire set operate correctly. If any of the TV game controls fail to move a ball, bat, player, rocketship or other image, the defect must clearly be in the TV game, and, most likely, in the control or game logic portion. As long as audio and video are received at the TV set, we know that, from the RF modulator on, everything else works correctly.

TV games generally use straight-line graphics and black and white or solid color images. This means that the video signals will have sharp, pulse-like shapes. Good resolution, or maximum video bandwidth, is essential. Many TV receivers do not provide the full 3.8 or 4 MHz of video bandwidth and, in addition, do not provide good vertical and horizontal linearity. These shortcomings are not as apparent on scenes, faces or moving images when viewing the usual TV programs. When the pattern of a TV game remains fixed on the screen, however, we become very sensitive to the lack of sharp edges, straight lines and overall picture quality. Invariably, the problem is not in the TV game but in the alignment of the TV set itself. The only remedy is an overall alignment of the tuner and IF section as described in Chapter 7, adjustment of the synchronizing and deflection circuits of Chapter 8, and the alignment of the monochrome and color circuits described in Chapter 9. This particular problem, poor frequency response of the TV set, is apparently one of the most frequent complaints when a TV game is connected to the set. Although it is possible that the video section of the TV game itself has poor frequency response, the most probable reason is still the alignment of the TV set.

TYPICAL PERSONAL COMPUTER
CONNECTION PROBLEMS

When we compare Figure 12.4, which shows TV game connections, to Figure 12.5, which shows a personal computer connection to the TV set, we can see that the antenna

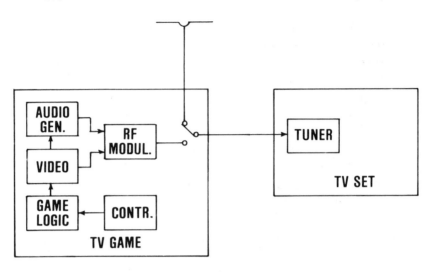

Figure 12.4: TV Game Connection

switch and RF modulator portions appear identical. The personal computer connection, however, differs from the game connection in one respect. When the antenna switch connects the TV set tuner directly to the antenna, the AC power for the personal computer cannot be shut off, as was possible for a TV game. A personal computer may be operated without connection to a TV set by using a printer or teletype terminal, and only the RF modulator itself should be shut off. In the RF modulator block diagram of Figure 12.2, you will note that B + is connected to the RF oscillator, 4.5-MHz modulator, and the color modulator. The dotted lines indicate that AC power to the modulator is disconnected when the antenna is connected directly to the TV set. When the modulator is selected, the power is automatically supplied to the modulator circuitry.

As discussed in the section on TV games, we know that the RF modulator and the TV set work correctly when a computer display appears on the screen. If keyboard entries do not result in the desired display, the defect is most likely in the keyboard or the computer portions, but the RF modulator is not at fault. The method presented

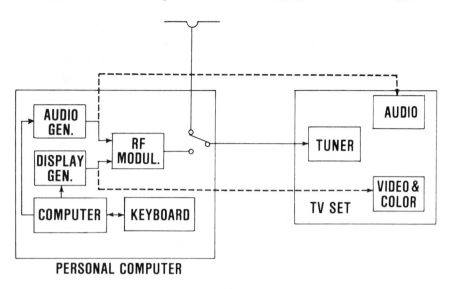

Figure 12.5: Personal Computer Connection

above for the VCR connection also applies to the alignment of the RF modulator oscillator and the corresponding channel on the TV set tuner. Aligning the TV tuner and RF circuits, as described in Chapter 7, will verify that the TV set operates correctly, and then the problem is probably in the RF modulator that is part of the personal computer.

The images generated by a computer are similar to those provided by TV games. The personal computer can be used for TV games, but alphanumerical text is its basic output. Text invariably consists of a two-level, black and white video signal with sharp edges, requiring maximum bandwidth as well as good horizontal and vertical linearity. If the edges of the letters or numerals appear fuzzy or washed out, the bandwidth of the TV receiver is most probably insufficient. Alignment of the IF video and color circuits, as described in Chapters 7 and 9, may improve this condition. If the letters appear bent, bowed or otherwise distorted, the vertical and horizontal deflection circuits of the TV set usually are at fault.

When a comparison is made between a computer CRT display and a standard broadcast TV receiver, the CRT display quality is usually superior to that of the TV set. The computer CRT display does not contain a TV tuner, IF, detector and video amplifier, and is designed for displaying text. In addition, the vertical and horizontal deflection circuits in the CRT displays are synchronized directly from the computer signals and do not require all the steps of sync clipping and separation. A properly aligned monochrome or color TV set should, however, be quite satisfactory for displays generated by a personal computer, as long as text displays do not exceed 64 characters per line.

CHAPTER 13

TROUBLESHOOTING MONOCHROME DEFECTS

Chapter 1 deals briefly with those monochrome defects that can be diagnosed using only the TV screen, the speaker and the front panel and secondary controls. We presented a block diagram in that chapter and explained the key functions of each block. Subsequent chapters have gone through more detailed circuit description and explained how a TV receiver, a monitor and a CRT computer display work.

This chapter covers specific troubleshooting methods and begins with an overall, ten-step troubleshooting procedure that will help you do a professional job on monochrome as well as color TV receivers, monitors and CRT computer displays. A list of essential test equipment is followed by helpful hints for signal-tracing monochrome defects. This signal-tracing procedure applies to those defects that are common to monochrome and color TV sets, monitors and CRT computer displays. Color TV receivers and color monitors are occasionally required to display black and white images. Troubleshooting the defects that can cause unwarranted color to appear in monochrome pictures is the subject of the concluding part of this chapter.

A PROFESSIONAL TROUBLESHOOTING PROCEDURE

The ten-step procedure described below may not be the only way to troubleshoot TV sets, monitors and CRT computer displays, but it is a complete and effective method to make sure that the job is done properly and the customer is satisfied.

1. *Verify the symptoms.* No matter how clearly the customer seems to describe the trouble, it is important to verify the symptoms, preferably in the presence of the customer. You will appreciate the importance of this step after you have listened to the descriptions

customers can give for such completely different troubles as sound in the picture, loss of color sync or an intermittent in the TV tuner.

2. *Isolate the defect to a function block.* You can use the method described in Chapter 1, together with the tables presented there for monochrome and color defects, or else depend on your own understanding of the operation of the TV set, monitor or CRT display. In either event, observing the symptoms should help you isolate the defect to one, or, at the most, two function blocks.

3. *Localize the trouble source.* Based on the known reliability of certain components and the frequency with which certain circuits become defective, we can often find the defective component or circuits on the first attempt. This chapter contains information on most frequent defects in TV receivers, monitors and CRT computer displays.

4. *Signal tracing.* If you have not found the defect as a result of the approach under paragraph 3 above, it may be necessary to trace specific signals, such as the audio, video or sync through a particular portion of the circuitry to find the defective component itself. A description of signal-tracing monochrome defects is included in this chapter.

5. *Component testing and substitution.* When you have isolated one or more components in the circuit causing the defect, it is often necessary to test each part individually. Some components, such as transformers and ICs, are best tested by substituting one known to be good.

6. *Repair or replacement.* Most electronic components must be replaced when they become defective and cannot be repaired. Connectors, printed wiring and some coils can be repaired. Many components in a TV receiver, monitor or CRT computer display are standard off-the-shelf items available from your elec-

tronics distributor, but some are available only from the manufacturer of the particular set.

7. *Adjustment and alignment.* Whenever a component has been replaced in a circuit that has some adjustment or alignment procedure, this procedure should be performed. While this adjustment or alignment may take some extra time and effort, it is essential for ultimate customer satisfaction. Chapters 7 through 10 cover alignment procedures for every portion of a TV set, monitor and CRT computer display.

8. *Checking the repair.* After the adjustment or alignment procedure, you have to check the performance of the receiver to make sure that no other defects exist. Because some types of defects depend on temperature, it is good practice to run the receiver for at least half an hour or longer to make sure the defect has really been cleared up.

9. *Checking overall performance.* Some types of defects tend to cover up the marginal function of other circuits. When the power supply has been shorted, for example, this may cover up the fact that the TV tuner is intermittent. For this reason it is good practice to tune in every available channel, operate the set in every possible mode, and check the function of all front panel controls, both when the set is cold and after a half-hour warm up.

10. *Demonstrate performance to the customer.* Until the customer can see the results of your efforts and agrees that the unit now works properly, there is little point in presenting a bill. It is also important to demonstrate reception on each active channel, and how each of the controls functions. This is the time to explain any remaining limitations, such as weak signals due to a distant station, so that the customer's satisfaction can be clearly established. Professional service technicians usually attach a sticker somewhere on the chassis with the date and type of defect

that was repaired, together with their name and phone number.

HOME OR SHOP REPAIR

One of the big questions for any professional service technician is whether a particular TV receiver, monitor or CRT computer display should be repaired in the owner's home or in the shop. Compact sets are usually difficult to take apart and more difficult to put together and for that reason, unless the defect is extremely simple and easy to repair, they are generally taken to the shop. A defect in a large color TV console, however, may require moving a large piece of furniture to and from the shop, and it may be more efficient to attempt a repair in the customer's home. The individual, on-the-spot judgment of the service technician has to govern in such cases. It is generally agreed, however, that any job that will take more than one hour of troubleshooting in the customer's home, or that will require the use of an oscilloscope, should be done in the shop. When a large console is involved and the shop has a color chassis test jig, it may be worthwhile to remove the chassis separately, leaving the cabinet and CRT with the customer.

The basic diagnosis about the type of trouble is made in the first three steps of the troubleshooting procedure described above. If the probable trouble source is an intermittent connection, and if we are not sure whether this is located in the TV tuner, the IF or the video section, then we will decide to move the set to the shop. When the color picture tube has to be replaced, the set should also be taken to the shop because we will have to perform purity and convergence adjustments. In these examples, the amount of time projected for the repair will all exceed the one-hour limit we stated earlier.

ESSENTIAL TEST EQUIPMENT

Technicians starting out in their profession usually want to invest the minimum amount of money in their test equipment. They believe that it is worthwhile to invest in quality test equipment only if the volume of business warrants it. Even for part-time service technicians, this policy is not very wise. You can expect a useful life of at least five years from any decent piece of test equipment. If you repair only 50 TV receivers, monitors or CRT computer displays in one year, using that particular test equipment and making a profit of only $50 per repair, you will have earned $2,500 with this test equipment. Experienced service technicians know that the money spent on quality test equipment is one of the best investments you can make. Test equipment is, after all, a tool, and every master mechanic knows that quality tools invariably pay for themselves many times over. If your starting capital is limited, you may be better off buying only the bare essentials in test equipment, concentrating on quality instead of quantity.

The beginner or part-time service technician may only use one set of test equipment but the full-time professional usually has one set of equipment as a bench set-up and another set, more compact, for portable use in the customer's home. We recommend the following items as the minimum essential test equipment for portable use for the beginning or part-time technician:

    one set of handtools
    flashlight
    a set of alligator clip leads
    assorted AC interlock cords
    digital volt-ohmmeter
    portable color bar generator (it usually contains a raster generator as well)

small TV receiver (especially useful for master antenna and cable TV systems).

As a typical bench set-up for one person, the following items are recommended as a bare minimum:

one set of handtools
adjustable bench light with magnifying lens
assorted clip leads, jack and plug combinations
assorted AC interlock cords
digital volt-ohmmeter
color bar generator (including dot and raster generators)
oscilloscope (should have at least 10-MHz bandwidth and be specially designed for TV work)
RF sweep generator (should cover all VHF channels, IF and video; internal, crystal controlled markers are very useful)
transistor tester (should have power transistor test capability)
tube tester (millions of TV receivers still use tubes)
capacity tester (the type that can also measure inductance)
audio oscillator (not essential but very handy)
110-V isolation transformer (able to handle 500 watts)
adjustable, regulated power supply (not essential but very handy for locating power supply defects).

More elaborate pieces of equipment such as alignment generators are very useful when the volume of business warrants their relatively high cost. The essential items described above will allow you to perform any kind of test that may be required in monochrome, color TV, monitors and CRT computer displays.

SIGNAL-TRACING

One of the most powerful servicing skills is the ability to trace signals through a complex circuit. In most TV work, this means using an oscilloscope to locate missing or incorrect signal levels in an existing circuit. We will use a case history to demonstrate proper use of the signal-tracing technique.

The TV was a late-model RCA, and was brought into the shop by the owner. His description was a terse "No picture." Finding the cause of the problem with signal-tracing is easier than ever, with the majority of television sets containing large amounts of integrated circuitry.

The bench technician hooked the TV up, and connected it to an antenna. He tuned to an operating station, and verified that there was sound, but no video or raster. He had noticed, however, the characteristic sound of static electricity that usually indicates the presence of high voltage to the picture tube.

Since sound was present, he noted that the tuner, and video IF, sound and detector stages were probably operating properly. A quick check with the high-voltage probe verified that high voltage was present on the CRT second anode. A good place to start looking for the problem is at the output of the video IF/detector, AFT IC. Figure 13.1 is a simplified block diagram of the suspected defective circuitry. A quick verification that video signal was present here indicated the proper operation of the tuner, video IF, detector and AFT circuits.

Moving to the output of the first video amplifier, the waveform was correct, indicating proper operation of this amplifier. The video signal was then sampled at the delay line, the next major component in the video chain, and found to be present. It was also present at the input of the last video stage, the luma/chroma amp IC. The output of this IC are the three-color signals, which are applied to the red, green and blue amplifiers.

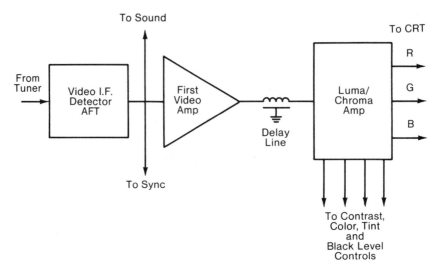

Figure 13.1: Simplified Video Circuitry

The output of this IC did not have correct waveforms present, therefore this video stage became a prime suspect. The best way to test for proper operation of a suspected IC is to measure the DC and AC voltages on the IC pins. Presence of proper power supply voltages, and input signals and voltage levels, with improper outputs almost certainly mean a defective component. On this particular IC there are outputs that connect to the color, tint, contrast and black level controls, and the voltage at the black level control IC pin was not reasonably close to the voltage stated on the schematic. In addition, some other voltages were out of tolerance. After verification that the IC had proper voltages on the power supply input pins, the technician substituted a new IC, which restored proper operation of the television.

As you can see, signal-tracing is simply a technique that provides an organized, symptomatic location of the defective stage, then narrowing the search to find the component or components responsible. A technician usually begins tracing the signal from a point where he believes the equipment is still working correctly. If this point does not have a correct signal present, the defect will be found closer to the antenna. Once a good signal has been found, the tracer proceeds one stage at a time toward the picture tube until an improper waveform is found. At that point, the suspected stage is probed with the oscilloscope and DVM to locate the defective component.

Pitfalls to watch out for when signal tracing include defective support stages causing the suspected stage to operate improperly. An example of this might be a dead video IF stage caused by improper operation of the AGC circuit. You can avoid this trap by making sure that all voltages being fed into the defective stage are well within tolerance range for the expected amount.

Another trap that is often encountered is circuit loading of the suspected stage by the presence of the oscilloscope or meter probe. If we connect a low-impedance probe to the input of a high-impedance circuit, for example, we may lower the amplifier gain substantially. To avoid this problem, use suitable probes on your test equipment, and use manufacturers' published test points, as these are likely to have been protected from circuit loading by test equipment.

Chapter 3 discusses the detailed functions of a monochrome TV receiver, and Figure 3.1 shows a detailed block diagram. Sixteen separate points are labeled on that diagram and corresponding waveforms are presented in Chapter 3. These waveforms are based on using a TV broadcast as signal source, but many of them apply equally well if a color bar generator or some other RF signal generator is used. For color TV receivers, the reader is referred to Chapter 5, which deals with the detailed color functions and contains a block diagram in Figure 5.1. Respective waveforms are also included in that chapter and referenced to points 20 through 28 of the block diagram in Figure 5.1. With an understanding of the principles of signal-tracing and the information contained in Chapters 3 and 5, you will have no difficulty in signal-tracing any defect.

TINTED MONOCHROME PICTURE

When only a part of the picture is tinted or when the colors vary over the picture, the defect is of a different nature (and is described in the next subheading). If the colored tint covers the entire screen, as shown in Figure 13.2 (see color insert), adjustment of the color temperature, screen controls, bias controls and the overall CRT set-up may be required. The following troubleshooting steps are recommended:

1. Tune in a monochrome broadcast or color broadcast with the intensity or color control set to minimum. Make sure that the tinting of the picture is uniform over the entire screen. Turn the contrast control down until only a very faint picture or the raster alone is visible.

2. Turn the brightness control up to obtain a fairly bright raster. If this raster is tinted, reduce the brightness control and adjust the background screen grid controls for a neutral gray background. If you can get a neutral gray raster and the tinting effect only occurs on a picture, the brightness and screen grid circuits should not be touched further because the trouble must be either in the Y or brightness amplifier or in the matrix section. Remember, however, that most color TV sets have a service switch, available from the rear, which will collapse the vertical sweep so that a single line is visible. See Chapter 8 for the procedure for adjusting a neutral gray or white picture.

3. If the background adjustments cannot provide a neutral shade for the entire screen, measure the DC voltages at the cathodes, control grids and screens. Compare the measured values with those stated in the manufacturer's instructions. If these instructions are unavailable, remember that the screen grids must

be at least 300 V or more positive with respect to the cathode, and the control grids must always be negative. The most likely components to fail in this particular curcuit section are the bypass capacitors, bleeder resistors, diodes or the brightness-limiting circuits. Some modern color TV receivers have elaborate high-voltage shut-down and brightness limiting circuits that, depending on component failures, could result in the tinted monochrome symptom.

4. If the raster can be adjusted for a neutral shade but the monochrome picture is still tinted, the defect is most likely in some part of the color decoder or matrixing section. To make sure that this defect is not due to misalignment, touch up the red, green or blue video gain controls. A definite check on the operation of the R, G, B video signals is possible by signal-tracing a color bar signal as described in Chapter 9. Oscilloscope measurements at each color picture tube control grid or cathode will indicate the relative amplitude of the R, G, B video.

5. Check the operation of the color killer circuit. Measure the color killer bias at each of the points in the color section where it is applied.

6. Although defects in the matrixing networks are relatively rare, it is possible that a resistor or one of the ICs has become defective. This type of defect is quite rare and requires detailed signal-tracing and substitution of suspected parts.

TINTED SPOTS IN MONOCHROME PICTURE

This defect is really a color defect, but it may be less noticeable on a color picture than when a color TV set receives a monochrome broadcast. The appearance of this symptom is illustrated in Figure 13.3 (color insert), and, in essence, represents a lack of color purity. Chapter 6 contained a detailed description of color TV picture tube operation, including the role of the purity magnet and the degaussing coil. When a symptom, as illustrated in Figure 13.3 (see color insert), is observed, adjustment of the purity magnet is the first attempt to correct this defect.

Tinted spots will also be visible without a monochrome picture, provided that the background raster is made sufficiently bright. In a color picture, a small loss of color purity may go unnoticed and many set owners only become aware of it when watching monochrome pictures. A defect in the automatic degaussing circuit may have existed for some time, and only when monochrome pictures are observed is the lack of degaussing apparent.

The troubleshooting procedure for this type of defect consists of first attempting to eliminate the tinted spots from the raster by adjusting the purity magnet assembly on the back of the color picture tube as described in Chapter 6. To check the operation of the degaussing circuit, it is necessary to allow the TV receiver to cool down and then measure the AC voltage across the degaussing coil during the turn-on period. The surge of AC through the degaussing coils may only last for a few seconds, but if it occurs we can be sure that degaussing takes place. If the degaussing current cannot be measured, an ohmmeter check of the series and parallel resistors as well as the degaussing coils themselves is required.

In some rare instances the color impurity can be caused by external fields, such as a large powerline transformer mounted nearby, or some other machinery using magnets or transformers. If the degaussing circuit works correctly and the purity provides some adjustment, three other defects could cause these symptoms. The convergence coil assembly itself may be defective, and this will also be apparent by poor convergence. The deflection yoke may have a slight unbalance or misalignment between certain windings and yet provide a linear horizontal and vertical scan. A deflection yoke defect of this type is extremely rare but should be considered if nothing else seems to cure the tinted spots in the monochrome picture. The third possibility is the picture tube itself, but if its operation is satisfactory in all other respects, it is extremely unlikely that the tinted spots are caused by the picture tube. In early color TV receivers certain internal structural defects occasionally caused tinted spots, but this is not very likely in modern color TV picture tubes.

COLOR FLASHES IN MONOCHROME PICTURE

When you see red, green and blue dots racing across a monochrome broadcast received on a color TV set, the most likely defect is in the color killer circuit. Random noise is picked up by the 3.58-MHz color amplifier and is amplified and passed through the color decoder and matrix. When the noise reaches the picture tube it will result in this type of symptom.

If the color killer section operates correctly, it senses the absence of the 8-cycle color burst on each horizontal sync pulse and provides a bias that shuts down the 3.58-MHz amplifier. The first step, therefore, is to measure the bias produced by the color killer when the TV set is tuned to a color broadcast and when it is turned to a monochrome broadcast. A defect in the color killer circuit itself may produce only part of the shut-down bias or the shut-down bias may not reach the 3.58-MHz color subcarrier amplifier. To verify that the defect is due to the color killer bias, we can short the input to the color decoder to ground and the color flashes across the screen disappear. If this color interference persists, however, the cause may be an open circuit, intermittent connection, or poor ground somewhere in the R, G and B output section.

POOR FOCUS

Poor focus, on monochrome as well as on color TV receivers, is invariably due either to incorrect DC voltage on the focus elements or to a defect in the picture tube itself. In early monochrome and color TV receivers and monitors, a permanent magnet ring was used on the outside of the picture tube neck to provide some focusing, but most modern TV receivers use a DC voltage that controls an electrostatic focusing element inside the electron gun. Where a focus potentiometer is provided, the first step will be to try adjusting it for best focus. The second step consists of measuring the voltage that goes to the picture tube focusing element and comparing it with the manufacturer's recommended values. In some color TV receivers, a resistive voltage divider with clip-on jumpers is provided in the high-voltage section to permit some adjustment of the focusing voltage. An open or shorted resistor can cause poor focus, but this can be easily determined by voltage and resistance measurements.

If the correct voltage is applied and focus is still poor, the most likely defect is in the picture tube itself. This can be remedied only by replacing the entire picture tube with one known to be good.

POOR CONVERGENCE

When the customer complains of seeing edges of the monochrome picture in either red, green or blue, or yellow and purple, we know that poor convergence is the cause of his complaint. Remember that convergence can be excellent over most of the screen and can be noticeably bad only on one side or the other, top or bottom, or in one or two corners. The description of the nontechnical viewer may confuse you as to what the real problem is, but one look at the actual picture will clearly show what kind of misconvergence is present. Chapter 6 contains a detailed explanation of the different convergence systems used and their adjustment procedures. The color pictures of Figures 6.12, 6.13, 6.14 and 6.15 show frequently encountered types of misconvergence as they are seen when a raster is applied to the screen. A monochrome picture resembles a raster in that no colors whatsoever should be apparent.

Convergence problems on projection televisions are especially noticeable and annoying. Due to the large magnification of the scanning lines on the projection screen, even slight misconvergence can be visible. With this in mind, manufacturers of projection TVs have taken extra steps in designing convergence circuitry, added extra adjustments and created a more sophisticated procedure for adjusting convergence. Follow the manufacturers' instructions for convergence of projection systems. According to a representative of Sony Corporation, a 25-inch CRT system can be 85 percent converged without causing a typical customer to complain. A projection system must be converged to within 95 percent of perfect before the customer is satisfied. This calls for extra circuitry to increase the accuracy of the convergence process.

In some older color TV receivers it may be difficult to provide a perfectly converged picture all over the screen, and while this may not be objectionable when a color broadcast is received, it becomes glaring on monochrome reception. Sometimes the set owner simply has to accept the fact that this is the best that can be achieved with this particular set and that perfect convergence is not possible. Whenever poor convergence is the symptom, the first step will be a complete convergence adjustment procedure. Resistors, capacitors, diodes or potentiometers, even the convergence circuits themselves, rarely become defective and cause the misconvergence. Simple volt and ohmmeter checks should be sufficient to find the defective component.

CHAPTER 14

TROUBLESHOOTING COLOR DEFECTS

Previous chapters have taught that color pictures are made from three primary colors and we have become familiar with the necessary alignment and adjustment procedures. Good color pictures depend on the proper operation of all portions of a color set, and the correct setting of front panel as well as secondary controls. Chapter 14 deals with those defects that affect the quality of color pictures, and applies to color TV monitors and receivers as well as to color CRT computer displays. We will refer to the detailed block diagram of a color TV set in Figure 14.1, and color illustrations in Figures 14.2 through 14.7 to help you troubleshoot these defects effectively. When you encounter a color defect, review the subheadings in this chapter to determine which symptom you have to deal with. Then you need only to follow the troubleshooting procedures listed for these particular symptoms.

NO COLOR

When good monochrome reception, both picture and sound, is obtained on color TV channels, we know that the TV tuner and IF section must be operating correctly. The most likely location of any defect will be in those parts of the TV receiver, monitor or CRT display that carry the color information. Referring to Figure 14.1, we can see that color information is carried by the 3.58-MHz amplifier, the color decoder, the R-Y, G-Y and B-Y amplifiers, the red, green and blue amplifiers, as well as the color burst, color sync and color killer sections. The following troubleshooting procedure deals with the most likely defect first and the least likely last.

1. When troubleshooting an old vacuum tube color TV set, check the filaments of all tubes in the color section to make sure they are operating.

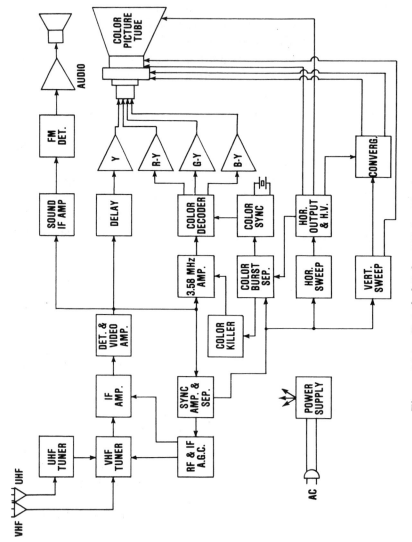

Figure 14.1: Detailed Color TV Set Block Diagram

340

2. With the TV set tuned to a channel known to transmit on color, adjust the fine tuning control or the automatic fine tuning (AFT) voltage to make sure that the tuner receives the station properly within its assigned bandpass. Repeat this on all other stations known to transmit in color. Adjust the intensity control for maximum and turn the hue or tint control through its complete range. If no color appears on the screen at this point, the back of the receiver will have to be removed and you will probably need some test equipment.

3. Check the set for loose plugs, cables and connectors. Also check for obvious mechanical defects, burnt spots or other physical damage.

4. Measure the output bias of the color killer section where it goes to the 3.58-MHz color subcarrier amplifier. A failure in the color killer circuit can cause excessive bias, which will cut off the 3.58-MHz amplifier.

5. Using the color bar generator and an oscilloscope, signal-trace the 3.58-MHz color subcarrier from the detector and video amplifier through the 3.58-MHz amplifier, the color decoder and each of the color difference amplifiers. For units with external matrixing circuits (see Figure 9.1), check these circuits as well. The color bar generator should be connected to the antenna terminals and the VHF tuner set to an unused channel. When working with color TV monitors and CRT computer displays, the output of the color bar generator should be the composite video signal and should be connected to the video input. A detailed discussion of signal-tracing with the color bar generator, including an explanation of the color bar patterns, is contained in Chapter 9.

6. If the color subcarrier signal can be traced to the input of the color demodulator or color processor IC, you

can only check some of the external networks. The oscilloscope should be able to pick up the 3.58-MHz reference signal generated by the oscillator and available at the oscillator tank circuit or the 3.58-MHz crystal. At some point, you should be able to locate the 8-cycle color burst, separated from the horizontal sync signal. In some rare instances a defect in the horizontal keying pulse circuit prevents the color burst from being removed and recognized, causing the color killer circuit to generate the same bias as when a monochrome picture is being received.

7. Before replacing a suspected IC, DC voltage measurements for all power supply points are suggested. As a last resort, however, the color decoder IC may have to be replaced.

WEAK COLORS

When the proper colors appear washed out and weak regardless of any of the front panel control adjustments, a color bar pattern such as the one shown in Figure 14.2 (see color insert) will be obtained. Note that the colors appear dim pastel shades rather than the fully saturated red, green and blue. To make sure that this type of defect is related only to the color circuits, try to tune in a monochrome picture or a color picture on another station. On distant or weak signal stations, the colors themselves may also be weak. In that event, a better antenna or transmission line system, rather than troubleshooting the receiver itself, may be required.

If color pictures appear weak on all color broadcasts, the adjustment of the intensity, or color gain, control should be able to increase or decrease the intensity of the colors. If adjusting this control does not change the intensity, the defect is most likely in the circuit involving this potentiometer. In the following troubleshooting procedure the most likely defect is discussed first and the least likely last.

1. A defective component in the intensity or color gain control circuit, or a defective component or misadjustment in the automatic color control (ACC) circuit, is the most frequent source of this type of trouble. This latter section provides automatic gain control for the 3.58-MHz color subcarrier signal, and a defect in the ACC circuit may keep this gain to a minimum. Measure all DC voltages in the ACC and intensity control circuits.

2. A defect or misadjustment in the color killer circuit may provide too much bias for good color pictures but insufficient bias to cut the 3.58-MHz amplifier off completely. Measure the bias voltage from the color killer circuit at the point where it enters the 3.58-MHz amplifier.

3. Misalignment of the 3.58-MHz resonant circuits for the 3.58-MHz amplifier input and/or output can also cause weak colors. Connect the color bar generator to the antenna terminals of a color TV receiver, or, without RF modulation, to the video input terminals of a color monitor or CRT display. Using the color bar generator and oscilloscope in the test set-up described in Chapter 9, adjust the 3.58-MHz resonant networks for maximum amplitude of the color bar signal.

4. The RF and IF sections of the color TV receiver are not likely trouble sources for weak color defects as long as the monochrome picture appears normal. If the monochrome picture lacks fine detail or if there is any other indication of misalignment of the RF tuner and the IF amplifier, the bandpass response of those sections could cause weak colors. The overall alignment procedure described in Chapter 7 may have

to be used, in rare cases, to determine whether weak colors are caused by the tuner and IF section.

COLOR SYNC TROUBLES

The detailed operation of the color sync system is described in Chapters 5 and 8. Figure 14.3 (see color insert) illustrates the appearance on the screen when the 3.58-MHz color reference signal from the local oscillator is not locked in with the 8-cycle color burst received from the TV station. The diagonal bars of mixed colors will tend to weave back and forth, and the number of bars will increase as the difference between the two frequencies increases. When the color sync is adjusted closer to the correct frequency, there will be fewer bars until, at the proper sync lock-in, a color picture will appear on the screen.

In most modern color TV receivers, color monitors and color CRT displays, the hue or tint control does not usually have sufficient range to change the frequency of the 3.58-MHz oscillator, but can only change the phase. A coarse adjustment of the frequency of this oscillator is usually accessible either from the rear of the unit, with the back cover removed, or else from the top or bottom of the chassis itself. Unless a component in the 3.58-MHz oscillator circuit has become defective and had to be replaced, this coarse adjustment should not be necessary. In the following troubleshooting procedure, the most likely defect of color sync troubles is discussed first and the least likely is taken up last.

1. The 8-cycle color reference burst transmitted from the TV station on each horizontal sync pulse is lost. Assuming that the sync pulses themselves are received correctly, this means that the color burst is lost in the color burst separator. The most likely cause

of this is a defect in the horizontal keying pulse circuit that gates the color burst separator. Signal-tracing the input and output of the color burst separator with the oscilloscope can be performed either by using the off-the-air signal from the TV station, or by connecting the color bar generator to the antenna terminals.

2. A defect in the automatic phase and frequency control circuit (AFPC) can also prevent proper synchronization. In most modern color TV receivers and monitors, the AFPC circuit as well as most of the oscillator are part of a single IC. External R-C networks, however, are required to filter the error signal from the AFPC detector to the oscillator, and a leaky capacitor or short circuit in these components can cause the symptoms of improper color sync. Ohmmeter tests or substitution of these components will determine where the defect lies.

3. In many color TV receivers, the color burst separator is followed by an amplifier stage or a tuned network at the input to the color sync circuit. A defect in either of these circuits will result in a loss of this 8-cycle color burst and therefore loss of color sync. Signal tracing with the oscilloscope is the best way to locate this defect.

4. A defective IC in the color burst separator and color sync section can also cause loss of color sync. Before replacing this IC, however, we suggest that you measure all DC voltages going to this IC and replace any external components, such as bypass capacitors. Replacing the IC itself is a last resort and can be done only with an exact replacement part.

ONE COLOR MISSING

A surprising number of TV viewers will accept color pictures in which one of the three primary colors is either totally missing or quite weak. Customer complaints on this type of defect are usually in the nature of "the colors don't look quite right," or, depending on which color is missing, "the pictures are too yellow," etc. We know from Chapter 4 that the three primary colors, red, green and blue, must be present in their proper relative amplitudes at the color picture tube in order to present a true, full-color picture. The best approach to complaints concerning wrong colors is the use of the color bar generator.

Figure 14.4 (color insert) shows the correct appearance of the color pattern. The yellow bar, a combination of red and green, appears at the left, and the pure green bar appears at the right. See detailed description given in Chapter 9 for the standard color bar pattern. Figure 14.5 (color insert) shows the same color bar pattern when the blue video is lost. Note that the green and yellow as well as the pure red bars appear perfectly normal, but that the loss of blue is indicated also by the fact that there is no purple and no greenish blue in the picture. If we use the color bar generator as a source of test signals, the screen display illustrated in Figure 14.5 (color insert) will tell us immediately that the blue component is missing. Similarly, loss of red or green would be immediately apparent on a color bar pattern.

If a color bar generator is not available, we can determine the lack of red because all white areas will be colored greenish, yellow areas will appear green, and all purple areas will appear blueish. A lack of green is indicated by a predominance of purple tones and yellow shades will become reddish. When the blue signal is missing from a normal picture, the predominant color in the picture will be various shades of yellow, a mixture of red and green. Areas such as the sky, which would be blue, will appear quite dark, with a greenish tint.

The following troubleshooting procedure applies equally to loss of each of the three colors, with the most likely defect discussed first and least likely defect discussed last.

1. Determine, if possible, by using the color bar generator, which of the three primary colors is missing. Concentrate all further work on the channel containing these colors.

2. Using either an off-the-air signal or the color bar generator, connect the oscilloscope to the pin on the color picture tube circuit that will carry the primary color that you have decided is missing. If a video signal is present at that point, adjust the drive or gain control for that particular primary color amplifier. If this has no effect on the amplitude of the video signal, voltage and resistance checks of this circuit are indicated.

3. With the TV set tuned to a nonoperating channel and the antenna terminal shorted, check the operation of the background, or screen grid, controls to make sure that a proper neutral gray or white raster can be obtained. If one of the screen controls cuts off its respective electron gun, the primary color concerned will not appear on the screen.

4. Use the oscilloscope to check the relative amplitudes of the video output signal from the color decoder on each of the three primary colors. In many receivers or monitors, a separate matrixing circuit is used. A simple component defect in this matrixing circuit can cause loss of a primary color. If the output of the color decoder appears correct but the video signals at the three drive amplifiers show a loss of one of the primary colors, voltage and resistance measurements of the components of that circuit should be made.

5. The color video signals reach the color picture tube through the picture tube socket, and, in many cases, a cable and connector arrangement. Poor contact, a loose connection, or cold solder joint can cause loss of the signal there. Check all cables, connectors and the kinescope socket itself.

ONE COLOR DOMINATES

This defect is, in some respects, the same as the one discussed above where one color is missing. It can often be confused with a misadjustment of the background or screen grid controls, and can apparently be compensated for to some extent by increasing the bias on the particular electron gun. Again, use of the color bar generator will quickly show which color dominates. Adjustment of the background, or screen grid, controls without any TV picture is the first step, followed by the same troubleshooting procedure as described for one color missing.

DIM, FUZZY RED AND BLUE PICTURE

This description will apply to a color TV picture in which the Y or brightness signal is missing or greatly reduced. In the block diagram of Figure 14.1 we have shown three separate color difference amplifiers and the Y or brightness signal added at the picture tube itself. In many color TV receivers, the Y or brightness signal is added to each of the color difference signals in separate amplifiers, and when the brightness signal itself is lost, the resulting pictures will appear fuzzy and relatively dim and will have predominantly red and blue hues. The following troubleshooting procedure deals with the most likely defect first and the least likely defect last.

1. To verify loss of the Y or brightness, turn the color intensity control to minimum. The resulting black and white picture should either be very dim or there should be no picture at all. This indicates loss of the Y or brightness signal.
2. In Chapter 13 the principles of signal-tracing have indicated that either Approach 1 or Approach 2 can be used. To determine where the brightness signal is lost, Approach 2, with the oscilloscope connected to

the output of the Y or brightness amplifier, should be followed. We can use either an off-the-air TV broadcast or the output of the color bar generator, connected to the antenna terminals on an unused channel.

3. When the Y or brightness amplifier is part of an IC, it makes sense to check all the external components first and to measure all DC voltages going to this IC before trying to replace it.

4. The contrast control is generally mounted on the front panel and connected to the circuits themselves by wires, and, possibly, a plug and jack arrangement. Intermittent or poor contacts, or cold solder joints, can cause this type of trouble.

5. The delay line itself is the least likely reason for defect, but both input and output signals should be checked with the oscilloscope.

EXCESSIVE INTENSITY, BRIGHTNESS OR CONTRAST

These three front panel controls can ordinarily be adjusted to provide a satisfactory balance between contrast (amplitude of the Y or brightness signal), intensity (amplitude of the three color signals) and brightness (background illumination of the color picture tube). When a defect occurs in any of these three color circuits, however, it may be impossible to reduce the respective parameter sufficiently and this will require misadjustment of the others. If the brightness, for example, is excessive, it may be necessary to adjust the intensity and contrast in order to get strong colors. Figure 14.6 (color insert) shows a color bar pattern with excessive brightness. Note that the three primary colors, red, green and blue, appear as pastel shades rather than the pure colors shown in Figure 14.4. In many instances, adjustment of the intensity or contrast controls will not compensate for excessive brightness, and the problem lies in the DC voltages, which determine the brightness.

Excessive contrast, and occasionally excessive intensity, may not be caused by the circuit sections controlled by these front panel controls but may be due to a defect in the automatic gain control (AGC), which determines the gain of the tuner and IF amplifier, as illustrated in Figure 14.1. In this type of defect, monochrome pictures will appear to have a very limited range of grays and most objects will be either black or white. Some widening of vertical black lines is also typical of excessive contrast. Troubleshooting this type of defect consists of measuring the AGC bias voltages generated by the AGC section and volt-ohmmeter measurements of those circuits.

Excessive intensity is most frequently due to a defect or misadjustment of the automatic color control (ACC) circuits. As in the case of excessive contrast, DC measurement of the ACC portion is the troubleshooting procedure recommended.

When brightness, contrast, or intensity cannot be adjusted by the troubleshooting procedures mentioned above, the DC power supply voltages should be checked carefully. In very rare instances excessive B+ voltages, caused by a component failure, can cause excessive gain in certain selected stages that receive their B+ voltages from these power supply points.

The least likely source of this defect is a change in resistance of some critical bias or load resistor that would cause the wrong DC voltages to appear at the Y or brightness amplifier, at the 3.58-MHz color subcarrier amplifier and at the brightness control itself.

CHANGING HUES

This type of defect is either a steady condition or a slowly varying situation. Figure 14.7 (color insert) illustrates the color bar pattern when the hue or tint control is set wrong. Note that the extreme left color bar is green instead of yellow, and the extreme right color bar is bluish green instead of green. In a properly working color TV receiver or monitor, adjustment of the hue or tint control will provide a correction. When it is not possible to obtain the proper hue, as indicated by the fact that flesh tones are either too purplish or too greenish, the most likely defect is in the tint control circuit itself. This control is usually a front panel or subpanel control and connected to the circuit itself by a plug and jack arrangement. Loose pins, intermittent contacts and cold solder joints in that area can be responsible for the defect.

When the wrong hue symptom cannot be corrected by the hue control, it may be due to a component defect in the phase shifting network that provides the two reference signals from the color sync section to the color decoder. A change in resistance or capacitance in this phase shifting network would be difficult to measure with the ohmmeter, and replacement of these R-C components is indicated for this type of defect.

When the hue changes gradually as the TV set warms up, the most likely defect is in the automatic frequency and phase control (AFPC) circuit, which compares the 8-cycle color reference burst with the locally generated 3.58-MHz oscillator output. The error signal from this AFPC circuit goes through a filter before it is applied to the oscillator itself, and a thermal defect in that filter is typical of the slowly changing hue symptom. Replacing all components in that circuit is usually the best solution.

One of the least likely defects causing slowly changing hue is the IC containing the color sync section and the color decoder itself. Because of the difficulty and expense in replacing these ICs with exact replacement parts, we measure all DC voltages first and replace all external parts connected to this IC. Changing hues is, fortunately, a relatively rare symptom and the defects causing it will always be within the color sync section.

CHAPTER 15

FINDING
THE
"IMPOSSIBLE"
DEFECT

Chapter 1 showed you how to diagnose over 75 percent of all TV defects by using only the screen and the various controls. In Chapters 13 and 14 specific troubleshooting procedures for the less frequent types of troubles that plague TV receivers, monitors and CRT computer displays have been presented. This, the last chapter, deals with those rare defects, probably less than 5 percent of the total, which seem to defy classification. These are "tough dog" problems that service technicians tell each other about. Even among the "impossible" defects, however, certain types can be distinguished. First we will discuss troubles caused by improper repairs or alignment, and then we will cover external and internal interference. The detailed procedure for locating intermittent defects is presented here, a procedure that is invariably successful.

Every experienced service technician remembers some really weird case, a set of symptoms that doesn't fit in any category or a stubborn defect that does not stay fixed. These are cases that seem to defy any rational approach and that resist logical analysis. The last part of this chapter contains a step-by-step method that will help you track down even the most elusive trouble. This is the method to use when everything else has failed.

STRANGE AND UNUSUAL DEFECTS

Suppose you get a color TV set that cannot produce any color pictures, but shows only rapidly changing black and white stripes regardless of what channel you are tuned to. There is no audio at normal volume control setting, but with the volume turned up all the way, strange whistles and noises are heard. It makes no difference if the antenna is connected, whether we are tuned to a VHF or UHF channel, and even connecting a color bar generator to the antenna terminals produces no color picture. When we measure the DC voltages, they appear to be approximately correct. The deflection circuits and the high voltage appear to operate correctly because a raster can be seen on the screen. After trying all controls, we find that when we set the AGC control close to maximum bias, we can dimly see the outlines of a very weak monochrome picture. If we continue to increase the AGC bias, the picture is cut off, and if we decrease the AGC bias just a little bit, we get the black and white stripes again.

This is certainly a difficult case, but it is a real one that the author has encountered. The problem was caused by an unskilled person who tried to align the IF section. By tuning all the resonant circuits to the same frequency, the IF section was brought into oscillation. When the AGC control set the bias high enough to reduce the IF gain, the oscillation stopped and it was possible to receive a picture. Because the IF gain was reduced so much, the picture appeared very weak. This particular TV receiver was restored to proper operation by a careful IF and tuner alignment, tuning each resonant circuit to its assigned frequency.

In another strange case, we observed a persistent loss of horizontal sync. On any channel the TV picture appeared cut into many fine lines, indicating that the horizontal oscillator frequency was much higher than the standard 15,750 Hz. Adjustment of the horizontal oscillator coil appeared to lower the frequency, but further adjustment made it higher again. Clearly, as the ferrite slug inside the coil produced maximum inductance, further turning of the adjustment screw reduced inductance. A careful visual check of the horizontal oscillator section revealed that the ceramic capacitor shunted across the oscillator coil had been soldered in place recently. When we checked its color coding, we found that the capacity was one-tenth of that specified in the circuit diagram. Apparently, the young son of the TV set owner had found the defective capacitor in the horizontal oscillator and had replaced it with one of the wrong value.

These two examples illustrate the strange and unusual defects that you will find when improper repairs or some kind of tampering has taken place. Sometimes the trouble is caused by screwdriver mechanics masquerading as skilled service technicians, sometimes well-meaning amateurs are at fault, and occasionally the set owner himself tries to save the cost of the service call. Whenever you run into a strange or unusual defect, ask the set owner if someone else has already tried to repair the receiver. Don't be surprised, however, if you are not told the truth. Traces of the amateur serviceman can often be found when the dust inside the chassis is disturbed; mounting screws are missing, alignment seals are broken or shield cans have screwdriver marks where the bogus repairman has tried to pry them out.

Almost all instances of attempted repairs or bungling require removal of the set to the shop and a thorough test and alignment procedure, which, of course, increases the cost of the service call. Be sure to explain this to the customer and point out the potential dangers to the amateur in servicing TV receivers. Explain the X-ray radiation hazards and the dangers of electric shock.

INTERFERENCE

Interference can be defined as the addition of unwanted signals to the desired signal. The most frequent type of external interference, static noise, is always received together with the desired RF signal. Other types of interference, such as a CB radio or a radio amateur transmission or RF pulses generated by a truck engine, appear on the screen, superimposed on the TV picture, and can be heard in the audio channel, added to the normal audio signal. Not all interference comes from the outside. The 60- or 120-Hz hum from a poorly filtered power supply is considered internal interference that will also appear in the picture and sound.

There are basically three ways in which an unwanted signal can interfere. The first is heterodyning, or beating with the desired signal, and the principles of heterodyning are illustrated in Figure 15.1. When the two frequencies, F1 and F2, enter the diode circuit, four frequencies will come out—the two original frequencies, their sum, and their difference. In addition to these fundamental frequencies, the harmonic frequencies indicated in Figure 15.1 are also present. While we have shown a diode in this illustration, any nonlinear impedance, such as a portion of a transistor, a vacuum tube or even a poor solder joint, can act as nonlinear impedance and cause heterodyne action.

An example of heterodyne interference is the case of the radio amateur who operates at 3.5 MHz. If his antenna is close enough, the TV set may pick up the signal directly in the video channel and it may appear on every TV channel as a fine grain interference on the screen. This interference will be present only for short periods of time because the radio amateur usually transmits briefly and then listens for a reply. If this radio amateur's transmitter does not transmit a very clean signal, it is easily possible that the twelfth harmonic of 3.5 MHz to 42 MHz, is picked up by the IF amplifier input stage and amplified along with the 41.25 to 45.75-MHz video IF signal. The same kind of beat will appear on the screen. We can distinguish radio interference from that caused by a diathermy machine by the fact that the interference pattern will be coarser and

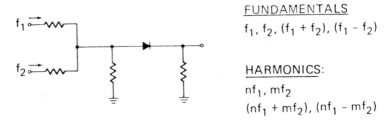

FUNDAMENTALS

f_1, f_2, $(f_1 + f_2)$, $(f_1 - f_2)$

HARMONICS:

nf_1, mf_2

$(nf_1 + mf_2)$, $(nf_1 - mf_2)$

Figure 15.1:   Principles of Heterodyning.
Tested Electronic Troubleshooting Methods, Walter H. Buchsbaum.
Prentice-Hall, Inc.

because a diathermy machine is usually turned on for at least ten to fifteen minutes.

The second type of interference is amplitude addition or modulation of two signals. A hum of 60 or 120 Hz is typical of this type of interference because it originates in the power supply and will vary the gain of the video and audio stages. In the third type of interference, a signal is generated within the circuit by internal oscillation, and that signal interferes with the desired signal.

Once we recognize that we are dealing with an interference defect, we have to locate the source of this interference. Is it external or internal? The most likely sources of external interference, such as an amateur or CB radio transmitter, diathermy equipment or automobile ignition, are not continuously present. Arcing from a street light or a utility power transformer, a neon sign or even a fluorescent light can be an almost constant source of interference but this does not occur often. Whatever causes the interference in the TV set itself, however, is always present. Here are some ways to determine whether the interference is external or internal:

1. Disconnect the VHF and UHF antenna transmission lines and short the tuner terminals together. Check to see if the interference is still there. When dealing with interference that appears only at certain times, be sure that the interference is present just before the antenna terminals are shorted.

2. With the antenna terminals shorted and the interference still present, rotate the TV receiver in various directions to see if the interference becomes weaker or stronger. If the interference pattern seems to change as the TV set is rotated, then the external signal is probably picked up by the chassis or some of the internal wiring.

3. With the antenna terminals still shorted, move the TV set to a shielded area, such as a concrete basement

or a space between concrete walls or large metal
structures. Note if the interference is reduced in this
new location.

4. The interference may be picked up by the AC powerline. If one is not already present, connecting a 0.1-
   MF capacitor across the AC powerline, inside the TV
   set, should reduce this type of interference. The capacitor should, of course, have a voltage rating of at
   least 400 V DC.

5. The final test of whether the interference is external
   or internal would be to either use another TV set in
   this location and see if the interference appears there
   too, or to remove the suspected TV set to your shop.

A. EXTERNAL INTERFERENCE

Most external interference comes either from communi-
cation transmitters or from industrial sources. Commu-
nication transmitters can usually be identified by the speech
or Morse code patterns and by the fact that transmissions
are usually brief and followed by long pauses. Citizens
band (CB) interference, as well as radio amateur interference, is more likely to take place at certain times of the
day. Late evening hours are particularly popular with amateur operators. Interference from police radio or from
VHF and UHF communications used by utility crews and
others is more frequent during the daytime and is also
characterized by brief transmissions. When the interference is limited to the normal working hours, an industrial
RF generator is the most likely source. Electric heating is
used in the plastics industry, inductance heating is used
in heat treating of metals and arc welding has a wide
application in industry. A diathermy machine is usually
used only during a doctor's office hours. All of these ac-
tivities generate RF signals that can interfere with TV
reception.

Interference due to the spark coil from a passing ve-
hicle appears as streaks racing across the screen. This

source of interference can often be identified simply by looking out the window or listening to the engine noise of an idling bus or truck.

The table of interference sources presented in Figure 15.2 shows frequency assignments of different RF services, indicating, where applicable, the harmonics, and shows where in the TV receiver the interference enters. A brief description of possible remedies is also included in this table.

If we can determine the frequency of the interfering signal, we can often design and construct a filter that will attenuate these unwanted signals. Many TV receivers already have filters at the input to the tuner, but additional reduction of strong local interference may be necessary.

In many instances, the interfering signals, such as ignition noise, are picked up primarily by the transmission line between the antenna and the TV tuner. If the source of interference is outside any of the normally used TV bands, the antenna itself may not pick them up nearly as strongly as the transmission line. When you suspect this type of trouble, the transmission line should be replaced by a coaxial cable, making sure that the outer braid, the shield, is well grounded. Some service technicians select a special coax cable that has a double-shielded outer conductor to reduce the likelihood of interference pickup even further. A variety of interference traps are commercially available, and your electronics distributor will probably know which frequencies give trouble in his particular area.

One special interference source is another TV receiver. Radiation from the local RF oscillator can be picked up by other TV receivers operating on another channel. This problem of oscillator radiation was covered in Chapter 12 in connection with RF switching between a TV receiver, an antenna, and a TV accessory such as a video cassette recorder, TV game or home computer. The best method of dealing with oscillator radiation from another TV set is to reduce the radiation at the source, the of-

FROM (mc.)	TO (mc.)	SERVICE	HARMONIC	ENTERS AT	REMEDY
.535	1.605	BC	—	2nd det., video, a.c.	Shielding, line filter
1.605	1.8	Aircraft, police	—	2nd det., video, a.c.	Shielding, line filter
1.8	2	Amateur, loran	—	2nd det., video, a.c.	Shielding, line filter
2.065	2.105	Maritime	10	IF	High-pass filter, shielding
3.2	3.4	Short-wave	7-8	IF	High-pass filter
			—	2nd det., video, a.c.	Shielding, line filter
3.5	4	Amateur	6-7	IF	High-pass filter
			—	2nd det., video, a.c.	Shielding, line filter
4.75	4.85	Short-wave	5	IF	High-pass filter, if shields
7	7.3	Amateur	3	IF, antenna	High-pass filter, if shields
11	11.975	Short-wave	2	IF, antenna	High-pass filter, if shields
14	14.35	Amateur	3	IF, 41 mc., antenna	High-pass filter, if shields
			4	Antenna, Channel 2	Modify antenna and lead-in
15.1	15.45	Short-wave	3	IF, 41 mc., antenna	High-pass filter, if shields
17.7	17.9	Short-wave	3	Antenna, Channel 2	Modify antenna and lead-in
21	21.45	Amateur	—	IF, antenna, a.c.	High-pass filter, shielding, line filter
21.45	21.75	Short-wave	—	IF, antenna	High-pass filter, if shields
21.85	22	Aircraft	—	Antenna	High-pass filter
22	22.72	Maritime	—	IF (rarely), antenna	High-pass filter
23.2	23.35	Aircraft	—	Antenna	High-pass filter
25.6	26.1	Short-wave	—	IF, antenna	High-pass filter, if shields
27.185	27.455	Industrial, medical	2	Antenna, Channel 2	Modify antenna
			—	IF, antenna, a.c.	High-pass filter, shielding, line filter
28	29.7	Amateur	2	Antenna, Channel 2	Modify antenna and lead-in
29.7	42	Gov't. fire, petroleum, etc.	2	Antenna, Channels 2-6	Modify antenna and lead-in
			—	IF, 41 mc.	High-pass filter, shielding
42	44	Police, highway	—	IF, 41 mc., antenna, a.c.	High-pass filter, shielding, line filter
44	50	Short-wave	—	IF, 41 mc., antenna, a.c.	High-pass filter, shielding, line filter
54	72	TV	Osc. radiation	Antenna	Modify antenna and lead-in, re-align and shield offender
76	88	TV	Osc. radiation	Antenna	Modify antenna and lead-in, re-align and shielf offender
88	108	FM	2	Antenna, Channels 7-13	Modify antenna and lead-in
			Image	Antenna, Channels 2-3	Wave trap
108	132	Aircraft	Image	Antenna, Channels 3-6	Wave trap
148	174	Gov't. railroad, police	Image	Antenna, Channels 7-13*	Wave trap
			3	Antenna, Channels 14-22	Modify antenna and lead-in
174	216	TV	Osc. radiation	Antenna	Modify antenna and lead-in, re-align and shield offender
216	220	Gov't	3	Antenna, Channels 43-46	Modify antenna and lead-in
220	225	Amateur	Image	Antenna, Channel 7	Wave trap
			3	Antenna, Channels 46-49	Modify antenna and lead-in
225	470	Aircraft, military	Image	Antenna, Channels 14-28*	
			2	Antenna, Channels 14-83	Modify antenna and lead-in
470	890	UHF TV	Osc. radiation	Antenna, Channels 14-83	Modify antenna and lead-in, re-align and shielf offender

*Where oscillator operates below incoming signal.

Figure 15.2: Table of Interference Sources.
Color TV Servicing, 3rd Ed., Walter H. Buchsbaum. Prentice-Hall, Inc.

fending TV set. Local oscillator radiation can be reduced or eliminated by proper grounding of the TV tuner and all its shielded components. Local oscillator radiation usually interferes on only one or two channels. Once we know which channels receive the offending radiation we can calculate the oscillator frequency and design a filter to attenuate the unwanted signals sufficiently.

In some instances the interference is so strong that it is picked up by the chassis or the wiring. In these cases, when the interference enters through the RF, video or audio itself, one remedy is to attempt to shield the bottom of the chassis. Before going to such lengths, however, the possibility of the interference coming in through the AC powerline should be investigated. Electronic distributors carry a variety of AC powerline interference filters or suppressors. These items usually contain a low pass filter that will cut off frequencies above 100 Hz or higher.

B. INTERNAL INTERFERENCE

Internal interference can be due to a number of different phenomena, and the remedy, of course, requires identification of the source of the interference.

1. *Internal oscillation.* Many of the high-gain amplifier stages in a TV receiver can start to oscillate themselves, due either to a defective component or to misalignment. These amplifiers usually have B + isolating networks, consisting of a series of resistors and a decoupling or bypass capacitor. Feedback networks that reduce the gain of an amplifier to safe limits can become defective or open circuit, causing oscillation. When the TV screen shows a pattern of bars or stripes moving across, in monochrome or in color, on one station or on every station, internal oscillation may be the problem. One rapid method of finding the stage where the oscillation occurs is to disable, by ground-

ing key points or by disconnecting B +, the following stages, in the sequence indicated:

RF oscillator in the tuner
last IF amplifier or video detector stage
the second video or brightness amplifier
the color sync oscillator
each of the three chroma drive amplifiers (R, G and B)
disable the audio, IF and drive amplifier.

If the oscillation continues as each of these stages is disabled, we know that the stages preceding them cannot have caused the oscillation.

A quick way to locate oscillations is to shunt a. 1-MFd capacitor across the B+ supply in each of the sections listed above. Check the screen or the loudspeaker each time to see what the effect of this bypass capacitor is. This procedure should be repeated by shunting the AGC bias points with this capacitor to make sure that they are properly filtered. Internal oscillation can also be due to misalignment of tuned amplifiers. This is particularly true in the video IF section and in the 4.5-MHz intercarrier audio system. A complete alignment procedure as described in Chapters 7 and 10 may be necessary to cure the oscillation.

2. *Beat pattern.* The most frequent type of beat interference occurs because the color subcarrier is approximately 900 KHz below the intercarrier sound IF. The resulting beat pattern is clearly visible on the screen, as illustrated in the color illustration of Figure 15.3. (See color insert.) This type of interference can usually be reduced sufficiently by careful alignment of the 4.5-MHz sound IF traps in the video detector and first video amplifier stage. The entire IF

amplifier section alignment should be checked, with special attention to the 41.25-MHz IF sound carrier.

The 3.58-MHz color sync signal is interleaved with the brightness signal and is not noticeable during color telecasts. When monochrome transmissions are received, however, and the frequency of the 3.58-MHz reference oscillator drifts, a fine weaving moire pattern can occasionally be seen. In most color TV receivers the color killer will prevent any signal from going through the 3.58-MHz amplifier, and a separate 3.58 MHz bandstop filter in the Y or brightness channel keeps that interference from the screen. Readjustment of this resonant circuit may be necessary to eliminate this type of beat.

3. *Vertical bars along one edge.* This type of interference is due to the so-called Barkhausen oscillations, a defect originating in horizontal output amplifier tubes. When solid state circuits, power transistors and ICs are used in the horizontal output section, this defect will not occur. Barkhausen oscillations can be cured either by changing tubes, rearranging the wiring to the deflection yoke or replacing the flyback transformer and deflection yoke.

4. *Arcing.* On the screen this looks very similar to ignition interference except that arcing can occur at regular intervals, depending on its cause. The most frequent source of arcing is the high-voltage section, where dirt or dust and a bad solder connection have combined to generate a relatively low-resistance path to ground. When the volume control is turned down, we can usually hear the arcing coming from the high-voltage cage. A detailed method of dealing with high-voltage arcing and corona, a purplish glow around the high voltage point, is contained in Chapter 8.

5. *Power supply hum.* Invariably due to poor power supply filtering, this can be either in the form of 60-Hz hum, in which case there will be one horizontal

bar across the screen, or 120-Hz, which means two horizontal bars across the screen. If the 60- or 120-Hz hum interference reaches the tuner, IF and video circuits, it will appear primarily as horizontal bars on the screen. If the hum is only on the B+ going to the audio section, it will be heard as a loud hum or buzz. If this type of interference reaches the horizontal sync or deflection circuits, this will mean scalloped edges and weaving of the picture. If the color pictures seem to vary in strips that get lighter and darker in a weaving motion, the interference has reached the color sync or phase control circuit, or else the color demodulator itself. The most frequent source of this type of defect is an open filter capacitor in one of the B+ lines.

6. *Poor ground connections.* Internal interference troubles are sometimes due to an open or high-resistance ground connection. All the different separators and shield cans that are used in a TV receiver, monitor and CRT computer display are effective only if they are grounded properly. In some instances a spring provides the ground contact and in others a solder connection. Whenever interference troubles are encountered, be sure to check the ground connections of all separators, shield cans, outer conductors of cables and ground points in general. A cold solder joint can provide a resistance of several thousand ohms between a supposedly grounded shield can and the chassis itself. Experienced service technicians frequently resolder all ground connections in the TV chassis whenever they encounter internal interference problems.

INTERMITTENT DEFECTS

This is the type of defect that the customer will describe in great detail, and when the service technician tries to verify the symptoms, the TV set, monitor or CRT computer display works perfectly. Obviously, it takes more time to find an intermittent defect, and the customer should be advised immediately that the repair of such a defect will be more expensive than a readily recognizable, steady defect. The basic troubleshooting approach, in most cases, is to change the intermittent defect into a permanent defect that can then be located and repaired in the usual manner.

The intermittent aspect of a defect is most frequently caused by either thermal or mechanical changes. In rare instances a component is voltage sensitive and becomes defective only when the AC line voltage is high. The defect either appears and disappears as a result of heating and cooling of a particular component, or else it occurs as a result of shock, vibration or mechanical position. If we can determine that the defect will only appear after a certain length of warm-up time, we can be pretty sure that we are dealing with a thermal intermittent. To make that defect permanent, we can often heat the suspected component and the defect will appear. If we find that the defect occurs whenever the TV receiver, monitor or CRT display is shaken, rattled or tapped in certain places, we have to try to locate, as closely as possible, the area of greatest mechanical sensitivity and then look for the defect itself.

Whether the defect is of thermal or mechanical origin, the troubleshooting procedure can be greatly simplified if we can localize it to a particular circuit. When only the sound is affected by the intermittent defect, for example, we can focus on the area containing the intercarrier 4.5-MHz sound IF section, the FM detector, and the audio amplifier. If the intermittent defect consists of a loss of vertical sync, indicated by the picture rolling up or down uncontrollably from time to time, we have to look only in the sync separator and the vertical oscillator section. Apply the symptom-function technique described in Chapter 1 and use the tables given in that chapter to isolate the intermittent defect to one functional block.

If the intermittent defect appears to be thermal, locate the particular functional block and its circuitry in the chassis. With the power on and the TV set operating properly, apply a heat gun or the radiant heat from a heavy soldering iron to the suspected area until the defect occurs. Continue the application of heat for another 30 seconds. Now you can troubleshoot that particular section, knowing that the intermittent component will measure as defective.

If you have determined that the intermittent defect is due to mechanical action and have isolated the defect by its symptoms to a specific functional block, tap each tube, transistor, IC, component, cable, shield and connector with a small rubber mallet or with the eraser portion of an ordinary pencil. Tap and check the various grounds and shielding points and, if any solder junction appears suspicious, resolder it with an appropriate-size soldering iron.

One of the most convenient ways to find intermittent components, hairline cracks, mechanical misalignment, and other types of intermittent defects is the instant freeze spraycan. Using the extender tube, you can create a small cold spot on the suspected portion of a circuit. Because metals contract in the cold much faster than do plastics, this makes the intermittent defect, particularly if it is mechanical, readily apparent. Caution is advised in the use of these sprays because many semiconductors do not operate at very low temperature and may be damaged if the freezing spray is applied too strongly.

For those rare instances where the voltage or current stress causes an intermittent operation of a particular component, the TV receiver, monitor or CRT computer display should be connected to a variable AC line voltage supply which is then set to provide 120 to 125 V AC to the power supply input.

The following list of likely intermittent defects represents the most frequently found problems in TV receivers, monitors and CRT computer displays:

1. *Poor connector contact.* Corrosion, dirt or mechanical misalignment can cause the plug and jack connection to be intermittent. The solder or crimp contact of the wire to the plug or jack should also be checked. Defective insulation or pieces of metal between contacts can cause intermittent short circuits.

2. *Broken wires.* A break in a solid conductor that is covered by insulation can occur as a result of the wrong setting of a wire-stripping machine. This defect may have been started when the wire stripper pinched the wire at the point where the insulation was cut off. The insulation then covered this pinched part, but vibration between the solder joint and the wire itself caused the break.

3. *Loose metal.* Cut-off pieces of wire or solder can move around the chassis and lodge themselves between two connections and cause an intermittent short circuit.

4. *Poor solder joints.* A universal disease in electronic equipment.

5. *Loose ground connection.* Corrosion and metal fatigue eventually cause lock washer or solder lug connections to be intermittent. Whenever you see screwtype ground connections, tighten them.

6. *Internal intermittents in ICs, transistors or tubes.* If heating or mechanical actuation causes one of these components to become defective, it must be replaced. Such internal defects are not very frequent but they can occur occasionally.

7. *Defective insulation between conductors.* Defective high voltage insulation in a flyback transformer can cause intermittent internal arcing and breakdown with resulting intermittent high-voltage defects. When the insulation inside a capacitor becomes defective, intermittent capacitor operation will occur. Either heating up or mechanical vibration will locate the intermittent component.

8. *PC board intermittents.* Broken, charred or cracked PC boards may still be operating but may become defective when the materials expand unevenly due to higher temperatures or when mechanical vibration causes the defect. Visual inspection will show this type of problem, but hairline cracks in the PC board conductors or solder-hair bridging are not as easily detected. Plated-through holes or eyelets and other through-the-board connection methods can be the source of intermittent defects.

9. *A cracked or broken tuning slug in a variable inductor.* While this is very rare, it represents a particularly hard-to-find intermittent defect. Variable inductors usually control either the frequency of an oscillator or the frequency response of a network. A broken or cracked tuning slug will cause intermittent changes that can easily give even a skilled service technician prematurely gray hair.

10. *Loose laminations or a cracked core in the transformer.* The flyback transformer uses ferrite cores that, when cracked, can cause strange, intermittent defects. Loose laminations in a power transformer or in a vertical or audio output transformer can cause audible noise. This type of vibration, however, is relatively easy to locate.

"LAST RESORT" TROUBLESHOOTING METHOD

Occasionally even the experienced and highly skilled service technician will encounter a TV set, monitor or CRT computer display that cannot be repaired by any of the methods described so far in this book. When you feel that you have "tried everything" and you have not located the trouble, when you have replaced all suspected parts and the defect is still there, possibly in some other form; in short, when you are ready to throw in the sponge, remember that "if a man makes it, a man can fix it." At this point, we recommend that you take a break, have a cup of coffee or postpone further work on the set until some other time.

When you have been working on the set for a while, things may get confused, wrong transistors or ICs may have been used as replacement, connections that you have opened for test purposes may not have been reconnected, cables may not be connected properly, temporary shorts may have been left in and so on. To keep the confusion from complicating the troubleshooting job, check the entire workbench for components that may have been removed from the set but that should be returned; look for components or connections that you yourself might have mistakenly installed.

After a suitable break, start work again, checking first to see that the set has been restored, as much as possible, to its original condition. The last-resort troubleshooting method described below should be performed without haste and with great care. Be sure to write down all results and keep them in logical order.

1. Measure all voltages in suspected stages that are listed in the manufacturer's voltage chart or schematic diagram and record them.
2. Signal-trace the video and all color signals from the detector to the color picture tube with the oscilloscope. Record the voltage amplitudes at each stage.
3. Signal-trace the vertical, horizontal and color sync signals from the detector to the respective sections.
4. Review the notes you have taken and compare them with the manufacturer's data. If manufacturer's data is not available, you might compare your notes with the data from a similar type of color TV receiver, monitor or CRT computer display.

In the course of the last-resort method, you will have encountered one or more significant differences in mea-

surements between the suspected section and the value
stated in the manufacturer's literature. This is where the
defective components are most likely located. In general,
capacitors are more prone to partial failure than resistors.
Inductors hardly ever change in value, but they can be
either open or shorted. ICs and other semiconductors are
temperature sensitive, but otherwise they either work or
they don't. Soldered connections may look OK and yet
be the source of the trouble. Wires, cables and connectors
are another source of hard-to-find defects. Remember, the
set worked correctly at one time. With patience, skill and
technical know-how you can find the trouble and restore
the set to proper operation.

APPENDIX I

BASIC COMPUTER-AIDED TROUBLESHOOTING PROGRAMS

BASIC COMMON-EMITTER AMPLIFIER CONFIGURATION WITH VOLTAGE (SHUNT) FEEDBACK, CURRENT (SERIES) FEEDBACK, BIAS RESISTOR AND OUTPUT LOAD RESISTANCE

The following troubleshooting program is highly generalized; it can be RUN for the complete network shown in Figure A-1, or it can be RUN as a program for an amplifier without feedback, without a bias resistor and without an output load resistance. Or, the program can be RUN with any chosen combination of feedback, bias and output load factors. In other words, any resistor can be "open-circuited" for computation by INPUTting a very large value, such as 1000 megohms. On the other hand, any resistor can be "short-circuited" for computation by INPUTting a very small value, such as .0001 ohm.

When voltage gain is measured, it is important to avoid transistor overload and resulting incorrectly measured values. In the case of a small-signal transistor, a base input signal of 4 mV rms is typical of good practice. Small-signal voltages can be measured with a digital voltmeter or with a sensitive oscilloscope. The Pi-R H-Parameter Verification Test included in the troubleshooting program answers the question: "Is it the transistor, or is it the associated circuitry?" For this test, the pi load shown in Figure A-2 is clipped to the base, emitter and collector terminals.

This is a "split-ticket" troubleshooting program wherein the RUN is first displayed on the video screen. Then, if the troubleshooter wishes to make a print-out, he INPUTs a Y in response to the query "Print Hard Copy Y/N?" on the video screen. If the operator INPUTs an N, the program then jumps to END. The advantage of "split-ticket" programming is that the troubleshooter can investigate various tolerance assignments in video RUNs. Then, if he decides that a permanent record of the analysis

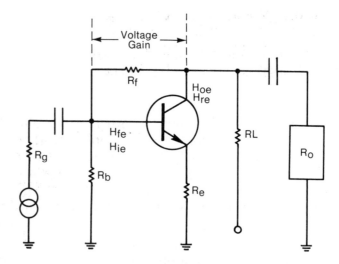

Figure A-1:   Basic CE amplifier with voltage (shunt) feedback, current (series) feedback, bias resistor and output load resistance.
Note: This is the basic CE amplifier arrangement. It is operated as a linear (small-signal) amplifier. The h parameters are provided in data sheets, or are available from transistor manufacturer. H parameters are easily measured, if desired. H_{fe} is the forward-current amplification with the output short-circuited for ac. H_{ie} is the base input impedance with the output short-circuited for ac. H_{oe} is the collector output admittance with the input open-circuited for ac. (H_{oe} is the reciprocal of the collector output resistance with the input open-circuited for ac.) H_{re} is the reverse-voltage amplification with the input open-circuited for ac.
Note: The same value of signal voltage will be measured at both ends of a coupling capacitor unless it is open or has lost a substantial amount of its rated capacitance.

is in order, he can INPUT a Y and a hard copy of the data will be RUN.

Another useful feature of this troubleshooting program is that it spells out the most critical parameter in the network with respect to the rated parameter values. This is helpful information, because time and effort can frequently be minimized by first checking out the most critical parameter. In the exemplified RUN, Re at low tolerance is the most critical parameter (it produces the great-

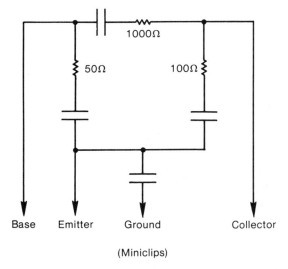

Base   Emitter   Ground   Collector

(Miniclips)

Figure A-2:   Pi load for Pi-*R H*-Parameter Verification Test.
Note: This pad includes three "swamping" resistors and three
blocking capacitors. The capacitor value should be sufficient to
present a virtual short-circuit for ac at the operating frequency. For
example, if the amplifier is tested at 1000 Hz, a suitable capacitor
value is 100 microfarads. At 10 kHz, a value of 10 microfarads is
suitable. The pad functions to swamp-out resistive off-tolerances, so
that the voltage gain that is developed by the rated transistor *h* parameters can be computed.

est error in voltage gain for a given tolerance). Note in
passing that *R*e at high tolerance produces the greatest
reduction in voltage gain for a given tolerance.

This troubleshooting program is written for the IBM
PC, or other compatible computers. Program conversion
to other types of computers is not unduly difficult, as
subsequently explained.

TROUBLESHOOTING PROGRAM No. 1

```
10   PRINT:PRINT "PRO#8.TAC": PRINT
20   PRINT"AMPLIFIER ANALYSIS; 3rd Echelon Troubleshooting Program": PRINT
30   PRINT "*** CE Amplifier With Voltage Feedback, Current Feedback, Bias
         Resistor and Output Load Resistance ***": PRINT:A$="########":
         DIM A(13):DIM B(13):DIM C(29)
40   PRINT "Identifies Most Critical Resistor": PRINT:B$="##.###":C$="##.###"
```

```
45   PRINT"Computes Normal & Off-Tolerance Voltage Gains": PRINT
50   PRINT "Provides Pi-R H-Parameter Computation":PRINT:INPUT "Hfe=";AA
60   INPUT "Hoe=";BB
70   INPUT "Hie=";CC
80   INPUT "Hre=";DD
90   INPUT "Re (Ohms)=";REE
100  INPUT "Rf (Ohms)=";RFF
110  INPUT "Rg (Ohms)=";RGG
120  INPUT "RL (Ohms)=";RLL
130  INPUT "Rb (Ohms)=";RBB
140  INPUT "Ro (Ohms)=";ROO
150  INPUT "Given % Tolerance=";T
160  RE=REE:RF=RFF:RG=RGG:RL=RLL:RB=RBB:RO=ROO:RG=RG*RB/(RG+RB):RL=RL*RO/(RL+RO):
C=CC+(RE*(1+AA))/(1+RE*BB):A=(AA-BB*RE)/(1+RE*BB):D=(DD+BB*RE)/(1+RE*BB):B=BB/(1
+RE*BB):G=AA*RL/((CC*BB-AA*DD)*RL+CC):M=M+1:CCC=C*RF/(RF+C):AAA=(A*RF-C)/(RF+C)
170  DDD=D+(C*(1-D))/(RF+C):BBB=B+((1+A)*(1-D)/(RF+CC)):J=(CCC+(BBB*CCC-AAA*DDD)*
RL)/(1+BBB*RL):SH=RG*J/(RG+J):Q=SH/(SH+RF)+RE/(RE+RL):GG=G/(1+Q*G):VBE=GG*RE/(RE
+RL)
180  PRINT
190  IF M=1 THEN 400
200  IF M=2 THEN 460
210  IF M=3 THEN 490
220  IF M=4 THEN 520
230  IF M=5 THEN 550
240  IF M=6 THEN 580
250  IF M=7 THEN 610
260  IF M=8 THEN 640
270  IF M=9 THEN 670
280  IF M=10 THEN 700
290  IF M=11 THEN 730
300  IF M=12 THEN 760
310  IF M=13 THEN 790
320  IF M=14 THEN 820
330  IF M=15 THEN 850
340  IF M=16 THEN 880
350  IF M=17 THEN 910
360  IF M=18 THEN 940
370  IF M=19 THEN 970
380  IF M=20 THEN 1000
390  IF M=21 THEN 1030
400   PRINT: PRINT "** NORMAL CHARACTERISTICS **": PRINT
410   PRINT "Collector Voltage Gain=";USING A$;-GG:
      A(1)=GG
420   PRINT "Base-Emitter Voltage Gain (approx.)=";USING B$;VBE: PRINT:C(1)=VBE
430   PRINT "** VOLTAGE GAIN WITH INDIVIDUAL PARAMETERS OFF-TOLERANCE BY GIVEN
            PERCENTAGE": PRINT
450  RLL=RLL+.01*T*RLL:GOTO 160
460   PRINT "Collector Voltage Gain, RL High Tol,=";USING A$;-GG:
      A(2)=GG
470   PRINT "Base-Emitter Voltage Gain (approx.)=";USING B$;VBE:C(2)=VBE
480  RLL=RLL/(1+.01*T):RLL=RLL-.01*T*RLL:GOTO 160
490   PRINT "Collector Voltage Gain, RL Low Tol,=";USING A$;-GG:
      A(3)=GG
500   PRINT "Base-Emitter Voltage Gain (approx.)=";USING B$;VBE:C(3)=VBE
510  RLL=RLL/(1-.01*T):RFF=RFF+.01*T*RFF:GOTO 160
520   PRINT "Collector Voltage Gain, Rf High Tol=";USING A$;-GG:
      A(4)=GG
530   PRINT "Base-Emitter Voltage Gain (approx.)=";USING B$;VBE:C(4)=VBE
540  RFF=RFF/(1+.01*T):RFF=RFF-.01*T*RFF:GOTO 160
550   PRINT "Collector Voltage Gain, Rf Low Tol,=";USING A$;-GG:
      A(5)=GG
560   PRINT "Base-Emitter Voltage Gain (approx.)=";USING B$;VBE:C(5)=VBE
570  RFF=RFF/(1-.01*T):REE=REE+.01*T*REE:GOTO 160
580   PRINT "Collector Voltage Gain, Re High Tol=";USING A$;-GG:
      A(6)=GG
590   PRINT "Base-Emitter Voltage Gain (approx.)=";USING B$;VBE:C(6)=VBE
600  REE=REE/(1+.01*T):REE=REE-.01*T*REE:GOTO 160
```

```
610   PRINT "Collector Voltage Gain, Re Low Tol,=";USING A$;-GG:
      A(7)=GG
620   PRINT "Base-Emitter Voltage Gain (approx.)=";USING B$;VBE:C(7)=VBE
630   REE=REE/(1-.01*T):RGG=RGG+.01*T*RGG:GOTO 160
640   PRINT "Collector Voltage Gain, Rg High Tol,=";USING A$;-GG:
      A(8)=GG
650   PRINT "Base-Emitter Voltage Gain (approx.)=";USING B$;VBE:C(8)=VBE
660   RGG=RGG/(1+.01*T):RGG=RGG-.01*T*RGG:GOTO 160
670   PRINT "Collector Voltage Gain, Rg Low Tol,=";USING A$;-GG:
      A(9)=GG
680   PRINT "Base-Emitter Voltage Gain (approx.)=";USING B$;VBE:C(9)=VBE
690   RGG=RGG/(1-.01*T):RBB=RBB+.01*T*RBB:GOTO 160
700   PRINT "Collector Voltage Gain, Rb High Tol=";USING A$;-GG:
      A(10)=GG
710   PRINT "Base-Emitter Voltage Gain (approx.)=";USING B$;VBE:C(10)=VBE
720   RBB=RBB/(1+.01*T):RBB=RBB-.01*T*RBB:GOTO 160
730   PRINT "Collector Voltage Gain, Rb Low Tol,=";USING A$;-GG:
      A(11)=GG
740   PRINT "Base-Emitter Voltage Gain (approx.)=";USING B$;VBE:C(11)=VBE
750   RBB=RBB/(1-.01*T):ROO=ROO+.01*T*ROO:GOTO 160
760   PRINT "Collector Voltage Gain, Ro High Tol,=";USING A$;-GG:
      A(12)=GG
770   PRINT "Base-Emitter Voltage Gain (approx.)=";USING B$;VBE:C(12)=VBE
780   ROO=ROO/(1+.01*T):ROO=ROO-.01*T*ROO:GOTO 160
790   PRINT "Collector Voltage Gain, Ro Low Tol,=";USING A$;-GG:
      A(13)=GG
800   PRINT "Base-Emitter Voltage Gain (approx.)=";USING B$;VBE:C(13)=VBE
810   ROO=ROO/(1-.01*T):AA=AA+.01*T*AA:GOTO 160
820   PRINT "Collector Voltage Gain, Hfe High Tol,=";USING A$;-GG:C(14)=GG
830   PRINT "Base-Emitter Voltage Gain (approx.)=";USING B$;VBE:C(15)=VBE
840   AA=AA/(1+.01*T):AA=AA-.01*T*AA:GOTO 160
850   PRINT "Collector Voltage Gain, Hfe Low Tol,=";USING A$;-GG:C(16)=GG
860   PRINT "Base-Emitter Voltage Gain (approx.)=";USING B$;VBE:C(17)=VBE
870   AA=AA/(1-.01*T):BB=BB+.01*T*BB:GOTO 160
880   PRINT "Collector Voltage Gain, Hoe High Tol,=";USING A$;-GG:C(18)=GG
890   PRINT "Base-Emitter Voltage Gain (approx.)=";USING B$;VBE:C(19)=VBE
900   BB=BB/(1+.01*T):BB=BB-.01*T*BB:GOTO 160
910   PRINT "Collector Voltage Gain, Hoe Low Tol,=";USING A$;-GG:C(20)=GG
920   PRINT "Base-Emitter Voltage Gain (approx.)=";USING B$;VBE:C(21)=VBE
930   BB=BB/(1-.01*T):CC=CC+.01*T*CC:GOTO 160
940   PRINT "Collector Voltage Gain, Hie High Tol,=";USING A$;-GG:C(22)=GG
950   PRINT "Base-Emitter Voltage Gain (approx.)=";USING B$;VBE:C(23)=VBE
960   CC=CC/(1+.01*T):CC=CC-.01*T*CC:GOTO 160
970   PRINT "Collector Voltage Gain, Hie Low Tol,=";USING A$;-GG:C(24)=GG
980   PRINT "Base-Emitter Voltage Gain (approx.)=";USING B$;VBE:C(25)=VBE
990   CC=CC/(1-.01*T):DD=DD+.01*T*DD:GOTO 160
1000  PRINT "Collector Voltage Gain, Hre High Tol,=";USING A$;-GG:C(26)=GG
1010  PRINT "Base-Emitter Voltage Gain (approx.)=";USING B$;VBE:C(27)=VBE
1020  DD=DD/(1+.01*T):DD=DD-.01*T*DD:GOTO 160
1030  PRINT "Collector Voltage Gain, Hre Low Tol,=";USING A$;-GG:C(28)=GG
1040  PRINT "Base-Emitter Voltage Gain (approx.)=";USING B$;VBE:C(29)=VBE
1050  DD=DD/(1-.01*T): PRINT
1060  B(1)=ABS(A(2)-A(1)):B(2)=ABS(A(3)-A(1)):B(3)=ABS(A(4)-A(1)):
      B(4)=ABS(A(5)-A(1)):B(5)=ABS(A(6)-A(1)):B(6)=ABS(A(7)-A(1)):
      B(7)=ABS(A(8)-A(1)):B(8)=ABS(A(9)-A(1)):B(9)=ABS(A(10)-A(1))
1070  B(10)=ABS(A(11)-A(1)):B(11)=ABS(A(12)-A(1)):B(12)=ABS(A(13)-A(1))
1080  FOR X=1 TO 13:NEXT X
1090  N=B(1)
1100  FOR X=2 TO 13
1110  IF B(X)>N THEN N=B(X)
1120  NEXT X
1130  IF N=B(1) THEN CH$="RL High Tol"
1140  IF N=B(2) THEN CH$="RL Low Tol"
1150  IF N=B(3) THEN CH$="Rf High Tol"
1160  IF N=B(4) THEN CH$="Rf Low Tol"
1170  IF N=B(5) THEN CH$="Re High Tol"
1180  IF N=B(6) THEN CH$="Re Low Tol"
```

```
1190 IF N=B(7) THEN CH$="Rg High Tol"
1200 IF N=B(8) THEN CH$="Rg Low Tol"
1210 IF N=B(9) THEN CH$="Rb High Tol"
1220 IF N=B(10) THEN CH$="Rb Low Tol"
1230 IF N=B(11) THEN CH$="Ro High Tol"
1240 IF N=B(12) THEN CH$="RO Low Tol"
1250  PRINT "MOST CRITICAL RESISTOR = ";CH$: PRINT
1260  PRINT "** Pi-R H-PARAMETER VERIFICATION TEST **": PRINT
1270  PRINT "Note: Clip 50-1000-100 Ohms Pi Load to Base, Collector, Emitter,
                and Ground Terminals": PRINT
1280 RL=100:RG=50:RF=1000
1290 G=AA*RL/((CC*BB-AA*DD)*RL+CC):C=CC*RF/(RF+CC):A=(AA*RF-CC)/(RF+CC):D=DD+(CC
*(1-DD))/(RF+CC):B=BB+((1+AA)*(1-DD)/(RF+CC)):J=(C+(B*C-A*D)*RL)/(1+B*RL):SH=RG*
J/(RG+J):Q=SH/(SH+RF):GG=G/(1+Q*G)
1300  PRINT "Normal Voltage Gain=";USING B$;-GG: PRINT
1310  PRINT "Note: If the transistor has rated values of h parameters, the
                normal voltage gain value will be measured.": PRINT
1320 INPUT "Print Hard Copy Y/N";CH$
1330 IF CH$="Y"THEN 1340 ELSE END
1340 LPRINT"AMPLIFIER ANALYSIS: 3rd Echelon Troubleshooting Program":LPRINT
1350 LPRINT "*** CE Amplifier With Voltage Feedback, Current Feedback, Bias
            Resistor and Output Load Resistance ***":LPRINT:A$="#########"
1360 LPRINT "Identifies Most Critical Resistor":LPRINT:B$="##.###":C$="##.###"
1370 LPRINT"Computes Normal & Off-Tolerance Voltage Gains":LPRINT
1380 LPRINT"Provides Pi-R H-Parameter Computation":LPRINT:LPRINT "Hfe=";AA
1390 LPRINT "Hoe=";BB
1400 LPRINT "Hie=";CC
1410 LPRINT "Hre=";DD
1420 LPRINT "Re (Ohms)=";REE
1430 LPRINT "Rf (Ohms)=";RFF
1440 LPRINT "Rg(Ohms=";RGG
1450 LPRINT "RL (Ohms)=";RLL
1460 LPRINT "Rb (Ohms)=";RBB
1470 LPRINT "Ro (Ohms)=";ROO
1480 LPRINT "Given % Tolerance=";T
1490 LPRINT:LPRINT "** NORMAL CHARACTERISTICS **":LPRINT
1500 LPRINT "Collector Voltage Gain=";USING A$;-A(1)
1510 LPRINT "Base-Emitter Voltage Gain (approx.)=";USING B$;C(1):LPRINT
1520 LPRINT "** VOLTAGE GAIN WITH INDIVIDUAL PARAMETERS OFF-TOLERANCE BY GIVEN
            PERCENTAGE":LPRINT
1530 LPRINT "Collector Voltage Gain, RL High Tol,=";USING A$;-A(2)
1540 LPRINT "Base-Emitter Voltage Gain (approx.)=";USING B$;C(2)
1550 LPRINT "Collector Voltage Gain, RL Low Tol,=";USING A$;-A(3)
1560 LPRINT "Base-Emitter Voltage Gain (approx.)=";USING B$;C(3)
1570 LPRINT "Collector Voltage Gain, Rf High Tol=";USING A$;-A(4)
1580 LPRINT "Base-Emitter Voltage Gain (approx.)=";USING B$;C(4)
1590 LPRINT "Collector Voltage Gain, Rf Low Tol,=";USING A$;-A(5)
1600 LPRINT "Base-Emitter Voltage Gain (approx.)=";USING B$;C(5)
1610 LPRINT "Collector Voltage Gain, Re High Tol=";USING A$;-A(6)
1620 LPRINT "Base-Emitter Voltage Gain (approx.)=";USING B$;C(6)
1630 LPRINT "Collector Voltage Gain, Re Low Tol,=";USING A$;-A(7)
1640 LPRINT "Base-Emitter Voltage Gain (approx.)=";USING B$;C(7)
1650 LPRINT  "Collector Voltage Gain, Rg High Tol,=";USING A$;-A(8)
1660 LPRINT "Base-Emitter Voltage Gain (approx.)=";USING B$;C(8)
1670 LPRINT "Collector Voltage Gain, Rg Low Tol,=";USING A$;-A(9)
1680 LPRINT "Base-Emitter Voltage Gain (approx.)=";USING B$;C(9)
1690 LPRINT "Collector Voltage Gain, Rb High Tol,=";USING A$;-A(10)
1700 LPRINT "Base-Emitter Voltage Gain (approx.)=";USING B$;C(10)
1710 LPRINT "Collector Voltage Gain, Rb Low Tol,=";USING A$;-A(11)
1720 LPRINT "Base-Emitter Voltage Gain (approx.)=";USING B$;C(11)
1730 LPRINT "Collector Voltage Gain, Ro High Tol,=";USING A$;-A(12)
1740 LPRINT "Base-Emitter Voltage Gain (approx.)=";USING B$;C(12)
1750 LPRINT "Collector Voltage Gain, Ro Low Tol,=";USING A$;-A(13)
1760 LPRINT "Base-Emitter Voltage Gain (approx.)=";USING B$;C(13)
1770 LPRINT "Collector Voltage Gain, Hfe High Tol,=";USING A$;-C(14)
1780 LPRINT "Base-Emitter Voltage Gain (approx.)=";USING B$;C(15)
1790 LPRINT "Collector Voltage Gain, Hfe Low Tol,=";USING A$;-C(16)
```

```
1800 LPRINT "Base-Emitter Voltage Gain (approx.)=";USING B$;C(17)
1810 LPRINT "Collector Voltage Gain, Hoe High Tol,=";USING A$;-C(18)
1820 LPRINT "Base-Emitter Voltage Gain (approx.)=";USING B$;C(19)
1830 LPRINT "Collector Voltage Gain, Hoe Low Tol,=";USING A$;-C(20)
1840 LPRINT "Base-Emitter Voltage Gain (approx.)=";USING B$;C(21)
1850 LPRINT "Collector Voltage Gain, Hie High Tol,=";USING A$;-C(22)
1860 LPRINT "Base-Emitter Voltage Gain (approx.)=";USING B$;C(23)
1870 LPRINT "Collector Voltage Gain, Hie Low Tol,=";USING A$;-C(24)
1880 LPRINT "Base-Emitter Voltage Gain (approx.)=";USING B$;C(25)
1890 LPRINT "Collector Voltage Gain, Hre High Tol,=";USING A$;-C(26)
1900 LPRINT "Base-Emitter Voltage Gain (approx.)=";USING B$;C(27)
1910 LPRINT "Collector Voltage Gain, Hre Low Tol,=";USING A$;-C(28)
1920 LPRINT "Base-Emitter Voltage Gain (approx.)=";USING B$;C(29)
1930 LPRINT
1940 B(1)=ABS(A(2)-A(1)):B(2)=ABS(A(3)-A(1)):B(3)=ABS(A(4)-A(1)):
     B(4)=ABS(A(5)-A(1)):B(5)=ABS(A(6)-A(1)):B(6)=ABS(A(7)-A(1)):
     B(7)=ABS(A(8)-A(1)):B(8)=ABS(A(9)-A(1)):B(9)=ABS(A(10)-A(1))
1950 B(10)=ABS(A(11)-A(1)):B(11)=ABS(A(12)-A(1)):B(12)=ABS(A(13)-A(1))
1960 FOR X=1 TO 13:NEXT X
1970 N=B(1)
1980 FOR X=2 TO 13
1990 IF B(X)>N THEN N=B(X)
2000 NEXT X
2010 IF N=B(1) THEN CH$="RL High Tol"
2020 IF N=B(2) THEN CH$="RL Low Tol"
2030 IF N=B(3) THEN CH$="Rf High Tol"
2040 IF N=B(4) THEN CH$="Rf Low Tol"
2050 IF N=B(5) THEN CH$="Re High Tol"
2060 IF N=B(6) THEN CH$="Re Low Tol"
2070 IF N=B(7) THEN CH$="Rg High Tol"
2080 IF N=B(8) THEN CH$="Rg Low Tol"
2090 IF N=B(9) THEN CH$="Rb High Tol"
2100 IF N=B(10) THEN CH$="Rb Low Tol"
2110 IF N=B(11) THEN CH$="Ro High Tol"
2120 IF N=B(12) THEN CH$="RO Low Tol"
2130 LPRINT "MOST CRITICAL RESISTOR = ";CH$:LPRINT
2140 LPRINT "** Pi-R H-PARAMETER VERIFICATION TEST **":LPRINT
2150 LPRINT "Note: Clip 50-1000-100 Ohms Pi Load to Base, Collector, Emitter,
              and Ground Terminals":LPRINT
2160 RL=100:RG=50:RF=1000
2170 G=AA*RL/((CC*BB-AA*DD)*RL+CC):C=CC*RF/(RF+CC):A=(AA*RF-CC)/(RF+CC):D=DD+(CC
*(1-DD))/(RF+CC):B=BB+((1+AA)*(1-DD)/(RF+CC)):J=(C+(B*C-A*D)*RL)/(1+B*RL):SH=RG*
J/(RG+J):Q=SH/(SH+RF):GG=G/(1+Q*G)
2180 LPRINT "Normal Voltage Gain=";USING B$;-GG:LPRINT
2190 LPRINT "Note: If the transistor has rated values of h parameters, the
              normal voltage gain value will be measured.": PRINT
2200 END
```

(TYPICAL RUN)

AMPLIFIER ANALYSIS; 3rd Echelon Troubleshooting Program

*** CE Amplifier With Voltage Feedback, Current Feedback, Bias
Resistor and Output Load Resistance ***

Identifies Most Critical Resistor

Computes Normal & Off-Tolerance Voltage Gains

Provides Pi-R H-Parameter Computation

Hfe= 50
Hoe= .00002
Hie= 1500
Hre= .0005

```
Re  (Ohms)= 100
Rf  (Ohms)= 50000
Rg (Ohms= 1500
RL  (Ohms)= 15000
Rb  (Ohms)= 5000
Ro  (Ohms)= 12000
Given % Tolerance= 50
```

** NORMAL CHARACTERISTICS **

```
Collector Voltage Gain=       -32
Base-Emitter Voltage Gain (approx.)= 0.469
```

** VOLTAGE GAIN WITH INDIVIDUAL PARAMETERS OFF-TOLERANCE BY GIVEN PERCENTAGE

```
Collector Voltage Gain, RL High Tol,=      -35
Base-Emitter Voltage Gain (approx.)= 0.446
Collector Voltage Gain, RL Low Tol,=      -24
Base-Emitter Voltage Gain (approx.)= 0.519
Collector Voltage Gain, Rf High Tol=      -36
Base-Emitter Voltage Gain (approx.)= 0.528
Collector Voltage Gain, Rf Low Tol,=      -23
Base-Emitter Voltage Gain (approx.)= 0.345
Collector Voltage Gain, Re High Tol=      -24
Base-Emitter Voltage Gain (approx.)=       1
Collector Voltage Gain, Re Low Tol,=      -48
Base-Emitter Voltage Gain (approx.)= 0.359
Collector Voltage Gain, Rg High Tol,=      -30
Base-Emitter Voltage Gain (approx.)= 0.443
Collector Voltage Gain, Rg Low Tol,=      -36
Base-Emitter Voltage Gain (approx.)= 0.528
Collector Voltage Gain, Rb High Tol=      -31
Base-Emitter Voltage Gain (approx.)= 0.462
Collector Voltage Gain, Rb Low Tol,=      -33
Base-Emitter Voltage Gain (approx.)= 0.490
Collector Voltage Gain, Ro High Tol,=      -36
Base-Emitter Voltage Gain (approx.)= 0.440
Collector Voltage Gain, Ro Low Tol,=      -23
Base-Emitter Voltage Gain (approx.)= 0.528
Collector Voltage Gain, Hfe High Tol,=      -32
Base-Emitter Voltage Gain (approx.)= 0.474
Collector Voltage Gain, Hfe Low Tol,=      -28
Base-Emitter Voltage Gain (approx.)= 0.414
Collector Voltage Gain, Hoe High Tol,=      -31
Base-Emitter Voltage Gain (approx.)= 0.465
Collector Voltage Gain, Hoe Low Tol,=      -32
Base-Emitter Voltage Gain (approx.)= 0.474
Collector Voltage Gain, Hie High Tol,=      -29
Base-Emitter Voltage Gain (approx.)= 0.427
Collector Voltage Gain, Hie Low Tol,=      -35
Base-Emitter Voltage Gain (approx.)= 0.523
Collector Voltage Gain, Hre High Tol,=      -32
Base-Emitter Voltage Gain (approx.)= 0.474
Collector Voltage Gain, Hre Low Tol,=      -31
Base-Emitter Voltage Gain (approx.)= 0.465
```

MOST CRITICAL RESISTOR = Re Low Tol

** Pi-R H-PARAMETER VERIFICATION TEST **

Note: Clip 50-1000-100 Ohms Pi Load to Base, Collector, Emitter,
      and Ground Terminals

Normal Voltage Gain=-2.949

Note: If the transistor has rated values of h parameters, the
      normal voltage gain value will be measured.

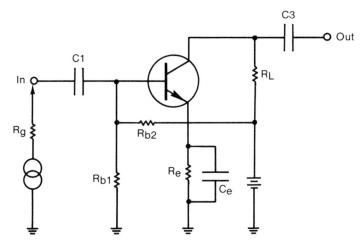

Figure A-3: Basic CE amplifier configuration with partially bypassed emitter resistor and voltage-divider base-bias resistors.

CE AMPLIFIER WITH PARTIALLY BYPASSED EMITTER RESISTORS AND VOLTAGE-DIVIDER BASE-BIAS RESISTORS

The following troubleshooting program is very practical because this form of high-frequency boost is in wide use. (See Figure A-3). This is also a highly generalized type of program that is applicable to circuitry that has only one bias resistor, or no bias resistors, or no output load. As previously noted, any resistor can be "open-circuited" for computation by INPUTting a very large value, or it can be "short circuited" for computation by INPUTting a very small value.

This troubleshooting program computes the shift in the $-3dB$ cutoff frequency that results from a given off-tolerance on individual parameters. Thereby, the troubleshooter can often "close-in" on a fault by noting the cutoff frequency shift that has occurred. The program also includes a supplementary troubleshooting routine to compute the normal values of maximum available high-frequency and low-frequency gain. In doubtful cases, this data can sometimes assist in pinpointing a circuit fault.

Note in passing that the troubleshooter can make a Pi-*R* *H*-Parameter Verification Test, if desired, in the same manner as explained for the previous troubleshooting program.

TROUBLESHOOTING PROGRAM No. 2

```
10 PRINT:PRINT "PRO#6.TAC":PRINT
20 PRINT "CE AMPLIFIER WITH PARTIALLY BYPASSED EMITTER RESISTOR AND
        VOLTAGE-DIVIDER BASE-BIAS RESISTORS":PRINT:
   PRINT "3rd Echelon Troubleshooting Program":PRINT
30 PRINT "(Note: Input coupling capacitor is normal)":PRINT:
   PRINT  "Computes Cutoff Frequency for Off-Tolerance Parameters": PRINT
40 INPUT "Ie (mA)=";IE
50 INPUT "Hfe=";FE
60 INPUT "Re (Ohms)=";RE
70 INPUT "Ce (Mfd)=";CE
80 INPUT "Rb1 (Ohms)=";RBO
90 INPUT "Rb2 (Ohms)=";RBT
100 INPUT "Rg (Ohms)=";RSS
110 INPUT "Given % Tolerance=";T
120 CER=10^8:A$="########":IEE=IE:FEE=FE:REE=RE:CEE=CE:ORB=RBO:TRB=RBT:SR=RS
130 GR=RBO*RBT/(RBO+RBT):GT=RS*GR/(RS+GR):ER=RE*CER/(RE+CER):FC=1/(6.2832*(ER+.0
25/IE+GT/FE)*CE*10^-6): PRINT
140  PRINT "* NORMAL -3dB CUTOFF FREQUENCY **": PRINT
150  PRINT "Cutoff Frequency (Hz)=";USING A$;FC: PRINT
160  PRINT "* -3dB CUTOFF F, INDIVIDUAL PARAMETERS OFF-TOLERANCE BY GIVEN
             PERCENTAGE *": PRINT
170 FE=FE+.01*T*FE
180 GR=RBO*RBT/(RBO+RBT):GT=RS*GR/(RS+GR):ER=RE*CER/(RE+CER):FC=1/(6.2832*(ER+.0
25/IE+GT/FE)*CE*10^-6)
190  PRINT "Cutoff Frequency (Hz), Hfe High Tol,=";USING A$;FC: PRINT
195 FE=FE/(1+.01*T):FE=FE-.01*T*FE
200 GR=RBO*RBT/(RBO+RBT):GT=RS*GR/(RS+GR):ER=RE*CER/(RE+CER):FC=1/(6.2832*(ER+.0
25/IE+GT/FE)*CE*10^-6)
210  PRINT "Cutoff Frequency (Hz), Hfe Low Tol=";USING A$;FC: PRINT
220 FE=FE/(1-.01*T):RE=RE+.01*T*RE
230 GR=RBO*RBT/(RBO+RBT):GT=RS*GR/(RS+GR):ER=RE*CER/(RE+CER):FC=1/(6.2832*(ER+.0
25/IE+GT/FE)*CE*10^-6)
240  PRINT "Cutoff Frequency (Hz), Re High Tol,=";USING A$;FC: PRINT
250 RE=RE/(1+.01*T):RE=RE-.01*T*RE
260 GR=RBO*RBT/(RBO+RBT):GT=RS*GR/(RS+GR):ER=RE*CER/(RE+CER):FC=1/(6.2832*(ER+.0
25/IE+GT/FE)*CE*10^-6)
270 PRINT "Cutoff Frequency (Hz), Re Low Tol,=";USING A$;FC:PRINT
280 RE=RE/(1-.01*T):CE=CE+.01*T*CE
290 GR=RBO*RBT/(RBO+RBT):GT=RS*GR/(RS+GR):ER=RE*CER/(RE+CER):FC=1/(6.2832*(ER+.0
25/IE+GT/FE)*CE*10^-6)
300  PRINT "Cutoff Frequency (Hz), Ce High Tol,=";USING A$;FC: PRINT
310 CE=CE/(1+.01*T):CE=CE-.01*T*CE
320 GR=RBO*RBT/(RBO+RBT):GT=RS*GR/(RS+GR):ER=RE*CER/(RE+CER):FC=1/(6.2832*(ER+.0
25/IE+GT/FE)*CE*10^-6)
330  PRINT "Cutoff Frequency (Hz), Ce Low Tol,=";USING A$;FC: PRINT
340 CE=CE/(1-.01*T):RBO=RBO+.01*T*RBO
350 GR=RBO*RBT/(RBO+RBT):GT=RS*GR/(RS+GR):ER=RE*CER/(RE+CER):FC=1/(6.2832*(ER+.0
25/IE+GT/FE)*CE*10^-6)
360  PRINT "Cutoff Frequency (Hz), Rb1 High Tol=";USING A$;FC: PRINT
370 RBO=RBO/(1+.01*T):RBO=RBO-.01*T*RBO
380 GR=RBO*RBT/(RBO+RBT):GT=RS*GR/(RS+GR):ER=RE*CER/(RE+CER):FC=1/(6.2832*(ER+.0
25/IE+GT/FE)*CE*10^-6)
390  PRINT "Cutoff Frequency (Hz), Rb1 Low Tol=";USING A$;FC: PRINT
```

```
400 RBO=RBO/(1-.01*T):RBT=RBT+.01*T*RBT
410 GR=RBO*RBT/(RBO+RBT):GT=RS*GR/(RS+GR):ER=RE*CER/(RE+CER):FC=1/(6.2832*(ER+.0
25/IE+GT/FE)*CE*10^-6)
420  PRINT "Cutoff Frequency (Hz), Rb2 High Tol=";USING A$;FC: PRINT
430 RBT=RBT/(1+.01*T):RBT=RBT-.01*T*RBT
440 GR=RBO*RBT/(RBO+RBT):GT=RS*GR/(RS+GR):ER=RE*CER/(RE+CER):FC=1/(6.2832*(ER+.0
25/IE+GT/FE)*CE*10^-6)
450  PRINT "Cutoff Frequency, Rb2 Low Tol,=";USING A$;FC: PRINT
460 RBT=RBT/(1-.01*T):IE=IE+.01*T*IE
470 GR=RBO*RBT/(RBO+RBT):GT=RS*GR/(RS+GR):ER=RE*CER/(RE+CER):FC=1/(6.2832*(ER+.0
25/IE+GT/FE)*CE*10^-6)
480  PRINT "Cutoff Frequency (Hz), Ie High Tol,=";USING A$;FC: PRINT
490 IE=IE/(1+.01*T):IE=IE-.01*T*IE
500 GR=RBO*RBT/(RBO+RBT):GT=RS*GR/(RS+GR):ER=RE*CER/(RE+CER):FC=1/(6.2832*(ER+.0
25/IE+GT/FE)*CE*10^-6)
510  PRINT "Cutoff Frequency (Hz), Ie Low Tol,=";USING A$;FC: PRINT
520 IE=IE/(1-.01*T):RS=RS+.01*T*RS
530 GR=RBO*RBT/(RBO+RBT):GT=RS*GR/(RS+GR):ER=RE*CER/(RE+CER):FC=1/(6.2832*(ER+.0
25/IE+GT/FE)*CE*10^-6)
540  PRINT "Cutoff Frequency (Hz), Rg High Tol,=";USING A$;FC: PRINT
550 RS=RS/(1+.01*T):RS=RS-.01*T*RS
560 GR=RBO*RBT/(RBO+RBT):GT=RS*GR/(RS+GR):ER=RE*CER/(RE+CER):FC=1/(6.2832*(ER+.0
25/IE+GT/FE)*CE*10^-6)
570  PRINT "Cutoff Frequency (Hz), Rg Low Tol,=";USING A$;FC: PRINT
580 RS=RS/(1-.01*T)
590  PRINT "SUPPLEMENTARY TROUBLESHOOTING PROGRAM: Normal Low-Frequency and
          High-Frequency Characteristics": PRINT
600 INPUT "Hfe=";AA
610 INPUT "Hoe=";BB
620 INPUT "Hie=";CC
630 INPUT "Hre=";DD
640 INPUT "Re (Ohms)=";RE
650 INPUT "RL (Ohms)=";EE
660 INPUT "Rg (Ohms)=";FF
670 INPUT "Rb1 (Ohms)=";RBO
680 INPUT  "Rb2 (Ohms)=";RBT
690 A$="#########":B$="######.##": PRINT
700 VB=RBO*RBT/(RBO+RBT):BV=FF*VB/(FF+VB):E=EE:F=BV:R=RE:C=CC+(RE*(1+AA))/(1+RE*
BB):A=(AA-BB*RE)/(1+RE*BB):D=(DD+BB*RE)/(1+RE*BB):B=BB/(1+RE*BB):J=(C+(B*C-A*D)*
E)/(1+RE*BB):K=(C+F)/(B*C-D*A+B*F):G=A*E/((C*B-A*D)*E+C):H=A/(B*E+1):I=G*H
710  PRINT "* LOW-FREQUENCY CHARACTERISTICS *": PRINT
720  PRINT "Maximum Available Low-Frequency Voltage Gain="; USING A$;-G: PRINT
730  PRINT "Maximum Available Low-Frequency Current Gain="; USING A$;-H: PRINT:
     I=G*H
740  PRINT "Maximum Available Low-Frequency Power Gain=";USING A$;I: PRINT:
     SP=10*LOG(I)/LOG(10)
750  PRINT "Maximum Available Low-Frequency Power Gain (dB)=";USING A$;SP:
     PRINT
760  PRINT "Low-Frequency Input Impedance (Ohms)=";USING A$;J: PRINT
770  PRINT "Low-Frequency Output Impedance (Ohms)=";USING A$;K: PRINT:
     RE=0
780  PRINT "* HIGH-FREQUENCY CHARACTERISTICS *": PRINT
790 VB=RBO*RBT/(RBO+RBT):BV=FF*VB/(FF+VB):E=EE:F=BV:R=RE:C=CC+(RE*(1+AA))/(1+RE*
BB):A=(AA-BB*RE)/(1+RE*BB):D=(DD+BB*RE)/(1+RE*BB):B=BB/(1+RE*BB):J=(C+(B*C-A*D)*
E)/(1+RE*BB):K=(C+F)/(B*C-D*A+B*F):G=A*E/((C*B-A*D)*E+C):H=A/(B*E+1):I=G*H
800  PRINT "Maximum Available High-Frequency Voltage Gain="; USING A$;-G: PRINT
810  PRINT "Maximum Available High-Frequency Current Gain="; USING A$;-H: PRINT:
     I=G*H
820  PRINT "Maximum Available High-Frequency Power Gain=";USING A$;I: PRINT:
     SP=10*LOG(I)/LOG(10)
830  PRINT "Maximum Available High-Frequency Power Gain (dB)=";USING A$;SP:
     PRINT
840  PRINT "High-Frequency Input Impedance (Ohms)=";USING A$;J: PRINT
850  PRINT "High-Frequency Output Impedance (Ohms)=";USING A$;K: PRINT
860 INPUT "Print Hard Copy Y/N";CH$
870 IF CH$="Y" THEN 900
880 IF CH$="N" THEN 1630
```

```
890 END
900 LPRINT "CE AMPLIFIER WITH PARTIALLY BYPASSED EMITTER RESISTOR AND
           VOLTAGE-DIVIDER BASE-BIAS RESISTORS":LPRINT:
    LPRINT "3rd Echelon Troubleshooting Program":LPRINT
901 LPRINT "(Note: Input coupling capacitor is normal)":LPRINT:
    LPRINT  "Computes Cutoff Frequency for Off-Tolerance Parameters":LPRINT
902 LPRINT "Ie (mA)=";IE
903 LPRINT "Hfe=";FE
904 LPRINT "Re (Ohms)=";REE
905 LPRINT "Ce (Mfd)=";CE
906 LPRINT "Rb1 (Ohms)=";RBO
907 LPRINT "Rb2 (Ohms)=";RBT
908 LPRINT "Rg (Ohms)=";RSS
909 LPRINT "Given % Tolerance=";T
910 IE=IEE:FE=FEE:RE=REE:CE=CEE:ORB=RBO:TRB=RBT:RS=SR
911 GR=RBO*RBT/(RBO+RBT):GT=RS*GR/(RS+GR):ER=RE*CER/(RE+CER):FC=1/(6.2832*(ER+.0
25/IE+GT/FE)*CE*10^-6):LPRINT:LPRINT "* NORMAL -3dB CUTOFF FREQUENCY *":LPRINT
920 LPRINT "Cutoff Frequency (Hz)=";USING A$;FC:LPRINT
930 LPRINT "* -3dB CUTOFF F, INDIVIDUAL PARAMETERS OFF-TOLERANCE BY GIVEN
           PERCENTAGE *":LPRINT
940 FE=FE+.01*T*FE
950 GR=RBO*RBT/(RBO+RBT):GT=RS*GR/(RS+GR):ER=RE*CER/(RE+CER):FC=1/(6.2832*(ER+.0
25/IE+GT/FE)*CE*10^-6)
960 LPRINT "Cutoff Frequency (Hz), Hfe High Tol,=";USING A$;FC:LPRINT
965 FE=FE/(1+.01*T):FE=FE-.01*T*FE
970 GR=RBO*RBT/(RBO+RBT):GT=RS*GR/(RS+GR):ER=RE*CER/(RE+CER):FC=1/(6.2832*(ER+.0
25/IE+GT/FE)*CE*10^-6)
980 LPRINT "Cutoff Frequency (Hz), Hfe Low Tol=";USING A$;FC:LPRINT
990 FE=FE/(1-.01*T):RE=RE+.01*T*RE
1000 GR=RBO*RBT/(RBO+RBT):GT=RS*GR/(RS+GR):ER=RE*CER/(RE+CER):FC=1/(6.2832*(ER+.
025/IE+GT/FE)*CE*10^-6)
1010 LPRINT "Cutoff Frequency (Hz), Re High Tol,=";USING A$;FC:LPRINT
1020 RE=RE/(1+.01*T):RE=RE-.01*T*RE
1030 GR=RBO*RBT/(RBO+RBT):GT=RS*GR/(RS+GR):ER=RE*CER/(RE+CER):FC=1/(6.2832*(ER+.
025/IE+GT/FE)*CE*10^-6)
1040 LPRINT "Cutoff Frequency (Hz), Re Low Tol,=";USING A$;FC:LPRINT
1050 RE=RE/(1-.01*T):CE=CE+.01*T*CE
1060 GR=RBO*RBT/(RBO+RBT):GT=RS*GR/(RS+GR):ER=RE*CER/(RE+CER):FC=1/(6.2832*(ER+.
025/IE+GT/FE)*CE*10^-6)
1070 LPRINT "Cutoff Frequency (Hz), Ce High Tol,=";USING A$;FC:LPRINT
1080 CE=CE/(1+.01*T):CE=CE-.01*T*CE
1090 GR=RBO*RBT/(RBO+RBT):GT=RS*GR/(RS+GR):ER=RE*CER/(RE+CER):FC=1/(6.2832*(ER+.
025/IE+GT/FE)*CE*10^-6)
1100 LPRINT "Cutoff Frequency (Hz), Ce Low Tol,=";USING A$;FC:LPRINT
1110 CE=CE/(1-.01*T):RBO=RBO+.01*T*RBO
1120 GR=RBO*RBT/(RBO+RBT):GT=RS*GR/(RS+GR):ER=RE*CER/(RE+CER):FC=1/(6.2832*(ER+.
025/IE+GT/FE)*CE*10^-6)
1130 LPRINT "Cutoff Frequency (Hz), Rb1 High Tol=";USING A$;FC:LPRINT
1140 RBO=RBO/(1+.01*T):RBO=RBO-.01*T*RBO
1150 GR=RBO*RBT/(RBO+RBT):GT=RS*GR/(RS+GR):ER=RE*CER/(RE+CER):FC=1/(6.2832*(ER+.
025/IE+GT/FE)*CE*10^-6)
1160 LPRINT "Cutoff Frequency (Hz), Rb1 Low Tol=";USING A$;FC:LPRINT
1170 RBO=RBO/(1-.01*T):RBT=RBT+.01*T*RBT
1180 GR=RBO*RBT/(RBO+RBT):GT=RS*GR/(RS+GR):ER=RE*CER/(RE+CER):FC=1/(6.2832*(ER+.
025/IE+GT/FE)*CE*10^-6)
1190 LPRINT "Cutoff Frequency (Hz), Rb2 High Tol=";USING A$;FC:LPRINT
1200 RBT=RBT/(1+.01*T):RBT=RBT-.01*T*RBT
1210 GR=RBO*RBT/(RBO+RBT):GT=RS*GR/(RS+GR):ER=RE*CER/(RE+CER):FC=1/(6.2832*(ER+.
025/IE+GT/FE)*CE*10^-6)
1220 LPRINT "Cutoff Frequency, Rb2 Low Tol,=";USING A$;FC:LPRINT
1230 RBT=RBT/(1-.01*T):IE=IE+.01*T*IE
1240 GR=RBO*RBT/(RBO+RBT):GT=RS*GR/(RS+GR):ER=RE*CER/(RE+CER):FC=1/(6.2832*(ER+.
025/IE+GT/FE)*CE*10^-6)
1250 LPRINT "Cutoff Frequency (Hz), Ie High Tol,=";USING A$;FC:LPRINT
1260 IE=IE/(1+.01*T):IE=IE-.01*T*IE
1270 GR=RBO*RBT/(RBO+RBT):GT=RS*GR/(RS+GR):ER=RE*CER/(RE+CER):FC=1/(6.2832*(ER+.
025/IE+GT/FE)*CE*10^-6)
```

```
1280 LPRINT "Cutoff Frequency (Hz), Ie Low Tol,=";USING A$;FC:LPRINT
1290 IE=IE/(1-.01*T):RS=RS+.01*T*RS
1300 GR=RBO*RBT/(RBO+RBT):GT=RS*GR/(RS+GR):ER=RE*CER/(RE+CER):FC=1/(6.2832*(ER+.
025/IE+GT/FE)*CE*10^-6)
1310 LPRINT "Cutoff Frequency (Hz), Rg High Tol,=";USING A$;FC:LPRINT
1320 RS=RS/(1+.01*T):RS=RS-.01*T*RS
1330 GR=RBO*RBT/(RBO+RBT):GT=RS*GR/(RS+GR):ER=RE*CER/(RE+CER):FC=1/(6.2832*(ER+.
025/IE+GT/FE)*CE*10^-6)
1340 LPRINT "Cutoff Frequency (Hz), Rg Low Tol,=";USING A$;FC:LPRINT
1350 RS=RS/(1-.01*T)
1360 LPRINT "SUPPLEMENTARY TROUBLESHOOTING PROGRAM: Normal Low-Frequency and
           High-Frequency Characteristics":LPRINT:PRINT
1370 PRINT "(Supplementary Program)":PRINT:INPUT "Hfe=";AA
1375 LPRINT "Hfe=";AA
1380 INPUT "Hoe=";BB
1385 LPRINT "Hoe=";BB
1390 INPUT "Hie=";CC
1395 LPRINT "Hie=";CC
1400 INPUT "Hre=";DD
1405 LPRINT "Hre=";DD
1410 INPUT "Re (Ohms)=";RE
1415 LPRINT "Re (Ohms)=";RE
1420 INPUT "RL (Ohms)=";EE
1425 LPRINT "RL (Ohms)=";EE
1430 INPUT "Rg (Ohms)=";FF
1435 LPRINT "Rg (Ohms)=";FF
1440 INPUT "Rb1 (Ohms)=";RBO
1445 LPRINT "Rb1 (Ohms)=";RBO
1450 INPUT "Rb2 (Ohms)=";RBT
1455 LPRINT "Rb2 (Ohms)=";RBT
1460 A$="##########":B$="######.##":LPRINT
1470 VB=RBO*RBT/(RBO+RBT):BV=FF*VB/(FF+VB):E=EE:F=BV:R=RE:C=CC+(RE*(1+AA))/(1+RE
*BB):A=(AA-BB*RE)/(1+RE*BB):D=(DD+BB*RE)/(1+RE*BB):B=BB/(1+RE*BB):J=(C+(B*C-A*D)
*E)/(1+RE*BB):K=(C+F)/(B*C-D*A+B*F):G=A*E/((C*B-A*D)*E+C):H=A/(B*E+1):I=G*H
1480 LPRINT "* LOW-FREQUENCY CHARACTERISTICS *":LPRINT
1490 LPRINT "Maximum Available Low-Frequency Voltage Gain="; USING A$;-G:LPRINT
1500 LPRINT "Maximum Available Low-Frequency Current Gain="; USING A$;H:LPRINT:
     I=G*H
1510 LPRINT "Maximum Available Low-Frequency Power Gain=";USING A$;I:LPRINT:
     SP=10*LOG(I)/LOG(10)
1520 LPRINT "Maximum Available Low-Frequency Power Gain (dB)=";USING A$;SP:
     LPRINT
1530 LPRINT "Low-Frequency Input Impedance (Ohms)=";USING A$;J:LPRINT
1540 LPRINT "Low-Frequency Output Impedance (Ohms)=";USING A$;K:LPRINT:
     RE=0
1550 LPRINT "* HIGH-FREQUENCY CHARACTERISTICS *":LPRINT
1560 VB=RBO*RBT/(RBO+RBT):BV=FF*VB/(FF+VB):E=EE:F=BV:R=RE:C=CC+(RE*(1+AA))/(1+RE
*BB):A=(AA-BB*RE)/(1+RE*BB):D=(DD+BB*RE)/(1+RE*BB):B=BB/(1+RE*BB):J=(C+(B*C-A*D)
*E)/(1+RE*BB):K=(C+F)/(B*C-D*A+B*F):G=A*E/((C*B-A*D)*E+C):H=A/(B*E+1):I=G*H
1570 LPRINT "Maximum Available High-Frequency Voltage Gain="; USING A$;-G:LPRINT

1580 LPRINT "Maximum Available High-Frequency Current Gain="; USING A$;-H:LPRINT
:    I=G*H
1590 LPRINT "Maximum Available High-Frequency Power Gain=";USING A$;I:LPRINT:
     SP=10*LOG(I)/LOG(10)
1600 LPRINT "Maximum Available High-Frequency Power Gain (dB)=";USING A$;SP:
     LPRINT
1610 LPRINT "High-Frequency Input Impedance (Ohms)=";USING A$;J:LPRINT
1620 LPRINT "High-Frequency Output Impedance (Ohms)=";USING A$;K:LPRINT
1630 END
```

(TYPICAL RUN)

CE AMPLIFIER WITH PARTIALLY BYPASSED EMITTER RESISTOR AND
VOLTAGE-DIVIDER BASE-BIAS RESISTORS

3rd Echelon Troubleshooting Program

(Note: Input coupling capacitor is normal)

Computes Cutoff Frequency for Off-Tolerance Parameters

Ie (mA)= 1.5
Hfe= 50
Re (Ohms)= 1000
Ce (Mfd)= .1
Rb1 (Ohms)= 10000
Rb2 (Ohms)= 100000
Rg (Ohms)= 1500
Given % Tolerance= 50

* NORMAL -3dB CUTOFF FREQUENCY *

Cutoff Frequency (Hz)=   1592

* -3dB CUTOFF F, INDIVIDUAL PARAMETERS OFF-TOLERANCE BY GIVEN
PERCENTAGE *

Cutoff Frequency (Hz), Hfe High Tol,=   1592

Cutoff Frequency (Hz), Hfe Low Tol=   1592

Cutoff Frequency (Hz), Re High Tol,=   1061

Cutoff Frequency (Hz), Re Low Tol,=   3183

Cutoff Frequency (Hz), Ce High Tol,=   1061

Cutoff Frequency (Hz), Ce Low Tol,=   3183

Cutoff Frequency (Hz), Rb1 High Tol=   1592

Cutoff Frequency (Hz), Rb1 Low Tol=   1592

Cutoff Frequency (Hz), Rb2 High Tol=   1592

Cutoff Frequency, Rb2 Low Tol,=   1592

Cutoff Frequency (Hz), Ie High Tol,=   1592

Cutoff Frequency (Hz), Ie Low Tol,=   1592

Cutoff Frequency (Hz), Rg High Tol,=   1592

Cutoff Frequency (Hz), Rg Low Tol,=   1592

SUPPLEMENTARY TROUBLESHOOTING PROGRAM: Normal Low-Frequency and
High-Frequency Characteristics

Hfe= 50
Hoe= .00002
Hie= 1500
Hre= .0005
Re (Ohms)= 1000
RL (Ohms)= 15000
Rg (Ohms)= 1500
Rb1 (Ohms)= 10000
Rb2 (Ohms)= 100000

* LOW-FREQUENCY CHARACTERISTICS *

Maximum Available Low-Frequency Voltage Gain=   -14

```
Maximum Available Low-Frequency Current Gain=      -38

Maximum Available Low-Frequency Power Gain=       536

Maximum Available Low-Frequency Power Gain (dB)=       27

Low-Frequency Input Impedance (Ohms)=    50858

Low-Frequency Output Impedance (Ohms)=   1050578

* HIGH-FREQUENCY CHARACTERISTICS *

Maximum Available High-Frequency Voltage Gain=     -476

Maximum Available High-Frequency Current Gain=      -38

Maximum Available High-Frequency Power Gain=     18315

Maximum Available High-Frequency Power Gain (dB)=       43

High-Frequency Input Impedance (Ohms)=    1575

High-Frequency Output Impedance (Ohms)=    90649
```

UNSYMMETRICAL 3-SECTION RC LEAD (DIFFERENTIATING) NETWORK

The unsymmetrical 3-section RC lead (differentiating) network shown in Figure A-4 is a basic arrangement used in various sections of electronic circuitry for high-pass filter action and for phase shifting. It is also used for voltage division in some applications. Although three sections are processed in this troubleshooting program, the 3- section network can also be RUN as a 2-section network or as a 1-section network. (Procedure is explained at the end of the program.)

The troubleshooting program is formatted as a survey routine. In other words, the RUN may address a single frequency, or it may address any desired number of frequencies with any specified increments (steps). In the exemplified RUN, survey is made at 1000 Hz and at 2000 Hz. Survey processing is often helpful in troubleshooting procedures inasmuch as an off-tolerance that does not "show up" at a low operating frequency will often "show up" prominently at a high operating frequency (or vice versa).

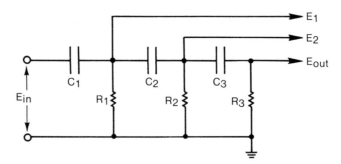

Figure A-4: Unsymmetrical 3-section RC lead (differentiating) network.

Note: This basic configuration provides three output voltages. As seen in the exemplified RUN, E_1 is less than E_{in}, E_2 is less than E_1 and E_{out} is less than E_{in}. Observe that if E_{out} is connected to a resistive load, this load resistance should be combined in parallel with R_3. In turn, the current drawn by the load will reduce the values of E_1, E_2 and E_{out}. Observe that this troubleshooting program can be RUN as a loaded 2-section configuration if R_3 is regarded as the load resistor, and a very large value is INPUTted for C_3. Then, E_2 is the output voltage, and $E_2 = E_{out}$.

TROUBLESHOOTING PROGRAM No. 3

```
1   PRINT:PRINT "PRO#101.TAC":PRINT:
    PRINT "UNSYMMETRICAL 3-SECTION RC LEAD (DIFFERENTIATING) NETWORK": PRINT:
    PRINT "3rd Echelon Troubleshooting Program": PRINT:A$="########"
2   PRINT "Computes Eout/Ein and Phase versus Frequency": PRINT:B$="####.##"
3   PRINT "Computes Sectional Eout/Ein Values": PRINT
4   PRINT "Computes Incidental Power Dissipation": PRINT:
    PRINT "Provides Survey Frequency Operation": PRINT
5   PRINT "Computes Eout/Ein for Off-Tolerance Parameters": PRINT:
    INPUT "R1 (Ohms)=";RO
6   INPUT "R2 (Ohms)=";RT
7   INPUT "R3 (Ohms)=";RQ
8   INPUT "C1 (Mfd)=";CO
9   INPUT "C2 (Mfd)=";CT
10  INPUT "C3 (Mfd)=";CQ
11  INPUT "Starting Frequency (Hz)=";H
12  INPUT "Survey End Frequency (Hz)=";FFF
13  INPUT "Frequency Increment (Hz)=";PP
14  INPUT "Given % Tolerance=";T
15  FF=FFF:FF=FF-H:N=0:G=H:  PRINT
16  F=G+N:  PRINT "f (Hz)=";F
17  XO=1/(6.2832*F*CO*10^-6):XT=1/(6.2832*F*CT*10^-6):XQ=1/(6.2832*F*CQ*10^-6)
18  RS=RO+RT:AB=(RS^2+XT^2)^.5:BA=ATN(XT/RS):AC=(RO^2+XO^2)^.5:CA=ATN(XO/RO)
19  AD=AB*AC:DA=BA+CA:AE=AD/RO:EA=DA:AF=AE*COS(EA):AG=AE*SIN(EA):AH=AF-RO
20  AJ=(AH^2+AG^2)^.5:JA=ATN(AG/AH):AK=RT/AJ:KA=-JA:KA=KA*360/6.2832
21  KA=KA-180:N=N+PP
22  IF ABS(KA)>180 THEN KA=KA+180
23  BC=(RT^2+XT^2)^.5:CB=ATN(XT/RT):BD=RO*BC:DB=CB:BE=RO+BD:BF=(RO^2+BC^2)^.5
24  FB=ATN(BC/RO):BG=BD/BF:GB=DB-FB:BH=BG*COS(GB):BJ=BG*SIN(GB):BK=BJ+XO
25  ZL=BG+RQ:LZ=BK+XQ:YL=(ZL^2+LZ^2)^.5:LY=ATN(LZ/ZL):IL=AK/YL:KA=KA*6.2832/360
```

```
26  LI=KA-LY:VO=IL*RQ:OV=LI*360/6.2832
27   PRINT "Eout/Ein=";USING B$;VO
28   PRINT"Phase Angle (Degrees)=";USING B$;OV
29  ZJ=(XQ^2+RQ^2)^.5:ET=VO*ZJ/RQ:JZ=(XT^2+RT^2)^.5:EQ=ET*JZ/RT
30   PRINT "E1/Ein=";USING B$;EO
31   PRINT "E2/Ein=";USING B$;ET
32  PD=EO^2/RO+ET^2/RT+VO^2/RQ
33   PRINT "Incidental Power Dissipation (mW)=";USING B$;1000*PD:
     PRINT "(For Ein=1 Volt)": PRINT
35  IF F>FF THEN 37
36   PRINT:GOTO 16
37  IF M=1 THEN 62
38  IF M=2 THEN 63
39  IF M=3 THEN 64
40  IF M=4 THEN 65
41  IF M=5 THEN 66
42  IF M=6 THEN 67
43  IF M=7 THEN 68
44  IF M=8 THEN 69
45  IF M=9 THEN 70
46  IF M=10 THEN 71
47  IF M=11 THEN 72
48  IF M=12 THEN 73
60   PRINT: PRINT "** CHARACTERISTICS WITH OFF-TOLERANCE PARAMETERS **": PRINT
61   PRINT "** Characteristics With R1 at High Tolerance **": PRINT:
     RO=RO+.01*T*RO:N=0:M=M+1:GOTO 16
62  RO=RO/(1+.01*T): PRINT "** Characteristics With R1 at Low Tolerance **":
     PRINT:RO=RO-.01*T*RO:N=0:M=M+1:GOTO 16
63  RO=RO/(1-.01*T): PRINT "** Characteristics With C1 at High Tolerance **":
     PRINT:CO=CO+.01*T*CO:N=0:M=M+1:GOTO 16
64  CO=CO/(1+.01*T): PRINT "** Characteristics With C1 at Low Tolerance **":
     PRINT:CO=CO-.01*T*CO:N=0:M=M+1:GOTO 16
65  CO=CO/(1-.01*T): PRINT"** Characteristics With R2 at High Tolerance **":
     PRINT:RT=RT+.01*T*RT:N=0:M=M+1:GOTO 16
66  RT=RT/(1+.01*T): PRINT "** Characteristics With R2 at Low Tolerance **":
     PRINT:RT=RT-.01*T*RT:N=0:M=M+1:GOTO 16
67  RT=RT/(1-.01*T): PRINT "** Characteristics With C2 at High Tolerance **":
     PRINT:CT=CT+.01*T*CT:N=0:M=M+1:GOTO 16
68  CT=CT/(1+.01*T): PRINT "** Characteristics With C2 at Low Tolerance **":
     PRINT:CT=CT-.01*T*CT:N=0:M=M+1:GOTO 16
69  CT=CT/(1-.01*T): PRINT "** Characteristics With R3 at High Tolerance **":
     PRINT:RQ=RQ+.01*T*RQ:N=0:M=M+1:GOTO 16
70  RQ=RQ/(1+.01*T): PRINT "** Characteristics With R3 at Low Tolerance **":
     PRINT:RQ=RQ-.01*T*RQ:N=0:M=M+1:GOTO 16
71  RQ=RQ/(1-.01*T): PRINT "** Characteristics With C3 at High Tolerance **":
     PRINT:CQ=CQ+.01*T*CQ:N=0:M=M+1:GOTO 16
72  CQ=CQ/(1+.01*T): PRINT "** Characteristics With C3 at Low Tolerance **":
     PRINT:CQ=CQ-.01*T*CQ:N=0:M=M+1:GOTO 16
73  CQ=CQ/(1-.01*T): PRINT:M=0:N=0
74   PRINT "Note: This 3-section program RUNs as a 2-section program if very
             large values are INPUTted for R3 and C3: It RUNs as a 1-section
             program if very large values are INPUTted for R2, C2,R3, and C3.":
     PRINT
76   PRINT "Note: This 3-section program RUNs as a loaded 2-section program if R3
             is considered as the load resistance, and a very large value is
             INPUTted for C3. (Then, E2/Ein becomes the load voltage)": PRINT
78   PRINT "Note: This 3-section program RUNs as a loaded 1-section program if R2
             is considered as the load resistance, and very large values are
             INPUTted for C2 and R3. (Then, E1/Ein becomes the load voltage)":
     PRINT
80  INPUT "Print Hard Copy Y/N";CH$
81  IF CH$="Y" THEN 83 ELSE END
82  END
83  LPRINT "R1=";RO:LPRINT "R2=";RT:LPRINT "R3=";RQ:LPRINT "C1=";CO:
    LPRINT "C2=";CT:LPRINT "C3=";CQ:LPRINT "Starting Frequency=";H:
    LPRINT "End Survey Frequency=";FFF:LPRINT"Frequency Increment=";PP
84  LPRINT "Given Tolerance=";T:LPRINT
115 FF=FFF:FF=FF-H:N=0:G=H:LPRINT
```

```
116 F=G+N:LPRINT "f (Hz)=";F
117 XO=1/(6.2832*F*CO*10^-6):XT=1/(6.2832*F*CT*10^-6):XQ=1/(6.2832*F*CQ*10^-6)
118 RS=RO+RT:AB=(RS^2+XT^2)^.5:BA=ATN(XT/RS):AC=(RO^2+XO^2)^.5:CA=ATN(XO/RO)
119 AD=AB*AC:DA=BA+CA:AE=AD/RO:EA=DA:AF=AE*COS(EA):AG=AE*SIN(EA):AH=AF-RO
120 AJ=(AH^2+AG^2)^.5:JA=ATN(AG/AH):AK=RT/AJ:KA=-JA:KA=KA*360/6.2832
121 KA=KA-180:N=N+PP
122 IF ABS(KA)>180 THEN KA=KA+180
123 BC=(RT^2+XT^2)^.5:CB=ATN(XT/RT):BD=RO*BC:DB=CB:BE=RO+BD:BF=(RO^2+BC^2)^.5
124 FB=ATN(BC/RO):BG=BD/BF:GB=DB-FB:BH=BG*COS(GB):BJ=BG*SIN(GB):BK=BJ+XO
125 ZL=BG+RQ:LZ=BK+XQ:YL=(ZL^2+LZ^2)^.5:LY=ATN(LZ/ZL):IL=AK/YL:KA=KA*6.2832/360
126 LI=KA-LY:VO=IL*RQ:OV=LI*360/6.2832
127 LPRINT "Eout/Ein=";USING B$;VO
128 LPRINT"Phase Angle (Degrees)=";USING B$;OV
129 ZJ=(XQ^2+RQ^2)^.5:ET=VO*ZJ/RQ:JZ=(XT^2+RT^2)^.5:EO=ET*JZ/RT
130 LPRINT "E1/Ein=";USING B$;EO
131 LPRINT "E2/Ein=";USING B$;ET
132 PD=EO^2/RO+ET^2/RT+VO^2/RQ
133 LPRINT "Incidental Power Dissipation (mW)=";USING B$;1000*PD:
    LPRINT "(For Ein=1 Volt)":LPRINT
135 IF F>FF THEN 137
136 LPRINT:GOTO 116
137 IF M=1 THEN 162
138 IF M=2 THEN 163
139 IF M=3 THEN 164
140 IF M=4 THEN 165
141 IF M=5 THEN 166
142 IF M=6 THEN 167
143 IF M=7 THEN 168
144 IF M=8 THEN 169
145 IF M=9 THEN 170
146 IF M=10 THEN 171
147 IF M=11 THEN 172
148 IF M=12 THEN 173
160 LPRINT:LPRINT "** CHARACTERISTICS WITH OFF-TOLERANCE PARAMETERS **":LPRINT
161 LPRINT "** Characteristics With R1 at High Tolerance **":LPRINT:
    RO=RO+.01*T*RO:N=0:M=M+1:GOTO 116
162 RO=RO/(1+.01*T):LPRINT "** Characteristics With R1 at Low Tolerance **":
    LPRINT:RO=RO-.01*T*RO:N=0:M=M+1:GOTO 116
163 RO=RO/(1-.01*T):LPRINT "** Characteristics With C1 at High Tolerance **":
    LPRINT:CO=CO+.01*T*CO:N=0:M=M+1:GOTO 116
164 CO=CO/(1+.01*T):LPRINT "** Characteristics With C1 at Low Tolerance **":
    LPRINT:CO=CO-.01*T*CO:N=0:M=M+1:GOTO 116
165 CO=CO/(1-.01*T):LPRINT"** Characteristics With R2 at High Tolerance **":
    LPRINT:RT=RT+.01*T*RT:N=0:M=M+1:GOTO 116
166 RT=RT/(1+.01*T):LPRINT "** Characteristics With R2 at Low Tolerance **":
    LPRINT:RT=RT-.01*T*RT:N=0:M=M+1:GOTO 116
167 RT=RT/(1-.01*T):LPRINT "** Characteristics With C2 at High Tolerance **":
    LPRINT:CT=CT+.01*T*CT:N=0:M=M+1:GOTO 116
168 CT=CT/(1+.01*T):LPRINT "** Characteristics With C2 at Low Tolerance **":
    LPRINT:CT=CT-.01*T*CT:N=0:M=M+1:GOTO 116
169 CT=CT/(1-.01*T):LPRINT "** Characteristics With R3 at High Tolerance **":
    LPRINT:RQ=RQ+.01*T*RQ:N=0:M=M+1:GOTO 116
170 RQ=RQ/(1+.01*T):LPRINT "** Characteristics With R3 at Low Tolerance **":
    LPRINT:RQ=RQ-.01*T*RQ:N=0:M=M+1:GOTO 116
171 RQ=RQ/(1-.01*T):LPRINT "** Characteristics With C3 at High Tolerance **":
    LPRINT:CQ=CQ+.01*T*CQ:N=0:M=M+1:GOTO 116
172 CQ=CQ/(1+.01*T):LPRINT "** Characteristics With C3 at Low Tolerance **":
    LPRINT:CQ=CQ-.01*T*CQ:N=0:M=M+1:GOTO 116
173 CQ=CQ/(1-.01*T):M=0:N=0
174 LPRINT "Note: This 3-section program RUNs as a 2-section program if very
            large values are INPUTted for R3 and C3: It RUNs as a 1-section
            program if very large values are INPUTted for R2, C2,R3, and C3.":
    LPRINT
176 LPRINT "Note: This 3-section program RUNs as a loaded 2-section program if
            R3 is considered as the load resistor, and a very large value is
            INPUTted for C3. (Then, E2/Ein becomes the load voltage)":LPRINT
178 LPRINT "Note: This 3-section program RUNs as a loaded 1-section program if
```

```
                 R2 is considered as the load resistor and very large values are
                 INPUTted for C2 and R3. (Then, E1/Ein becomes the load voltage)":
      LPRINT
180 END

(TYPICAL RUN)


R1= 1000
R2= 2000
R3= 3000
C1= .25
C2= .15
C3= .1
Starting Frequency= 1000
End Survey Frequency= 2000
Frequency Increment= 1000
Given Tolerance= 50


f (Hz)= 1000
Eout/Ein=   0.43
Phase Angle (Degrees)= -88.98
E1/Ein=   0.56
E2/Ein=   0.49
Incidental Power Dissipation (mW)=   0.49
(For Ein=1 Volt)


f (Hz)= 2000
Eout/Ein=   0.65
Phase Angle (Degrees)= -45.35
E1/Ein=   0.69
E2/Ein=   0.67
Incidental Power Dissipation (mW)=   0.85
(For Ein=1 Volt)


** CHARACTERISTICS WITH OFF-TOLERANCE PARAMETERS **

** Characteristics With R1 at High Tolerance **

f (Hz)= 1000
Eout/Ein=   0.44
Phase Angle (Degrees)= -79.67
E1/Ein=   0.57
E2/Ein=   0.50
Incidental Power Dissipation (mW)=   0.40
(For Ein=1 Volt)

f (Hz)= 2000
Eout/Ein=   0.62
Phase Angle (Degrees)= -38.70
E1/Ein=   0.67
E2/Ein=   0.64
Incidental Power Dissipation (mW)=   0.63
(For Ein=1 Volt)

** Characteristics With R1 at Low Tolerance **

f (Hz)= 1000
Eout/Ein=   0.35
Phase Angle (Degrees)=-109.33
E1/Ein=   0.45
E2/Ein=   0.40
Incidental Power Dissipation (mW)=   0.53
(For Ein=1 Volt)
```

```
f (Hz)= 2000
Eout/Ein=   0.63
Phase Angle (Degrees)= -63.07
E1/Ein=   0.67
E2/Ein=   0.65
Incidental Power Dissipation (mW)=   1.24
(For Ein=1 Volt)


** Characteristics With C1 at High Tolerance **

f (Hz)= 1000
Eout/Ein=   0.51
Phase Angle (Degrees)= -76.74
E1/Ein=   0.66
E2/Ein=   0.58
Incidental Power Dissipation (mW)=   0.69
(For Ein=1 Volt)



f (Hz)= 2000
Eout/Ein=   0.69
Phase Angle (Degrees)= -36.49
E1/Ein=   0.74
E2/Ein=   0.71
Incidental Power Dissipation (mW)=   0.96
(For Ein=1 Volt)


** Characteristics With C1 at Low Tolerance **

f (Hz)= 1000
Eout/Ein=   0.27
Phase Angle (Degrees)=-112.85
E1/Ein=   0.34
E2/Ein=   0.30
Incidental Power Dissipation (mW)=   0.19
(For Ein=1 Volt)


f (Hz)= 2000
Eout/Ein=   0.51
Phase Angle (Degrees)= -66.61
E1/Ein=   0.55
E2/Ein=   0.53
Incidental Power Dissipation (mW)=   0.53
(For Ein=1 Volt)


** Characteristics With R2 at High Tolerance **

f (Hz)= 1000
Eout/Ein=   0.50
Phase Angle (Degrees)= -77.54
E1/Ein=   0.60
E2/Ein=   0.56
Incidental Power Dissipation (mW)=   0.54
(For Ein=1 Volt)



f (Hz)= 2000
Eout/Ein=   0.68
Phase Angle (Degrees)= -36.51
E1/Ein=   0.71
E2/Ein=   0.70
Incidental Power Dissipation (mW)=   0.82
(For Ein=1 Volt)


** Characteristics With R2 at Low Tolerance **

f (Hz)= 1000
```

```
Eout/Ein=   0.29
Phase Angle (Degrees)=-110.87
E1/Ein=   0.48
E2/Ein=   0.33
Incidental Power Dissipation (mW)=   0.37
(For Ein=1 Volt)


f (Hz)= 2000
Eout/Ein=   0.54
Phase Angle (Degrees)= -67.32
E1/Ein=   0.64
E2/Ein=   0.56
Incidental Power Dissipation (mW)=   0.82
(For Ein=1 Volt)

** Characteristics With C2 at High Tolerance **

f (Hz)= 1000
Eout/Ein=   0.47
Phase Angle (Degrees)= -81.47
E1/Ein=   0.56
E2/Ein=   0.53
Incidental Power Dissipation (mW)=   0.53
(For Ein=1 Volt)


f (Hz)= 2000
Eout/Ein=   0.67
Phase Angle (Degrees)= -40.46
E1/Ein=   0.70
E2/Ein=   0.69
Incidental Power Dissipation (mW)=   0.88
(For Ein=1 Volt)

** Characteristics With C2 at Low Tolerance **

f (Hz)= 1000
Eout/Ein=   0.34
Phase Angle (Degrees)=-105.83
E1/Ein=   0.56
E2/Ein=   0.38
Incidental Power Dissipation (mW)=   0.42
(For Ein=1 Volt)


f (Hz)= 2000
Eout/Ein=   0.58
Phase Angle (Degrees)= -58.46
E1/Ein=   0.68
E2/Ein=   0.60
Incidental Power Dissipation (mW)=   0.76
(For Ein=1 Volt)

** Characteristics With R3 at High Tolerance **

f (Hz)= 1000
Eout/Ein=   0.49
Phase Angle (Degrees)= -83.04
E1/Ein=   0.59
E2/Ein=   0.52
Incidental Power Dissipation (mW)=   0.53
(For Ein=1 Volt)


f (Hz)= 2000
Eout/Ein=   0.70
```

```
Phase Angle (Degrees)= -43.61
E1/Ein=   0.74
E2/Ein=   0.72
Incidental Power Dissipation (mW)=   0.91
(For Ein=1 Volt)


** Characteristics With R3 at Low Tolerance **


f (Hz)= 1000
Eout/Ein=   0.31
Phase Angle (Degrees)=-100.51
E1/Ein=   0.52
E2/Ein=   0.46
Incidental Power Dissipation (mW)=   0.44
(For Ein=1 Volt)



f (Hz)= 2000
Eout/Ein=   0.52
Phase Angle (Degrees)= -49.23
E1/Ein=   0.61
E2/Ein=   0.59
Incidental Power Dissipation (mW)=   0.73
(For Ein=1 Volt)


** Characteristics With C3 at High Tolerance **


f (Hz)= 1000
Eout/Ein=   0.45
Phase Angle (Degrees)= -82.09
E1/Ein=   0.54
E2/Ein=   0.48
Incidental Power Dissipation (mW)=   0.48
(For Ein=1 Volt)



f (Hz)= 2000
Eout/Ein=   0.65
Phase Angle (Degrees)= -41.48
E1/Ein=   0.68
E2/Ein=   0.66
Incidental Power Dissipation (mW)=   0.83
(For Ein=1 Volt)


** Characteristics With C3 at Low Tolerance **


f (Hz)= 1000
Eout/Ein=   0.36
Phase Angle (Degrees)=-105.70
E1/Ein=   0.60
E2/Ein=   0.53
Incidental Power Dissipation (mW)=   0.54
(For Ein=1 Volt)



f (Hz)= 2000
Eout/Ein=   0.62
Phase Angle (Degrees)= -56.51
E1/Ein=   0.73
E2/Ein=   0.70
Incidental Power Dissipation (mW)=   0.91
(For Ein=1 Volt)


Note: This 3-section program RUNs as a 2-section program if very
large values are INPUTted for R3 and C3: It RUNs as a 1-section
program if very large values are INPUTted for R2, C2,R3, and C3.
```

Note: This 3-section program RUNs as a loaded 2-section program if
R3 is considered as the load resistor, and a very large value is
INPUTted for C3. (Then, E2/Ein becomes the load voltage)

Note: This 3-section program RUNs as a loaded 1-section program if
R2 is considered as the load resistor and very large values are
INPUTted for C2 and R3. (Then, E1/Ein becomes the load voltage)

UNSYMMETRICAL 3-SECTION RC LAG (INTEGRATING) NETWORK

The unsymmetrical 3-section RC lag (integrating) network shown in Figure A-5 is similar to the preceding arrangement except that series R and shunt C are used instead of series C and shunt R. Its applications are also similar to its differentiating counterpart, and it can be RUN as a 2-section configuration or as a 1-section configuration.

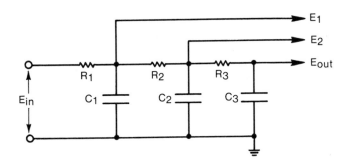

Figure A-5: Unsymmetrical 3-section RC lag (integrating) circuit.

TROUBLESHOOTING PROGRAM No. 4

```
1   PRINT:PRINT "PRO#100.TAC":PRINT:
    PRINT "UNSYMMETRICAL 3-SECTION RC LAG (INTEGRATING) NETWORK": PRINT
2   PRINT "3rd Echelon Troubleshooting Program": PRINT:
    PRINT "Computes Eout/Ein and Phase versus Frequency": PRINT:
    PRINT "Provides Survey Frequency Data":PRINT
3   PRINT "Computes Sectional Eout/Ein Values": PRINT
4   PRINT "Computes Incidental Power Dissipation": PRINT
5   PRINT "* Computes Eout/Ein for Off-Tolerance Parameters *": PRINT:
    A$="#######":B$="####.##"
6   PRINT "This Routine Also RUNs as a 2-Section or 1-Section Program": PRINT:
    INPUT "R1 (Ohms)=";R0
```

```
7 INPUT "R2 (Ohms)=";RT
8 INPUT "R3 (Ohms)=";RO
9 INPUT "C1 (Mfd)=";CO
10 INPUT "C2 (Mfd)=";CT
11 INPUT "C3 (Mfd)=";CQ
12 INPUT "Starting Frequency (Hz)=";H
13 INPUT "Survey End Frequency (Hz)=";FFF
14 N=0:G=H:FF=FFF:FF=FF-H:M=0:
   INPUT "Frequency Increment (Hz)=";PP
15 INPUT "Given % Tolerance=";T:GOTO 40
16 F=G+N: PRINT "f (Hz)=";F
17 XO=1/(6.2832*F*CO*10^-6):XT=1/(6.2832*F*CT*10^-6):XQ=1/(6.2832*F*CQ*10^-6)
18 AB=(RO^2+XO^2)^.5:BA=ATN(XO/RO):LK=XO+XT:BC=(RT^2+LK^2)^.5
19 CB=ATN(LK/RT):AC=BC*AB:CA=CB+BA:AD=AC/XO:DA=CA+6.2832/4:AE=AD*COS(DA)
20 EA=AD*SIN(DA):BE=EA+XO:CE=(AE^2+BE^2)^.5:EC=ATN(BE/AE):AN=XT/CE
21 NA=-EC-6.2832/4:NA=NA*360/6.2832:AB=RO*XO:BA=-6.2832/4
22 AF=AD*SIN(DA):AG=AE+RT:AH=(AG^2+AF^2)^.5:HA=-ATN(AF/AG):AJ=AH*XT
23 JA=HA-6.2832/4:AK=AF-XT:KA=FA-6.2832/4:AL=(AG^2+AK^2)^.5:LA=-ATN(AK/AG)
24 AM=AJ/AL:MA=JA-LA:ZN=AM:NZ=MA:NZ=NZ*360/6.2832+180:PQ=-NA*6.2832/360
25 QP=-NZ*6.2832/360:RS=AN*COS(PQ):SR=AN*SIN(PQ):RR=RS+RO:IT=SR+XQ
26 RU=(RR^2+IT^2)^.5:IL=AN/RU:VO=IL*XO:ZI=(RQ^2+XQ^2)^.5:IZ=ATN(XQ/RQ)
27 BF=IZ-3.1416/2:NA=NA*6.2832/360:OV=-NA+BF:OV=OV*360/6.2832-180:N=N+PP
28  PRINT"Eout/Ein=";USING B$;VO
29  PRINT"Phase Angle (Degrees=";USING B$;-OV
31 ZJ=(XQ^2+RQ^2)^.5:ET=VO*ZJ/XQ:JZ=(XT^2+RT^2)^.5:EO=ET*JZ/XT
32  PRINT "E1/Ein=";USING B$;EO
33  PRINT "E2/Ein=";USING B$;ET
34  PRINT "Incidental Power Dissipation (mW)=";USING B$;1000*(1-EO)^2/RO+1000*(E
T-EO)^2/RT+1000*(VO-ET)^2/RQ: PRINT "(For Ein=1 Volt)": PRINT
36 IF F>FF THEN 42
37 GOTO 16
38 END
40  PRINT"Given % Tolerance=";T: PRINT:GOTO 16
41 END
42 IF M=1 THEN 62
43 IF M=2 THEN 63
44 IF M=3 THEN 64
45 IF M=4 THEN 65
46 IF M=5 THEN 66
47 IF M=6 THEN 67
48 IF M=7 THEN 68
49 IF M=8 THEN 69
50 IF M=9 THEN 70
51 IF M=10 THEN 71
52 IF M=11 THEN 72
53 IF M=12 THEN 73
60 PRINT: PRINT "** CHARACTERISTICS WITH INDIVIDUAL PARAMETERS OFF-TOLERANCE BY
GIVEN PERCENTAGE **": PRINT
61  PRINT "* Characteristics With R1 at High Tolerance *": PRINT:
    RO=RO+.01*T*RO:N=0:M=M+1:GOTO 16
62 RO=RO/(1+.01*T): PRINT "* Characteristics With R1 at Low Tolerance *": PRINT:
   RO=RO-.01*T*RO:N=0:M=M+1:GOTO 16
63 RO=RO/(1-.01*T): PRINT "* Characteristics With C1 at High Tolerance *": PRINT
:  CO=CO+.01*T*CO:N=0:M=M+1:GOTO 16
64 CO=CO/(1+.01*T): PRINT "* Characteristics With C1 at Low Tolerance *": PRINT:
   CO=CO-.01*T*CO:N=0:M=M+1:GOTO 16
65 CO=CO/(1-.01*T): PRINT "* Characteristics With R2 at High Tolerance *": PRINT
:  RT=RT+.01*T*RT:N=0:M=M+1:GOTO 16
66 RT=RT/(1+.01*T): PRINT "* Characteristics With R2 at Low Tolerance *": PRINT:
   RT=RT-.01*T*RT:N=0:M=M+1:GOTO 16
67 RT=RT/(1-.01*T): PRINT"* Characteristics With C2 at High Tolerance *": PRINT:
   CT=CT+.01*T*CT:N=0:M=M+1:GOTO 16
68 CT=CT/(1+.01*T): PRINT "* Characteristics With C2 at Low Tolerance *": PRINT:
   CT=CT-.01*T*CT:N=0:M=M+1:GOTO 16
69 CT=CT/(1-.01*T): PRINT "* Characteristics With R3 at High Tolerance *": PRINT
:  RQ=RQ+.01*T*RQ:N=0:M=M+1:GOTO 16
```

```
70 RQ=RQ/(1+.01*T): PRINT "* Characteristics With R3 at Low Tolerance *": PRINT:
   RQ=RQ-.01*T*RQ:N=0:M=M+1:GOTO 16
71 RQ=RQ/(1-.01*T): PRINT "* Characteristics With C3 at High Tolerance *": PRINT
:  CQ=CQ+.01*T*CQ:N=0:M=M+1:GOTO 16
72 RQ=RQ/(1+.01*T): PRINT "* Characteristics With C3 at Low Tolerance *": PRINT:
   CQ=CQ-.01*T*CQ:N=0:M=M+1:GOTO 16
73 CQ=CQ/(1-.01*T): PRINT
74 PRINT "Note: This routine RUNs as a 2-section program if very small values
          are INPUTted for R3 and C3. It RUNs as a 1-section program if very
          small values are INPUTted for R2, C2, R3, and C3.": PRINT
76 PRINT "Note: This 3-section program RUNs as a loaded 2-section program if R3
          is considered as the load resistor, and a very large value is
          INPUTted for C3. (The load voltage is then E2/Ein)": PRINT
78 PRINT "Note: This 3-section program RUNs as a loaded 1-section program if R2
          is considered as the load resistor, and a very large value is
          INPUTted for C2. (The load voltage is then E1/Ein)": PRINT
80 INPUT "Print Hard Copy Y/N";CH$
81 IF CH$="Y" THEN 82 ELSE END
82 LPRINT:LPRINT "R1=";RO:LPRINT "R2=";RT:LPRINT "R3=";RQ:LPRINT "C1=";CO:
   LPRINT "C2=";CT:LPRINT "C3=";CQ:LPRINT "Starting Frequency=";H:
   LPRINT "Survey End Frequency=";FFF:N=0:G=H:FF=FFF:FF=FF-H:M=0
83 LPRINT "Given % Tolerance=";T:GOTO 140
116 F=G+N:LPRINT "f (Hz)=";F
117 XO=1/(6.2832*F*CO*10^-6):XT=1/(6.2832*F*CT*10^-6):XQ=1/(6.2832*F*CQ*10^-6)
118 AB=(RO^2+XO^2)^.5:BA=ATN(XO/RO):LK=XO+XT:BC=(RT^2+LK^2)^.5
119 CB=ATN(LK/RT):AC=BC*AB:CA=CB+BA:AD=AC/XO:DA=CA+6.2832/4:AE=AD*COS(DA)
120 EA=AD*SIN(DA):BE=EA+XO:CE=(AE^2+BE^2)^.5:EC=ATN(BE/AE):AN=XT/CE
121 NA=-EC*6.2832/4:NA=NA*360/6.2832:AB=RO*XO:BA=-6.2832/4
122 AF=AD*SIN(DA):AG=AE+RT:AH=(AG^2+AF^2)^.5:HA=-ATN(AF/AG):AJ=AH*XT
123 JA=HA-6.2832/4:AK=AF-XT:KA=FA-6.2832/4:AL=(AG^2+AK^2)^.5:LA=-ATN(AK/AG)
124 AM=AJ/AL:MA=JA-LA:ZN=AM:NZ=MA:NZ=NZ*360/6.2832+180:PQ=-NA*6.2832/360
125 OP=-NZ*6.2832/360:RS=AN*COS(PQ):SR=AN*SIN(PQ):RR=RS+RO:IT=SR+XQ
126 RU=(RR^2+IT^2)^.5:IL=AN/RU:VO=IL*XQ:ZI=(RQ^2+XQ^2)^.5:IZ=ATN(XQ/RQ)
127 BF=IZ-3.1416/2:NA=NA*6.2832/360:OV=-NA+BF:OV=OV*360/6.2832-180:N=N+PP
128 LPRINT"Eout/Ein=";USING B$;VO
129 LPRINT "Phase Angle (Degrees=";USING B$;-OV
131 ZJ=(XQ^2+RQ^2)^.5:ET=VO*ZJ/XQ:JZ=(XT^2+RT^2)^.5:EO=ET*JZ/XT
132 LPRINT "E1/Ein=";USING B$;EO
133 LPRINT "E2/Ein=";USING B$;ET
134 LPRINT "Incidental Power Dissipation (mW)=";USING B$;1000*(1-EO)^2/RO+1000*(
    ET-EO)^2/RT+1000*(VO-ET)^2/RQ:LPRINT "(For Ein=1 Volt)":LPRINT
136 IF F>FF THEN 142
137 GOTO 116
138 END
140 LPRINT:GOTO 116
141 END
142 IF M=1 THEN 162
143 IF M=2 THEN 163
144 IF M=3 THEN 164
145 IF M=4 THEN 165
146 IF M=5 THEN 166
147 IF M=6 THEN 167
148 IF M=7 THEN 168
149 IF M=8 THEN 169
150 IF M=9 THEN 170
151 IF M=10 THEN 171
152 IF M=11 THEN 172
153 IF M=12 THEN 173
160 LPRINT:LPRINT"** CHARACTERISTICS WITH INDIVIDUAL PARAMETERS OFF-TOLERANCE BY
    GIVEN PERCENTAGE **":LPRINT
161 LPRINT "* Characteristics With R1 at High Tolerance *":LPRINT:
    RO=RO+.01*T*RO:N=0:M=M+1:GOTO 116
162 RO=RO/(1+.01*T):LPRINT "* Characteristics With R1 at Low Tolerance *":LPRINT
:   RO=RO-.01*T*RO:N=0:M=M+1:GOTO 116
163 RO=RO/(1-.01*T):LPRINT "* Characteristics With C1 at High Tolerance *":LPRIN
T:  CO=CO+.01*T*CO:N=0:M=M+1:GOTO 116
```

```
164 CO=CO/(1+.01*T):LPRINT "* Characteristics With C1 at Low Tolerance *":LPRINT
:   CO=CO-.01*T*CO:N=0:M=M+1:GOTO 116
165 CO=CO/(1-.01*T):LPRINT "* Characteristics With R2 at High Tolerance *":LPRIN
T:  RT=RT+.01*T*RT:N=0:M=M+1:GOTO 116
166 RT=RT/(1+.01*T):LPRINT "* Characteristics With R2 at Low Tolerance *":LPRINT
:   RT=RT-.01*T*RT:N=0:M=M+1:GOTO 116
167 RT=RT/(1-.01*T):LPRINT"* Characteristics With C2 at High Tolerance *":LPRINT
:   CT=CT+.01*T*CT:N=0:M=M+1:GOTO 116
168 CT=CT/(1+.01*T):LPRINT "* Characteristics With C2 at Low Tolerance *":LPRINT
:   CT=CT-.01*T*CT:N=0:M=M+1:GOTO 116
169 CT=CT/(1-.01*T):LPRINT "* Characteristics With R3 at High Tolerance *":LPRIN
T:  RQ=RQ+.01*T*RQ:N=0:M=M+1:GOTO 116
170 RQ=RQ/(1+.01*T):LPRINT "* Characteristics With R3 at Low Tolerance *":LPRINT
:   RQ=RQ-.01*T*RQ:N=0:M=M+1:GOTO 116
171 RQ=RQ/(1-.01*T):LPRINT "* Characteristics With C3 at High Tolerance *":LPRIN
T:  CQ=CQ+.01*T*CQ:N=0:M=M+1:GOTO 116
172 CQ=CQ/(1+.01*T):LPRINT "* Characteristics With C3 at Low Tolerance *":LPRINT
:   CQ=CQ-.01*T*CQ:N=0:M=M+1:GOTO 116
173 CQ=CQ/(1-.01*T):LPRINT
174 LPRINT "Note: This routine RUNs as a 2-section program if very small values
             are INPUTted for R3 and C3. It RUNs as a 1-section program if very
             small values are INPUTted for R2, C2, R3, and C3.":LPRINT
176 LPRINT "Note: This 3-section program RUNs as a loaded 2-section program if
             R3 is considered as the load resistor, and a very large value is
             INPUTted for C3. (The load voltage is then E2/Ein)":LPRINT
178 LPRINT "Note: This 3-section program RUNs as a loaded 1-section program if
             R2 is considered as the load resistor, and a very large value is
             INPUTted for C2. (The load voltage is then E1/Ein)":LPRINT
179 END
```

(TYPICAL RUN)

```
R1= 1000
R2= 2000
R3= 3000
C1= .25
C2= .15
C3= .1
Starting Frequency= 500
Survey End Frequency= 1000
Given % Tolerance= 50

f (Hz)= 500
Eout/Ein=   0.33
Phase Angle (Degrees= 126.57
E1/Ein=   0.62
E2/Ein=   0.45
Incidental Power Dissipation (mW)=   0.16
(For Ein=1 Volt)

f (Hz)= 1000
Eout/Ein=   0.10
Phase Angle (Degrees= 176.08
E1/Ein=   0.44
E2/Ein=   0.21
Incidental Power Dissipation (mW)=   0.34
(For Ein=1 Volt)
```

```
** CHARACTERISTICS WITH INDIVIDUAL PARAMETERS OFF-TOLERANCE BY GIVEN PERCENTAGE
**

* Characteristics With R1 at High Tolerance *

f (Hz)= 500
Eout/Ein=   0.26
Phase Angle (Degrees= 135.54
E1/Ein=   0.49
E2/Ein=   0.35
Incidental Power Dissipation (mW)=   0.19
(For Ein=1 Volt)


f (Hz)= 1000
Eout/Ein=   0.07
Phase Angle (Degrees= 183.38
E1/Ein=   0.32
E2/Ein=   0.15
Incidental Power Dissipation (mW)=   0.32
(For Ein=1 Volt)


* Characteristics With R1 at Low Tolerance *

f (Hz)= 500
Eout/Ein=   0.43
Phase Angle (Degrees= 111.45
E1/Ein=   0.81
E2/Ein=   0.59
Incidental Power Dissipation (mW)=   0.10
(For Ein=1 Volt)


f (Hz)= 1000
Eout/Ein=   0.15
Phase Angle (Degrees= 160.75
E1/Ein=   0.67
E2/Ein=   0.31
Incidental Power Dissipation (mW)=   0.29
(For Ein=1 Volt)


* Characteristics With C1 at High Tolerance *

f (Hz)= 500
Eout/Ein=   0.28
Phase Angle (Degrees= 135.74
E1/Ein=   0.53
E2/Ein=   0.39
Incidental Power Dissipation (mW)=   0.24
(For Ein=1 Volt)


f (Hz)= 1000
Eout/Ein=   0.08
Phase Angle (Degrees= 185.63
E1/Ein=   0.34
E2/Ein=   0.16
Incidental Power Dissipation (mW)=   0.45
(For Ein=1 Volt)


* Characteristics With C1 at Low Tolerance *

f (Hz)= 500
Eout/Ein=   0.38
Phase Angle (Degrees= 114.08
E1/Ein=   0.72
E2/Ein=   0.52
Incidental Power Dissipation (mW)=   0.11
(For Ein=1 Volt)
```

```
f (Hz)= 1000
Eout/Ein=   0.13
Phase Angle (Degrees= 159.63
E1/Ein=   0.59
E2/Ein=   0.27
Incidental Power Dissipation (mW)=   0.23
(For Ein=1 Volt)
```

* Characteristics With R2 at High Tolerance *

```
f (Hz)= 500
Eout/Ein=   0.27
Phase Angle (Degrees= 135.67
E1/Ein=   0.65
E2/Ein=   0.37
Incidental Power Dissipation (mW)=   0.15
(For Ein=1 Volt)
```

```
f (Hz)= 1000
Eout/Ein=   0.07
Phase Angle (Degrees= 184.85
E1/Ein=   0.47
E2/Ein=   0.16
Incidental Power Dissipation (mW)=   0.31
(For Ein=1 Volt)
```

* Characteristics With R2 at Low Tolerance *

```
f (Hz)= 500
Eout/Ein=   0.40
Phase Angle (Degrees= 113.27
E1/Ein=   0.60
E2/Ein=   0.54
Incidental Power Dissipation (mW)=   0.17
(For Ein=1 Volt)
```

```
f (Hz)= 1000
Eout/Ein=   0.13
Phase Angle (Degrees= 159.97
E1/Ein=   0.39
E2/Ein=   0.29
Incidental Power Dissipation (mW)=   0.39
(For Ein=1 Volt)
```

* Characteristics With C2 at High Tolerance *

```
f (Hz)= 500
Eout/Ein=   0.25
Phase Angle (Degrees= 135.48
E1/Ein=   0.60
E2/Ein=   0.34
Incidental Power Dissipation (mW)=   0.20
(For Ein=1 Volt)
```

```
f (Hz)= 1000
Eout/Ein=   0.07
Phase Angle (Degrees= 182.68
E1/Ein=   0.44
E2/Ein=   0.15
Incidental Power Dissipation (mW)=   0.35
(For Ein=1 Volt)
```

* Characteristics With C2 at Low Tolerance *

```
f (Hz)= 500
Eout/Ein=   0.45
Phase Angle (Degrees= 110.42
```

```
E1/Ein=   0.68
E2/Ein=   0.62
Incidental Power Dissipation (mW)=   0.11
(For Ein=1 Volt)


f (Hz)= 1000
Eout/Ein=   0.16
Phase Angle (Degrees= 161.20
E1/Ein=   0.45
E2/Ein=   0.33
Incidental Power Dissipation (mW)=   0.32
(For Ein=1 Volt)


* Characteristics With R3 at High Tolerance *

f (Hz)= 500
Eout/Ein=   0.26
Phase Angle (Degrees= 137.99
E1/Ein=   0.62
E2/Ein=   0.45
Incidental Power Dissipation (mW)=   0.17
(For Ein=1 Volt)


f (Hz)= 1000
Eout/Ein=   0.07
Phase Angle (Degrees= 184.55
E1/Ein=   0.44
E2/Ein=   0.21
Incidental Power Dissipation (mW)=   0.34
(For Ein=1 Volt)


* Characteristics With R3 at Low Tolerance *

f (Hz)= 500
Eout/Ein=   0.41
Phase Angle (Degrees= 108.49
E1/Ein=   0.62
E2/Ein=   0.45
Incidental Power Dissipation (mW)=   0.16
(For Ein=1 Volt)


f (Hz)= 1000
Eout/Ein=   0.15
Phase Angle (Degrees= 157.33
E1/Ein=   0.44
E2/Ein=   0.21
Incidental Power Dissipation (mW)=   0.34
(For Ein=1 Volt)


* Characteristics With C3 at High Tolerance *

f (Hz)= 500
Eout/Ein=   0.26
Phase Angle (Degrees= 137.99
E1/Ein=   0.62
E2/Ein=   0.45
Incidental Power Dissipation (mW)=   0.17
(For Ein=1 Volt)


f (Hz)= 1000
Eout/Ein=   0.07
Phase Angle (Degrees= 184.55
E1/Ein=   0.44
E2/Ein=   0.21
Incidental Power Dissipation (mW)=   0.34
(For Ein=1 Volt)
```

```
* Characteristics With C3 at Low Tolerance *

f (Hz)= 500
Eout/Ein=   0.41
Phase Angle (Degrees= 108.49
E1/Ein=   0.62
E2/Ein=   0.45
Incidental Power Dissipation (mW)=   0.16
(For Ein=1 Volt)

f (Hz)= 1000
Eout/Ein=   0.15
Phase Angle (Degrees= 157.33
E1/Ein=   0.44
E2/Ein=   0.21
Incidental Power Dissipation (mW)=   0.34
(For Ein=1 Volt)

Note: This routine RUNs as a 2-section program if very small values
are INPUTted for R3 and C3. It RUNs as a 1-section program if very
small values are INPUTted for R2, C2, R3, and C3.

Note: This 3-section program RUNs as a loaded 2-section program if
R3 is considered as the load resistor, and a very large value is
INPUTted for C3. (The load voltage is then E2/Ein)

Note: This 3-section program RUNs as a loaded 1-section program if
R2 is considered as the load resistor, and a very large value is
INPUTted for C2. (The load voltage is then E1/Ein)
```

PROGRAM CONVERSION

Program conversion from the IBM PC to other types of computers is not unduly difficult. However, there are coding differences that must be observed. The best way to become familiar with program conversion is to compare the same routine with coding for another computer, as exemplified in Figure A-6. Here, comparative codings are shown for the IBM PC, Commodore 64 and Apple IIe.

Input/Output (I/O) commands for the printer are different for these three computers. Also, print formats are different. In other words, the answer will be printed out to a large number of decimal places unless a suitable print format is used in coding the program. In the case of the IBM PC, the print format employs an A string, such as A$ = "######.##." The answer will then be printed out to two decimal places.

In the case of the Commodore 64 and the Apple IIe, another type of print format must be used. This print format is based on the integer function. If the answer is

IBM PC

```
5 REM PRG 5 WITH PRINTER
10 PRINT "BASIC FET AMPLIFIER ANALYSIS BASED ON OFF-TOLERANCE PARAMETERS"
15 LPRINT "BASIC FET AMPLIFIER ANALYSIS BASED ON OFF-TOLERANCE PARAMETERS"
20 PRINT "GENERALIZED TROUBLESHOOTING PROGRAM No. 5":PRINT
25 LPRINT "GENERALIZED TROUBLESHOOTING PROGRAM No. 5":LPRINT
```

COMMODORE 64

```
5 REM PRG 5 WITH PRINTER
10 PRINT "BASIC FET AMPLIFIER ANALYSIS BASED ON OFF-TOLERANCE PARAMETERS"
12 OPEN1,4
15 PRINT#1,"BASIC FET AMPLIFIER ANALYSIS BASED ON OFF-TOLERANCE PARAMETERS"
17 CLOSE1,4
20 PRINT "GENERALIZED TROUBLESHOOTING PROGRAM NO.5":PRINT
22 OPEN1,4
25 PRINT#1,"GENERALIZED TROUBLESHOOTING PROGRAM NO.5":PRINT#1,:CLOSE1,4
```

APPLE IIe

```
5   REM  PRG 5 WITH PRINTER
20  PRINT "BASIC FET AMPLIFIER A
    NALYSIS BASED ON OFF-TOLERAN
    CE PARAMETERS"
25  PRINT  CHR$ (4);"PR#1"
30  PRINT "BASIC FET AMPLIFIER A
    NALYSIS BASED ON OFF-TOLERAN
    CE PARAMETERS"
35  PRINT  CHR$ (4);"PR#0"
40  PRINT "GENERALIZED TROUBLESH
    OOTING PROGRAM NO. 5": PRINT

45  PRINT  CHR$ (4);"PR#1"
50  PRINT "GENERALIZED TROUBLESH
    OOTING PROGRAM NO. 5": PRINT

55  PRINT  CHR$ (4);"PR#0"
```

Figure A-6: Comparative program codings for the IBM PC, Commodore 64, and Apple IIe personal computers.

to be printed out to two decimal places, the command is PRINT .01*INT(100*X), where X is the variable value to be printed out. Observe that the computed answer is processed by first moving the decimal point two places to the right, eliminating following numerals, then moving the decimal point two places to the left and finally printing out the answer.

Note in passing that capital O cannot be used for numeral 0 in coding programs. Numeral 0 is displayed on the video screen as Ø. This can be a confusing situation for the beginner, inasmuch as Ø on the video screen will be printed out as capital O on the printout. However, after the programmer has "learned the ropes," no confusion will result from the inconsistency.

After a program has been converted, it is advisable to save it on floppy disk. Here again, considerable differences must be observed with I/O commands for disk drives. The disk-operating-system instruction book for the particular computer should be consulted, or instruction sought from a friend who is familiar with the requirements.

Index

A

Absorption trap, 153
Accessible rear control, 53
Actual color circuits, 209-17
Adjustment of parts, 323
AFPC detector, 210-11
AFT, 135
AGC, 6 45-47
Alignment, 159-63
    manufacturer's instructions, 160, 161
Alignment of parts, 323
American Commercial TV System
    Standards, 33-36
Antenna combiners, 276
Antenna problems, 267-68
Antenna splitters, 273-75
Arcing, 188-89, 365-66
Audio amplifiers, 37
Audio circuits, 231-36
Audio output stage, 55
Automatic color circuits, 217-18
Automatic color correction, 209
Automatic degaussing, 106
Automatic fine tuning signal:
    see AFT
Automatic frequency and phase control:
    see AFPC detector

Automatic frequency control, 52
Automatic gain control:
    see AGC
Automatic gain control voltages:
    see AGC
Autotransformer, 54

B

Balance of colors, 13
Baluns, 266
Bandpass adjustments, 223
BDC, 293
Beam limiter, 185
Beat pattern, 365
Beta VCRs, 307
Bifilar transformer, 153
Binary code, 57
Black and white TVs:
    see Monochrome TVs
"Black arts," 61
Black level, 31
Blanking pulse, 30, 55
Blanking section, 55
Block down converter:
    see BDC
Blocking oscillator, 51

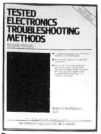

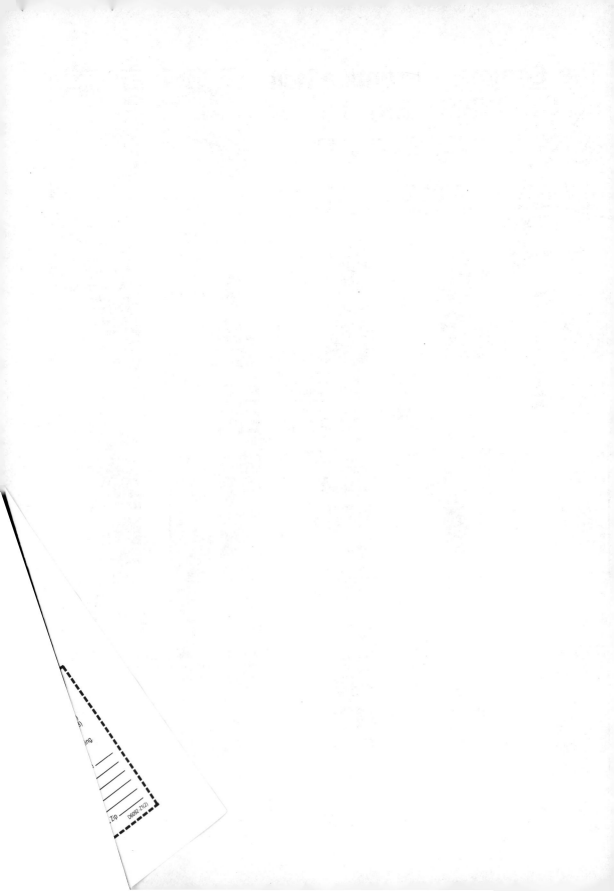